Multiple Methods
of Teaching Mathematics
in the Elementary School

Multiple Methods of
in the

Charles H. D'Augustine

OHIO UNIVERSITY

Teaching Mathematics Elementary School

Harper & Row, Publishers

NEW YORK, EVANSTON, AND LONDON

To E. T. D., E. D. N., and R. K.

Contents

Preface

THIS book is designed to be used in colleges of education when students have had the equivalent of three semester hours of mathematics which have included the following: number systems, including a study of their structure and properties relating to operations on these systems; set notation and set operations; and numeration systems, modern and ancient, with certain basic concepts relative to characteristics of these numeration systems.

This book does not presuppose that a student has had the appropriate geometry and therefore supplements methods of teaching this topic with some content new to the student.

I believe that this text presents many features that heretofore have not been incorporated in a single methods text. One of these features is the involvement of prospective teachers in the creation of exercises that can lead children to make discoveries of various number sentence patterns; the creation of such exercises is developed extensively in each chapter dealing with operations on numbers. I believe that the ability of a teacher to create problems that will lead to mathematical discoveries is a prerequisite to developing effective discovery techniques.

A second feature of this text is that alternate methods of teaching a given concept are presented. For example, not only are the methods of using sets, arrays, and the cross products of sets to teach the basic multiplication facts introduced, but the methods of using patterns, properties, the multiplication table, and number lines to teach these facts are also presented.

A third feature of this text is that the study of measurement is organized around basic principles of teaching measure which are applicable to measure in general and not just to certain measures. For example, not only are these principles applicable when one is teaching area measure, but they are also applicable when one is teaching measure relating to water pressure or measure relating to the magnetic field of the earth. Though common measures, such as time, linear measure, area measure, and volume measure, are presented, the emphasis is on developing broad concepts relating to measure per se, rather than to any measure in particular.

A fourth feature of this text is that the geometry is presented along both a topological and a geometric basis. The geometric figures are developed around a properties-classification system. Careful attention is given both to the relationships and properties by which one can distinguish one subset of points in space from another and to the construction of a teachable and logical sequence of geometric concepts.

xiii

The following schematic diagram illustrates how the number systems through the fractional numbers and integers are developed in this text.

| WHOLE NUMBERS | → | FRACTIONAL NUMBERS | | INTEGERS |

| Defined as the number property of either a discrete set or an empty set. Two sets are said to have the same number property when they can be put into a one-to-one correspondence. | Defined as the quotient of two whole numbers, where the divisor is not zero. (These fractional numbers are regarded for all practical purposes as being the nonnegative rationals.) | Defined as directed numbers, the nonnegative elements of which are isomorphic to the set of whole numbers. (However, for all practical purposes, the set of whole numbers is considered as a subset of the set of integers.) |

I believe that a methods text should prepare an elementary school teacher for the future, as well as for the present. With this in mind, I have tried to anticipate trends and directions of the elementary movement and to focus this methods text on those aspects of the modern elementary program that provide the teacher with the best opportunity to adapt to future content and curriculum innovations.

Topics such as vector spaces, linear algebras, logical systems, game theory, and statistics have been omitted entirely from this book. There are those who advocate these topics, and there is some evidence that they will play a role in the elementary curriculum in a decade or more. Nevertheless, I believe that there is not yet sufficient experimental evidence to suggest methods of teaching such topics to elementary school children.

I wish to thank my colleagues and students who offered valuable suggestions in the construction of this text. I am particularly grateful to teachers and students in Leon, West Palm Beach, and Broward counties in Florida and to the Marietta, Chesapeake, Jackson, Logan, Lancaster, and Athens school systems in Ohio and to teachers in these systems. I am indebted to Jo Ann Sargent and Jan Krupp for the technical assistance they rendered in the preparation of this book.

C.H.D'A.

Multiple Methods
of Teaching Mathematics
in the Elementary School

Historical Prelude

From the Colonial Period to 1870

ELEMENTARY school mathematics has not always played a major role in our educational system. Whether or not a child studied "ciphering" was dictated by the occupation or trade for which he was being prepared. For example, during our country's Colonial period, special schools were organized for training in ciphering because the Dutch West India Company needed men with such training to act as "keepers of the stores."[1] (Ciphering is synonymous with what we currently identify as the computational aspects of arithmetic.) It was not a mark of distinction to be able to cipher, however; in fact, the aristocracy of the Colonial period felt that a person who could cipher was suited only for menial work.[2] Thus, arithmetic did not hold a place of eminence in the Colonial schools. Reading and writing were designated as essentials and were listed as required subject matter in laws as early as 1679, but arithmetic often was omitted from the Colonial school curriculum.[3]

Elementary school mathematics of a very basic nature was found in some grammar schools of the later part of the seventeenth century and the early part of the eighteenth century. Although girls in general did not learn anything about arithmetic, boys going into a trade had to learn how to write a column of figures and also how to do simple addition and subtraction.[4]

General political acceptance of the value of arithmetic as a school subject was slow in developing. In the later part of the seventeenth century, ciphering was given official sanction by the settlers of Pennsylvania. In 1789, Massachusetts passed a law to make "arithmetic" a mandatory school subject.[5] The South was the last section of the then-settled country to include arithmetic

---

[1] W. H. Kilpatrick, *The Dutch Schools of New Netherlands and Colonial New York*, U.S. Department of the Interior, Bureau of Education, Washington, D.C.: U.S. Government Printing Office, Bulletin 12, 1912.

[2] Walter Scott Monroe, *Development of Arithmetic as a School Subject*, U.S. Department of the Interior, Bureau of Education, Washington, D.C.: U.S. Government Printing Office, Bulletin 10, 1917, p. 5.

[3] Walter Herbert Small, *Early New England Schools*, Boston: Ginn and Company, 1914, p. 358.

[4] David Eugene Smith and Jekuthiel Ginsburg, *A History of Mathematics in America Before 1900*, Chicago: The Mathematical Association of America, 1934, p. 2.

[5] Clifton Johnson, *Old-Time Schools and School Books*, New York: The Macmillan Company, 1917, p. 301.

I

in its curriculum—the idea of universal education was not recognized there, and only the children of landed gentry were educated. But even this education was college preparatory in nature and thus excluded the "practical" or "applied" subjects, such as arithmetic.[6]

By 1800, arithmetic was generally taught in the schools. One might characterize the nature of this arithmetic instruction as "working problems from rules." Practice or drill on the operations of arithmetic was almost nonexistent. (An interesting aspect of some arithmetic books of this period is that they included such topics as conic sections, geometry, and trigonometry.[7]) Texts of the time can be classified as "commercial" arithmetic texts because a large number of the problems and rules contained in them concerned trade and commerce.[8] The arithmetic books of the first 20 years of the nineteenth century, then, were not designed for teaching the young child. Arithmetic was seldom, in any case, taught to children below the age of 10. As a matter of fact, it was considered to signify approaching manhood when a boy started to study the subject.[9]

The method of presenting arithmetic was essentially teacher-to-pupil. Only the teacher had a book; the pupils were each given a quire of blank pages sewed together to form a booklet into which they copied the teacher's dictated problems. It is interesting to note that textbooks during this period were organized from the abstract to the concrete. Furthermore, no individualized instruction was given—the role of the teacher was primarily to keep order and to "hear" the children's lessons. All computations were recorded in the pupil's book, and there were no provisions for "oral" or mental arithmetic activities.

About 1820, the character of arithmetic texts began to change. Topics were better sequenced, and instruction in arithmetic was begun as early as the age of 5.[10] Large numbers of drill exercises made their appearance in the texts. The method of presentation now went from the concrete to the abstract, and the introduction of abstract symbolism was delayed. An attempt was made to motivate the child by introducing concepts through applied problems.[11] Then for about 40 years there were frequent revisions of arithmetic textbooks by authors who attempted to keep pace with the changing conditions and needs in society.[12]

---

[6] Monroe, *op. cit.*, p. 11.

[7] Nicolas Pike, *A New and Complete System of Arithmetic*, Newbury-Port: John MyCall, 1788.

[8] Louis Charles Karpinski, *The History of Arithmetic*, New York: Rand McNally & Company, 1925, p. 144.

[9] Monroe, *op. cit.*, p. 46.

[10] Monroe, *op. cit.*, p. 63.

[11] Newton Edward and Herman G. Richey, *The School in the American Social Order*, Boston: Houghton Mifflin Co., 1947, pp. 765–767.

[12] Monroe, *op. cit.*, p. 89.

There is evidence that, around 1866, formal courses of study were being developed. In California, for example, a first-grade child was required to be able to count to 50, using kernels of corn or beans, and to study form, including lines, parallel lines, vertical lines, and angles.[13]

1870 to 1900

During the later part of the nineteenth century, several divergent factors were influencing the arithmetic curriculum. The "formal discipline" advocates made their mark on the arithmetic curriculum in the form of extensive arithmetic drill, which it was thought would serve to strengthen by exercise certain faculties of the child's brain. This need for more drill to train the mind led to the idea that one textbook was inadequate to contain all the necessary exercises for meeting the requirements of this educational philosophy.

While the "Formalists" were influencing the curriculum, others were experimenting with it in a different way. In 1873, Francis Parker organized the Quincy, Massachusetts, school system in a way that has come to be thought of as quite modern for that day.[14] Arithmetic was approached inductively, through objects, rather than through rules.

1900 to 1950

During the early 1900s, there was a concerted effort to relate the problems of elementary arithmetic to the problems that the adult would encounter. This movement is often called the "Social Utility Movement." As the major determining factor for selection of content in the elementary curriculum, the Social Utility Movement led to such extremes as teaching concepts of tariff and taxation to elementary school children.

A second factor that influenced the arithmetic curriculum during the early 1900s, when social usage as the basis of curriculum selection was waning, was the acceptance of the "Connectionist" theory of learning. One of the outcomes of the utilization of this theory was the complete atomization of the computational skills. Arithmetic became a series of fragmented learning experiences "fixed" in the brain for "automatic mastery" through extensive

[13] Roy W. Cloud, *Education in California*, Stanford, Calif.: Stanford University Press, 1952, p. 42.
[14] Lawrence A. Cremin, *The Transformation of the School*, New York: Alfred A. Knopf, Inc., 1961, p. 128.

drill. In other words, just as drill as a means of training the brain was falling into disrepute, a new champion, the Connectionist psychologist, was re-establishing its value.[15]

During the late 1920s a study undertaken by the Committee of Seven sought to determine the mental age at which various arithmetic topics could be taught.[16] In spite of the fact that the method of presenting each topic was highly restricted, the report exerted a wide influence. For 20 years, the grade placement of topics became frozen on the basis of this report. This happened despite the fact that a great amount of evidence showing this restriction to be unnecessary was collected by child-study specialists. Research after research gave evidence that when and where a topic is placed in the curriculum depends upon how it is taught.

While the content at each grade level remained fixed, the curriculum was being strongly influenced by the child-study movement in other ways. Evidence that children learn best by progressing from the concrete to the abstract caused greater use of manipulative devices in the elementary school. Research on the reading levels of children influenced the publication of series of arithmetic texts whose word problems in general reflected a lag of six months to a year in reading-level difficulty. Problems became oriented toward the child's experiences. Research indicated that arithmetic was best learned over a broad period of time, which gave rise to the spiral approach in teaching.

An outgrowth of the concern for the needs of the child was the "Progressive Movement." One of the consequences of this movement was the unstructured, unsequenced arithmetic curriculum. Arithmetic experiences were structured around the direct needs of the child as he participated in some type of unit activity. For example, if the first-grade child were playing store and needed to know division, he would be taught the division that he needed to solve his problem. But this type of instruction was found wanting, because it left the child with large gaps in his knowledge of arithmetic. A desirable result of the movement, however, was the general recognition that meaningful learning experiences create a highly desirable learning environment for the child. Meaningful motivation causes the child to apply greater effort to a problem, and he attains greater mastery than the less motivated child.

After 1920, the curriculum also was influenced by the advocates of Gestalt psychology, in which the total organization of learning is stressed. The organization of learning concentrated on the whole, rather than on the atomistic parts, as advocated by the Connectionists. Drill or practice became less

---

[15] Edward L. Thorndike, *The Psychology of Arithmetic*, New York: The Macmillan Company, 1922, pp. 141–155.

[16] C. W. Washburne, "The Grade Placement of Arithmetic Topics: A Committee of Seven's Investigation," *Report of the Society's Committee on Arithmetic, Twenty-ninth Yearbook, Part II*, National Society for the Study of Education, Bloomington, Ill.: Public School Publishing Company, 1930.

extensive, because mastery required less drill when it followed learning in a meaningful context.

After 1930, mathematics education began stressing the idea that meaning must be developed along with a skill. This trend became known as the "Meaning Movement."

The "Modern" Movement

The term *modern* is probably a misnomer for the current elementary school mathematics program, as most mathematics in the modern program was "discovered" or "created" before 1900. A more apt expression might be *revolution mathematics*, because the curricular reform contains many of the characteristics one normally associates with a revolution.

The "seeds" for the change in the curriculum were present for at least three decades, and it was from an accumulation of a large number of favorable forces that the change occurred. The beginnings of the revolution consisted of

1. A continuing accumulation of information on how children learn
2. An accumulation of knowledge of the basic structure of mathematics
3. Some successful attempts to unify the concepts of mathematics
4. An awareness that continuity between grade levels was not sufficient
5. An awareness that arithmetic was totally oriented toward computational skills
6. An awareness that the sequence of elementary mathematics was historical, rather than logical
7. An awareness that greater mathematical competence was being required by business and industry in contemporary society
8. An awareness that the background and training of the elementary teacher was more extensive than in the past

The forces that generated the revolution in mathematics in the 1950s are highly complex and interrelated. It would be difficult to identify any one major contributing factor. Certainly the rapid growth of our technical society dictated that more people had to be better prepared in mathematics. This preparation, to be adequate, had to reflect the idea of flexibility, because our technical society was changing at a very rapid pace. Although such a rapid technical change precludes our being able to predict accurately the type of mathematics a person will need 20 years from now, it does permit us to see that the mathematics presented to the student should be so structured that concepts can be added to it from whatever direction the student moves. The modern elementary mathematics curriculum reflects this change.

Curriculum change has many built-in dampers. Our methods of training and retraining elementary teachers serve as dampers in any effort to reform the elementary school curriculum. The teacher near retirement, the teacher weak in an area, the administrator with no goal other than making peace with the public, the advocate of the status quo, the noncertified teacher, the adoption techniques for new materials, the failure of previous attempts at curriculum revision, all tend to impede curriculum change. Heretofore, these impeders have been successful in blunting attempts at curriculum revision. They have succeeded in muddying the water to such an extent that any attempt at an impartial evaluation of a curriculum innovation has been nearly impossible.

The emergence of a strong and dynamic National Council of Teachers of Mathematics (NCTM) is one of the major forces that has provided the cadre and intellectual guidance to promote and sustain the elementary mathematics revolution. The council has served as a sounding board and disseminator of the "new" mathematics. It has actively supported curriculum research and innovation. It has stabilized the revolution by providing wide dissemination of the results of research and curriculum innovations, as well as by providing critical appraisals of each new curriculum proposal.

A new force entered the scene concurrent with the modern mathematics, a force that made the modern mathematics movement difficult to impede, a force with built-in modifying features that promise continued impetus. This new force consists of the availability of large amounts of money and trained personnel for constructing and evaluating materials and for training other personnel. Directly and indirectly, it is attributable to the federal government. In 1957, by an act of Congress, the National Science Foundation (NSF) was created. Its function is to provide funds for the retraining of teachers, for mathematics-curriculum projects, and for supporting curriculum research. Teachers trained in NSF Institutes have provided school systems with well-trained teachers who are capable of developing and sustaining curriculum change within the school system. Heretofore, it was often the case that when the "transient experts" on curriculum reform left the system, the curriculum change they had initiated departed with them.

Several private and NSF-sponsored projects developed materials that, by their very nature, contributed to the wide acceptance of modern elementary mathematics by the elementary teacher. Such projects as the School Mathematics Study Group (SMSG), Greater Cleveland Mathematics Program (GCMP), University of Illinois Arithmetic Project (UIAP), Madison Project, Ball State Project, and Minnesota Elementary Curriculum Project, as well as numerous less extensive projects, developed materials for both the elementary child and the elementary teacher.

No curriculum movement is capable of sustaining itself unless the teacher-training institutions train teachers who are able to participate in the movement. The Committee on Undergraduate Programs in Mathematics was instrumental in successfully promoting a type of mathematics for prospective elementary teachers that could convey the essence and structure of mathematical systems.

From the way the mathematics revolution has developed, it is easy to predict that the curriculum change has only begun. The idea of continuous evaluation has received wide acceptance and will promote a constant search for better techniques for teaching mathematics. The computer has made possible the evaluation of educational research that contains many variables. This will provide the curriculum expert with a constant source of data for instituting promising curriculum innovations.

The better-trained student in mathematics will make a better mathematics teacher, who will in turn teach other better-trained students, and so on. This will mean that different materials will be needed for both, and a constant evaluation and revision of elementary materials will be promoted. In the next chapter, we shall discuss the nature of the modern curriculum and its implications for teaching.

REFERENCES

CLOUD, ROY W., *Education in California*, Stanford: Stanford University Press, 1952, p. 42.

CREMIN, LAWRENCE A., *The Transformation of the School*, New York: Alfred A. Knopf, Inc., 1961, p. 128.

DEANS, E., *Elementary School Mathematics—New Directions*, Washington, D.C.: U.S. Department of Health, Education and Welfare, 1963.

EDWARD, NEWTON, and HERMAN G. RICHEY, *The School in the American Social Order*, Boston: Houghton Mifflin Company, 1947, pp. 765–767.

GLENNON, VINCENT J., and students, *Teaching Arithmetic in the Modern School*, Syracuse: Bureau of School Service, School of Education, Syracuse University, 1953, p. 139.

JOHNSON, CLIFTON, *Old-Time Schools and School Books*, New York: The Macmillan Company, 1917, p. 301.

KARPINSKI, LOUIS CHARLES, *The History of Arithmetic*, New York: Rand McNally & Company, 1925, p. 144.

KILPATRICK, W. H., *The Dutch Schools of New Netherlands and Colonial New York*, U.S. Department of the Interior, Bureau of Education, Washington, D.C.: U.S. Government Printing Office, Bulletin 12, 1912.

MONROE, WALTER SCOTT, *Development of Arithmetic as a School Subject*, U.S. Department of the Interior, Bureau of Education, Washington, D.C.: U.S. Government Printing Office, Bulletin 10, 1917.

NATIONAL COUNCIL OF TEACHERS OF MATHEMATICS, *An Analysis of New Mathematics Programs*, Washington, D.C.: The National Council of Teachers of Mathematics, 1963.

PIKE, NICOLAS, *A New and Complete System of Arithmetic*, Newbury-Port: John MyCall, 1788.

ROSENBLOOM, PAUL C., "Mathematics K-12," *Educational Leadership*, vol. 1,9 pp. 359–363, March, 1962.

SMALL, WALTER HERBERT, *Early New England Schools*, Boston: Ginn and Company, 1914, p. 358.

SMITH, DAVID EUGENE, and JEKUTHIEL GINSBURG, *A History of Mathematics in America Before 1900*, Chicago: The Mathematical Association of America, 1934, p. 2.

THORNDIKE, EDWARD L., *The Psychology of Arithmetic*, New York: The Macmillan Company, 1922, pp. 141–155.

WASHBURNE, C. W., "The Grade Placement of Arithmetic Topics: A Committee of Seven's Investigation," *Report of the Society's Committee on Arithmetic, Twenty-ninth Yearbook, Part II*, National Society for the Study of Education, Bloomington, Ill.: Public School Publishing Company, 1930.

WEAVER, J. F., "Basic Considerations in the Improvement of Elementary School Mathematics Programs," *The Arithmetic Teacher*, vol. 7, pp. 269–273, October, 1960.

Discovery of mathematical patterns can be used to motivate a child to learn mathematics.

1

The Essence of Modern Mathematics Methods

1.1. *Introduction*

WHAT DISTINGUISHES modern elementary school mathematics from the "traditional" arithmetic program which the majority of elementary teachers were taught? As mentioned previously, the content, per se, is not modern, with a few exceptions. For example, in the Historical Prelude we saw that some of the topics currently identified as new, such as the study of lines, angles, parallel lines, and so on, were an integral part of the curriculum of a California first-grader in 1866.

If the mathematics, for the most part, is not modern, then what does constitute modern elementary school mathematics? The following phrases might be used to describe the modern elementary program: a structural approach; greater student involvement; greater flexibility; provision for individual differences; greater emphasis on a unified and consistent approach; better balance among the computational aspects of mathematics, the social applications of mathematics, and the creative aspects of mathematics; greater precision of language; greater emphasis on meanings; and incorporation of the results of recent educational and psychological research on learning.

The reader will note that most of these phrases are descriptions of degrees of emphasis; they are not clear reversals of what has been done earlier. This is not to say that we can find *no* ideas that are truly new to the elementary mathematics curriculum. Topics such as inequalities, variables, and set notation, to mention just a few, are new. But these topics cannot be divorced from all of the previous descriptions of the modern mathematics curriculum. Their inclusion is not accidental or just for a "glamour effect" but serves to unify the curriculum and provide it with flexibility. Nondecimal bases also represent a recent addition to the elementary curriculum. Their study aids the child in getting a clear understanding of his own decimal base.

Let us now take a look in depth at each of the characteristics that describes the modern elementary mathematics program.

1.2. *Structural Properties*

Mathematics is a well-structured body of knowledge. The basic structure of the mathematics the elementary child studies is one of beauty and simplicity. The terms *commutative*, *associative*, *identity*, and *distributive* are the labels we attach to certain patterns that determine a large part of the basic structure at the elementary level.

These, and other basic patterns, form the structure whereby number systems can be studied and compared systematically. In Figure 1.1, we see

Commutative patterns

$$\triangle + \square = \square + \triangle \qquad \triangle \times \square = \square \times \triangle$$

WHOLE NUMBERS	$3 + 4 = 4 + 3$	$7 \times 6 = 6 \times 7$
FRACTIONAL NUMBERS	$3 + 4 = 4 + 3$ $\dfrac{3}{4} + \dfrac{2}{7} = \dfrac{2}{7} + \dfrac{3}{4}$	$7 \times 6 = 6 \times 7$ $\dfrac{6}{7} \times \dfrac{3}{8} = \dfrac{3}{8} \times \dfrac{6}{7}$
INTEGERS	$^-3 + {}^+4 = {}^+4 + {}^-3$	$^-6 \times {}^-8 = {}^-8 \times {}^-6$
RATIONAL NUMBERS	$^-3 + {}^+4 = {}^+4 + {}^-3$ $\dfrac{^+1}{3} + \dfrac{^-6}{7} = \dfrac{^-6}{7} + \dfrac{^+1}{3}$	$^-6 \times {}^-8 = {}^-8 \times {}^-6$ $\dfrac{^-2}{8} \times \dfrac{^+2}{3} = \dfrac{^+2}{3} \times \dfrac{^-2}{8}$

FIGURE 1.1

how the commutative pattern holds for whole numbers, fractional numbers, integers,* and rational numbers.

A concept such as the commutative property of addition provides a bridge whereby a child can move smoothly from addition on the subset of the fractional numbers, the whole numbers, to addition on the entire set of fractional numbers.

This basic structure is useful not only in developing the mathematics concepts that are now being taught in the schools from elementary grades to college levels, but is useful also in forming a framework upon which the child should be able to add efficiently other mathematics, as yet uncreated, that he will certainly encounter in the near future of our rapidly changing society.

As we shall see in later sections, focusing on the structural nature of the number systems being studied will lead to an economy of effort in terms of learning the concepts relating to these systems. Smooth transition from one number system to another is made possible by relating the common elements of structure of both systems. Recognition of common structural elements leads to the discovery and proof of theorems paralleling those proved for the previous number system, thus accelerating the search for and acquisition of new knowledge.

A flexible program can be developed via the use of structural properties. As we shall see in the next section, the use of structural properties will provide the teacher with a valuable tool in meeting the individual needs of students.

1.3. *Involvement or Discovery*

Involvement of the student probably should rank at the top of a list describing the major distinctions between the traditional and the modern curricula. The child ceases to be a spectator in the learning process and becomes instead an active participant. This participation takes many forms. It may involve the child in searching for a pattern within a sequence of problems constructed by the teacher. See Figure 1.2.

It may take the form of the child's responding orally or mentally to a sequence of well-designed questions presented by the teacher. For example:

"How many objects do we have in our first set? How many objects do we have in our second set?"

"If we put the two sets together, how many objects will we have in our new set?"

* In this text, the non-negative integers and the whole numbers are treated as being related isomorphically. In this text, the whole numbers are not defined as a subset of the integers.

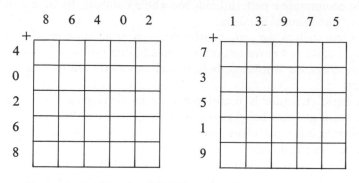

Designed to help the child discover the generalizations:
even + even = even   odd + odd = even

FIGURE 1.2

It may take the form of the child's reacting to a well-designed learning experience presented in his textbook or in a programmed text. It may take the form of his reacting and interacting with other children when he is constructing a mathematics project or exhibit.

It may take the form of his making discoveries and extending these discoveries to a generalization. This is quite similar to and includes searching for patterns, except that it can occur in any teaching context. It is characterized by the child's creating a hypothesis arising out of some learning situation, his testing his hypothesis with more examples, and his formulating a generalization. Finally, although not necessarily at the elementary level, the child may prove his generalization.

Other techniques for promoting discovery include, at one end of the spectrum, a nondirected discovery technique conducive to inquiry within the general framework of a learning situation. Some specifications for this type of discovery are

1. The teacher must have a superior grasp of the subject matter in order to be able to recognize and focus on significant things discovered by the students
2. The teacher must have sufficient grasp of the subject matter to recognize when students are at the end of a blind alley and need to be redirected to more productive avenues of thought
3. The teacher needs to have the ability to interject just the right question at just the right time in order to produce a discovery
4. The teacher needs to have the ability to sense when the inherent discoveries have been exhausted.

Teaching with a nondirected discovery method is a highly desirable goal toward which to work, but it is probably not a technique the novice should experiment with during his first trials of teaching elementary school mathematics; it requires a high degree of sensitivity to the pace at which a group learns, and this sensitivity is usually developed through teaching experience.

At the other end of the spectrum is the directed discovery technique in which there exists one solution, one pattern, or one generalization to be discovered. The teacher presents the problem in such a way that variations from expected outcomes are not likely to occur. For example, suppose that you have taught your children that $2 + 2 = 4$ and $3 + 3 = 6$ and $4 + 4 = 8$, and you would like them to discover, using a pattern, that $5 + 5 = 10$.

You might present your students with the following sentences:

$$2 + 2 = 4$$
$$3 + 3 = 6$$
$$4 + 4 = 8$$
$$5 + 5 = \square$$

You might then ask the students to study the pattern and see if they can guess what 5 plus 5 must be equal to. (After arriving at the speculation that the answer is 10, the children can check their guess by putting together two sets of five.)

You will also be shown how to test, nonverbally, the child's "awareness" of these properties. For example, exercises such as

Because $49,672 + 321,872 = 371,544$
then $321,872 + 49,672 = \square$
or simply $49,672 + 321,872 = 321,872 + \square$

test the child's "awareness" of the commutative property of addition on the set of whole numbers.

You will also be shown how to construct exercises that can be used to lead the child toward a generalization. For example, an exercise such as

Find a number that will make the following sentence true: $3 + \square = \square + 3$

is useful in taking the child from an awareness of the commutative property for a limited number of instances to a more generalized form. A listing of the various solutions obtained by different members of the class guides the child toward the realization that if each whole number were used as a replacement, each new sentence would be true.

In actual practice a teacher will employ a discovery technique that lies somewhere between the two ends of the spectrum. He will fit the degree of direction given (of the number of "limits" given) to the ability level of his students and take into consideration his depth of understanding of the problem, which might be uncovered by giving less direction.

Not every activity or concept lends itself to the discovery technique. The following list illustrates some of the many topics that lend themselves to the discovery technique at the elementary level:

	Example
1. Basic facts	What rectangular arrays can be constructed using a set of eight blocks? *Answer:* A 2-by-4 array $(2 \times 4 = 8)$, a 4-by-2 array $(4 \times 2 = 8)$, a 1-by-8 array $(1 \times 8 = 8)$, and an 8-by-1 array $(8 \times 1 = 8)$
2. Generalizations	Odd + odd = even, $n - n = 0$, odd × odd = odd, $n - 0 = n$, $(n + m) \div p = (n \div p) + (m \div p)$, etc.
3. Geometric "constructions"	If you are allowed to use any two triangles, how can you construct a three-sided figure? four-sided? five-sided? etc.
4. Properties	Find each sum. Can you find a pattern? $4 + 3 = \square$ $9 + 3 = \square$ $3 + 4 = \square$ $3 + 9 = \square$ $7 + 8 = \square$ $8 + 7 = \square$
5. Mathematical patterns	See if you can find a pattern that will help you answer the following question: What is the sum of the first 400 odd numbers? $1 + 3 = 4$ $1 + 3 + 5 = 9$ $1 + 3 + 5 + 7 = 16$ $1 + 3 + 5 + 7 + 9 = 25$
6. Algorithms	Can you find a way to multiply 19×21 mentally? *An answer:* Because $(n - 1) \times (n + 1) = n^2 - 1$, then $(20 - 1) \times (20 + 1) = 20^2 - 1 = 399$

1.4. *Meeting Individual Differences*

Getting the students involved gives the teacher more opportunity to meet individual differences. With each child involved, the teacher can get around to those students who require individual attention. This ability to view the results of each child's efforts gives the teacher a much better opportunity to know individual strengths and weaknesses than ever was possible in the era of "spectator" learning.

The content of the curriculum itself has been designed to meet individual needs. For example, the division algorithm shown in Figure 1.3 has been found to be efficient and flexible, meeting the needs of both the "slow" learner and the "fast" learner. This algorithm (an algorithm is a prescribed computational scheme for arriving at an answer) allows each child to attack a division problem at his own skill level, rather than attempting to make each child conform to the skill level required by the older traditional division algorithm.

23) 497	
230	10
267	
230	10
37	
23	1
14	21

23) 497	
460	20
37	
23	1
14	21

Worked by a student classified by his teacher as a slow learner

Worked by a student classified by his teacher as an average learner

FIGURE 1.3

Although there are some algorithms that tend to meet individual differences better than others, there will be times in your teaching when you have children who are at a prealgorithm stage for which no algorithm is suitable. Special activities are necessary for these students.

The structure of the subject provides another way to meet the individual needs of children. To illustrate, let us consider two children, John and Mary, who are fourth-graders. John knows his ones, twos, and fives multiplication facts. (A multiplication fact is of the form $\square \times \triangle = \bigcirc$, where both the $\square$ and $\triangle$ are replaced by numerals naming whole numbers less than 10. Thus, $6 \times 9 = 54$, and $1 \times 0 = 0$ are examples of multiplication facts.) Mary knows the ones, twos, threes, fours, and fives multiplication facts, as well as $10 \times 1 = 10$, $10 \times 2 = 20$, $10 \times 3 = 30$, $10 \times 4 = 40$, $10 \times 5 = 50$, and $10 \times 6 = 60$.

Both of these students have discovered also the following patterns: $\triangle \times \square = \square \times \triangle$, and $\triangle \times (\bigcirc + \square) = (\triangle \times \bigcirc) + (\triangle \times \square)$. In addition, Mary has discovered the generalization: $\triangle \times (\bigcirc - \square) = (\triangle \times \bigcirc) - (\triangle \times \square)$, when $\bigcirc > \square$. Their teacher wishes to have them discover, mathematically, the product of 6 sixes. John and Mary have learned that by finding suitable names for six they can find the product of two numbers. John chooses $(5 + 1)$

as a name for six and uses the distributive property as follows: $6 \times (5 + 1) = (6 \times 5) + (6 \times 1) = 30 + 6 = 36$.

Mary has proceeded to discover that $6 \times (5 + 1) = 36$, $6 \times (4 + 2) = 36$, $6 \times (3 + 3) = 36$, and $6 \times (10 - 4) = 36$. She has also decided that 6×9 must be equal to 54, if $(6 \times 9) - (6 \times 3) = 36$, and $6 \times 3 = 18$.

As the reader can see, this particular property allows each individual to attack a problem at his skill level. It provides for economy of effort, because the slow learner does not need to return to a concrete situation for every new concept. (It is, however, best to remember that this slow learner will need more experience with concrete situations as concepts are developed than will the fast learner. The teacher should be aware, too, that he has other non-concrete situational techniques with which to simplify the abstraction for the child.)

In some cases, there exist independent algorithms that meet the individual needs of the students. The multiplication algorithms depicted in Figure 1.4 are typical of those that can be used to meet the needs of different individuals. In the algorithm at the left, the child is not required to remember the 4 tens obtained by multiplying 6 and 7 while he is obtaining the product of 6 and 5 tens. He simply records each partial product as it is obtained. The algorithm at the right sacrifices simplicity of thought for conciseness of recording and is thus less suitable for the slow learner than the algorithm at the left.

$$
\begin{array}{r}
57 \\
\times\ \ 6 \\
\hline
42 \\
300 \\
\hline
342
\end{array}
\qquad\qquad
\begin{array}{r}
57 \\
\times\ \ 6 \\
\hline
342
\end{array}
$$

A complete partial products   A standard multiplication
algorithm   algorithm

FIGURE 1.4

1.5. *Unification and Consistency*

Traditional elementary school mathematics was often a sequence of disjointed learning experiences. For many traditional elementary teachers, whole numbers and fractional numbers represented completely unrelated ideas. Little or no thought was given to the fact that the whole numbers constituted a subset of the set of fractional numbers. Little thought was given to extending the concepts from the subset to the set.

The teaching of fractional numbers often represented a fragmented approach. To most children who were products of the traditional approach, "fractions" meant those fractional numbers between zero and one. When the teacher strayed out of this range, the term *improper fraction* was given to those "unmentionables" not in the zero to less-than-one range. The fractional number zero was even more "unmentionable." Teaching concepts related to the set of whole numbers was fragmented. Frequently, no attempt was made to establish the close relationship between the operation of addition and its inverse, subtraction, or between multiplication and its inverse, division.

Under the leadership of competent mathematicians such as The Reverend Stanley Bezuska, Boston College; Newton Hawley, Stanford University; Robert Pingry, University of Illinois; and Paul C. Rosenbloom, University of Minnesota, great strides were made in unifying the curriculum. The mathematicians encouraged the inclusion of such topics as sets, inequalities, structural properties, nonmetric geometry, nondecimal bases, and functions, because, from their own broad perspective of mathematics, they knew that these topics would unify, clarify, and promote meaning.

1.6. *Balance*

The major emphases of the elementary mathematics program during the traditional era were computational skills and social applications. Almost totally ignored was the essence of mathematics. The fact that mathematics is a dynamic science that is constantly changing was overlooked by the creators of the traditional curriculum. The beautiful patterns awaiting discovery by the inquisitive young mind were shunted aside by those who failed to recognize that these patterns offered the key to making mathematics functional, as well as to making it an exciting, adventuresome subject. It was not until the mathematician added to the curriculum the ingredients of mathematics that he found creative and inspiring that the subject reached its full potential for arousing the child's natural instinct to search for discoveries.

A careful presentation of computational skills, accompanied by application of these skills, probably did an adequate job of preparing the child for the *now*, but it did little to build a flexible structure on which he could build in the future. It was only after adding the study of structural properties to the curriculum that one could hope to prepare a child for the mathematics he would need in the future.

1.7. *Precision of Language*

The mathematician and the semanticist helped to develop a more precise language for the elementary mathematics curriculum. Insistence on distinguishing the name of a thing from the thing itself caused greater emphasis to be given to such ideas as number and numeral, geometric figures and their pictures, fractional numbers and fractions.

This new precision of language is especially evident in the language we now use to talk about fractional numbers. For example, a statement such as "Invert the divisor" is not allowed, because the divisor is a number (which is an abstract idea), and it would not be possible to invert it any more than to "Erase the number five from the board." Such expressions as "the top number," "Add the numbers down," and "22 has 2 twos" were also found to have faulty semantic bases.

This precision of language was incorporated into the mathematical area of measure, as well as into the area of number and numeration systems. Because no measure is exact, it was felt that the equality relation existing for numbers was not an appropriate relation for measure; therefore, the expression "equal in measure" was coined.

In Figure 1.5, we can see several ways this concept of equality of measure is designated.

12 inches $\overset{m}{=}$ 1 foot

(Read: 12 inches are equal in measure to 1 foot)

2 pints $\overset{m}{=}$ 1 quart

(Read: 2 pints are equal in measure to 1 quart)

$m\angle ABC = 90°$

(Read: the measure of angle ABC is 90°)

$\overset{m}{AB} = 3$ inches

(Read: the measure of line segment AB is 3 inches)

FIGURE 1.5

Precision of language became very pronounced in the area of geometry. This precision resulted in the coining of the following precise and correct statements: The set of boundary points constitutes the square; dots are pictures of points; a line (in the Euclidean sense) implies a straight line and there cannot exist curved lines; an angle and its measure are distinct ideas; and so on.

1.8. *Emphasis on Meaning*

Although the "meaning movement" predates modern mathematics by 20 years, its impact was not fully established until the advent of the modern mathematics movement.

The following statements represent findings from research done before 1950: There exists a greater retention and understanding if understanding precedes practice; primary children can systematically be taught meaningful mathematics if sufficient concrete experiences are provided; reliance on incidental learning experiences in arithmetic at the primary level results in large gaps in concept skills; meaningful learning is closely associated with an understanding of the structure of a number system; meaningful arithmetic offers the promise of aiding the child in reconstructing a concept when he has forgotten it.

1.9. *Incorporation of Recent Research*

In order to present a comprehensive discussion of the incorporation of recent research into the elementary curriculum, several hundred pages of discourse would be required. Because of the limitation on space, we shall look at only a few of the major areas of research that have had a significant impact on the elementary curriculum.

Greater availability of funds for research, more refined statistical techniques, better-designed research projects, more willingness to question the how and why of teaching of various mathematics topics—all have led to more and better mathematics-education research. In this section, we shall not attempt to evaluate the hundreds of reports of mathematics-education research. We shall, however, look at how certain research in the areas of meaning, methods, and curriculum has influenced the modern elementary mathematics curriculum.

The general acceptance of the results of recent readiness research has led to some major changes in the elementary curriculum. For example, the theory that there is an "ideal" time to teach each concept, as formulated by the Committee of Seven study in the 1920s, has been discredited by numerous researchers, such as Robert Davis, Newton Hawley, William Hull, Anthony Kallet, Patrick Suppes, and Jean Piaget.

Moving from a highly restricted concept of readiness, research has revealed that readiness is a "fluid" concept depending for interpretation on the teacher's presentation technique and level of abstraction, as well as on the continuous variable of the individual child's maturation. The child's readiness can be influenced by his physical maturation as well as by the depth of his previous experiences with the concept under consideration.

Davis[1] demonstrated that one could teach the basic algebraic concepts to fourth-, fifth-, and sixth-grade students if he used presentation techniques appropriate to the children's previous experiences. Piaget[2] pointed out that the prerequisite concepts needed for the mastery of plane geometry concepts were possessed by children at the age of 11.

---

[1] Robert Davis, "Algebra in Grades Four, Five and Six," *Grade Teacher*, vol. 79, p. 57, April, 1962.

[2] Jean Piaget, B. Inhelder, and A. Szeminska, *The Child's Conception of Geometry*, New York: Basic Books, Inc., 1960, pp. 389–408.

In addition to research conducted by individuals and teams of researchers, such as the School Mathematics Study Group, the Greater Cleveland Mathematics Project, the University of Illinois Arithmetic Project, the Madison Project, and the Minnesota Project, broad curriculum-research studies gave extensive support to the results of "readiness researchers." This support showed that thousands of elementary children could be taught concepts that previously had been held for presentation in high school and college.

One effect of this interpretation of readiness has been to develop a nonstatic curriculum. No longer is it possible to predict that by Christmas time, at a certain grade level, a specific topic will have been introduced. No longer is there *the* method appropriate for introducing a concept, because the method will vary in level of abstraction depending on the maturity of the children and on their previous experiences.

The implication for the beginning teacher is that he must be able to vary the presentation techniques to meet the needs of the students, rather than attempting to meet the students with a fixed curriculum. It also means that the teacher must have a good knowledge of a logical sequential development of a topic, because he will be expected to find out where the children's skill levels are and then develop their concepts from this point with the methods appropriate for their readiness level.

The implication of this readiness research requires that the teacher be responsible for selecting the essential topics to be covered at a given grade. When studying the methods presented in this text, keep in mind that a "perfect" method to fit all circumstances and levels of readiness does not exist. It will be the teacher's task to select and modify methods to meet the needs of the students.

A second area in which research has significantly affected the curriculum is in the area of the development of meanings. Numerous experimenters, such as William Brownell, Harold Moser, Esther Swenson, Henry Van Engen, and Glenadine Gibb have demonstrated that teaching the meaning behind algorithms leads to better transfer to new situations, leads to better insight into existing relationships, and provides a structure on which concepts can be reviewed easily when forgotten through disuse.

Van Engen and Gibb[3] demonstrated that when division was taught via a "subtractive" algorithm, children were able to extend their skills to new and more complex situations. Similar results were obtained by Brownell and Moser,[4] who found that children who were taught subtraction in a meaningful

---

[3] Henry Van Engen and Glenadine Gibb, *General Mental Functions Associated with Division*, Educational Service Studies, No. 2, Cedar Falls, Iowa: Iowa State Teachers College, 1956.

[4] William Brownell and Harold Moser, *Meaningful Versus Mechanical Learning—A Study in Grade III Subtraction*, Research Monograph No. 8, Durham, N.C.: Duke University Press, 1949.

way were better able to transfer to new situations than were children who were taught the same concept in a less meaningful way.

One implication of these research studies is that the presentation of modern elementary mathematics requires that the teacher be knowledgeable in the meanings of the various algorithms. He must know the "whys" behind the various algorithms and he must know how to present these meanings to the child.

Recent research studies on how children learn point out that the best techniques for teaching and learning vary from child to child. Numerous studies reflect the lack of an effective method or process for all children. For example, Van Engen and Gibb[5] found that children of low intellectual ability had less trouble with division when the subtractive process was used than when a conventional method was used. Rheins and Rheins[6] found that the "decomposition method" was more effective for teaching subtraction to the less intelligent student than was the "equals addition" method.

With the knowledge that different children learn by different techniques, the teacher assumes the responsibility for being able to teach a wide variety of techniques and algorithms. As you grow professionally, you will be required to accumulate more and more techniques of teaching in order to increase your effectiveness.

EXERCISES

1. Name 10 characteristics of the modern mathematics movement.
2. Are the characteristics of modern mathematics completely new, or are they largely a matter of degree?
3. What is one of the functions of structural concepts in the elementary mathematics curriculum?
4. Describe two techniques of involvement or discovery.
5. How do the techniques of modern mathematics meet individual differences?
6. How has the elementary mathematics curriculum been made more consistent?
7. In what ways has a balanced elementary mathematics curriculum been achieved?
8. In what way has language been made more precise in the elementary mathematics curriculum?

[5] Van Engen and Gibb, *op. cit.*

[6] Gladys B. Rheins and Joel J. Rheins, "A Comparison of Two Methods of Compound Subtraction: The Decomposition and the Equal Additions Method," *The Arithmetic Teacher*, vol. 2, pp. 63–67, October, 1955.

9. What are some of the ways research has influenced the elementary mathematics curriculum?
10. Let's explore: Using an elementary school mathematics series, find concepts in one of the following areas that would lend themselves to the discovery technique:
a. Generalizations   b. Geometry   c. Properties   d. Patterns

REFERENCES

BROWNELL, WILLIAM A., "Arithmetical Abstractions—Progress Toward Maturity of Concepts Under Differing Programs of Instruction," *The Arithmetic Teacher*, vol. 10, pp. 322–329, October, 1963.

BROWNELL, WILLIAM A., "The Place of Meaning in the Teaching of Arithmetic," *Elementary School Journal*, vol. 47, pp. 256–265, January, 1947.

BROWNELL, WILLIAM A., "The Progressive Nature of Learning in Mathematics," *The Mathematics Teacher*, vol. 37, pp. 147–157, April, 1944.

BROWNELL, WILLIAM A., "When Is Arithmetic Meaningful?" *Journal of Educational Research*, vol. 38, pp. 481–498, March, 1945.

BUSWELL, GUY T., "Arithmetic," *The Implications of Research for the Classroom Teacher, Joint Yearbook*, American Educational Research Association and the Department of Classroom Teachers, National Education Association, Washington, D.C.: National Education Association, 1939, pp. 190–198.

BUSWELL, GUY T., "Needed Research on Arithmetic," *The Teaching of Arithmetic, Fiftieth Yearbook, Part II*, National Society for the Study of Education, Chicago: University of Chicago Press, 1951, pp. 282–297.

CARPENTER, FINLEY, "The Effect of Different Learning Methods on Concept Formation," *Science Education*, vol. 40, pp. 282–285, October, 1956.

DAVIS, R. B., "Algebra in Grades Four, Five and Six," *Grade Teacher*, vol. 79, pp. 57 ff., April, 1962.

DIENES, Z. P., "The Growth of Mathematical Concepts in Children Through Experience," *Educational Research*, vol. 2, no. 1, pp. 9–28, 1959.

FEHR, HOWARD F., "A Philosophy of Arithmetic Instruction," *The Arithmetic Teacher*, vol. 2, pp. 27–32, April, 1955.

FEHR, HOWARD F., "Modern Mathematics and Good Pedagogy," *The Arithmetic Teacher*, vol. 10, pp. 402–411, November, 1963.

FOLSOM, M., "Why the New Mathematics?" *The Instructor*, vol. 73, pp. 7 ff., December, 1963.

GIBB, E. GLENADINE, "A Review of a Decade of Experimental Studies which Compared Methods of Teaching Arithmetic," *Journal of Educational Research*, vol. 46, pp. 603–608, April, 1953.

GLENNON, VINCENT J., and C. W. HUNNICUTT, *What Does Research Say About Arithmetic?*, Washington, D.C.: Association for Supervision and Curriculum Development, a department of the National Education Association, 1958, p. 77.

HEDDENS, JAMES W., and KENNETH J. SMITH, "The Readability of Elementary Mathematics Books," *The Arithmetic Teacher*, vol. 11, pp. 466–468, November, 1964.

HENDRIX, GERTRUDE, "Prerequisite to Meaning," *The Mathematics Teacher*, vol. 43, pp. 334–339, November, 1950.

HILDRETH, G., "Principles of Learning Applied to Arithmetic," *The Arithmetic Teacher*, vol. 1, pp. 1–5, October, 1954.

ILG, FRANCES, and LOUISE AMES, "Developmental Trends in Arithmetic," *Journal of Genetic Psychology*, vol. 79, pp. 3–28, September, 1951.

JACKSON, H. C., "Creative Thinking and Discovery," *The Arithmetic Teacher*, vol. 8, pp. 107–111, March, 1961.

JARVIS, OSCAR T., "An Analysis of Individual Differences in Arithmetic," *The Arithmetic Teacher*, vol. 11, pp. 471–473, November, 1964.

JOHNSON, HARRY C., "What Do We Mean by Discovery?" *The Arithmetic Teacher*, vol. 2, pp. 538–539, December, 1964.

KARSH, BERT Y., "Learning by Discovery," *The Arithmetic Teacher*, vol. 2, pp. 226–231, April, 1964.

KING, E. G., "Greater Flexibility in Abstract Thinking through Frame Arithmetic," *The Arithmetic Teacher*, vol. 10, pp. 183–187, April, 1963.

KNIPP, MINNIE B., "An Investigation of Experimental Studies which Compare Methods of Teaching Arithmetic," *Journal of Experimental Education*, vol. 13, pp. 23–30, September, 1944.

KOENKER, R. H., "Twenty Methods for Improving Problem Solving," *The Arithmetic Teacher*, vol. 5, pp. 74–78, March, 1958.

MARKS, J. L., "The Uneven Progress of the Revolution in Elementary School Mathematics," *The Arithmetic Teacher*, vol. 10, pp. 474–478, December, 1963.

MORTON, ROBERT L., "Language and Meaning in Arithmetic," *Educational Research Bulletin*, vol. 34, pp. 197–204, November, 1955.

PAGE, D. A., *Number Lines, Functions and Fundamental Topics*, Urbana, Ill.: University of Illinois, Arithmetic Project, 1961.

PIAGET, JEAN, "How Children Form Mathematical Concepts," *Scientific American*, vol. 189, no. 3, pp. 74–79, 1953.

PINCUS, M., "An Adventure in Discovery," *The Arithmetic Teacher*, vol. 11, pp. 28–29, January, 1964.

SCHMINKE, C. W., "A Time for Precision," *The Arithmetic Teacher*, vol. 2, pp. 395–401, October, 1964.

SUPPES, PATRICK, and FREDERICK BINFORD, "Experimental Teaching of Mathematical Logic in the Elementary School," *The Arithmetic Teacher*, vol. 12, pp. 187–195, March, 1965.

TILTON, JOHN W., "Individualized and Meaningful Instruction in Arithmetic," *Journal of Educational Psychology*, vol. 38, pp. 83–88, February, 1947.

UICSM Project Staff, "Arithmetic with Frames," *The Arithmetic Teacher*, vol. 4, pp. 119–124, April, 1957.

WALLACH, MICHAEL A., "Research on Children's Thinking," *Child Psychology*, *Sixty-second Yearbook*, National Society for the Study of Education, Chicago: University of Chicago Press, 1963.

WEAVER, J. FRED, "Research on Arithmetic Instruction—1957," *The Arithmetic Teacher*, vol. 5, pp. 109–119, April, 1958.

WEAVER, J. FRED, "Six Years of Research on Arithmetic Instruction: 1951–1956," *The Arithmetic Teacher*, vol. 4, pp. 89–99, April, 1957.

WIRTZ, R. W., "Nonverbal Instruction," *The Arithmetic Teacher*, vol. 10, pp. 72–77, February, 1963.

WRIGHTSTONE, J. WAYNE, "Influence of Research on Instruction in Arithmetic," *The Mathematics Teacher*, vol. 45, pp. 187–192, March, 1952.

Problems derived from advertisements can motivate a child to learn mathematics.

2

Introduction to Problem Solving

2.1. *What Is Problem Solving?*

PROBLEM solving is the process of reorganizing concepts and skills into a new pattern of application that opens a path to a goal. This is in contrast to the application of a habitual pattern to reach a previously attained goal. For example, suppose your goal on the first day of school were to get to this class. There were several alternative ways of reaching this goal. Some of these are as follows:

You could have looked up the classroom number and location in the schedule of classes and then, using this information, have found your way to class;

Or you could have found someone who was taking this class and followed him to class;

Or you could have attempted to reach your goal by visiting each classroom in the school and asking the people in each classroom what course was being taught in that room;

Or if you had an idea in which building courses of this type were taught, you could have come to this building and asked someone in the hall where the class was being taught.

Perhaps each of these techniques had helped you solve similar problems in the past. Or, perhaps you selected one of them as the method that had been the most efficient in the past. However, getting to class on the second day is a habitual application of your recent problem-solving experience and hence ceases to be identified as a problem-solving situation.

2.2. *The Teacher's Responsibilities*

There are two factors that play a role in problem solving for which you as the teacher have a prime responsibility for nurturing. These factors are the concepts and skills that a child brings to a problem-solving situation and his repertoire of previously solved problems.

For example, suppose we pose the following problem to a sixth-grade class:

> You are an engineer and it is your responsibility to find the distance across a gorge so that you can draw up plans for a bridge to cross this gorge. How would you go about finding the distance across the gorge?

A student might bring to this problem some or all of the following:

1. An understanding of linear measure
2. A knowledge of measuring instruments
3. A knowledge of concepts relating to right triangles
4. A knowledge of proportion and rules of proportion with respect to various geometric figures
5. Experience in solving problems involving linear measurements where both direct and indirect methods have led to satisfactory solutions

The child's normal path to the goal of determining the distance across the gorge—that is, by direct measurement—is blocked. He will not be able to use a habitual response pattern and thus is faced with a real problem situation. His solution might consist of getting a string to the other side of the gorge by an arrow, or a helicopter, or by some other means, and then retrieving the string and associating the length of the string with the distance across the gorge. Or, it might consist of a more sophisticated approach such as triangulation or using proportional sides of a triangle.

The degree of flexibility and sophistication that the child can exhibit will be directly proportional to the number of concepts you have helped him develop and the extensiveness of his repertoire of solved problems of a similar nature.

2.3. *Developing the Child's Repertoire*

Before investigating some of the areas from which problems can be selected, let us examine some of the vehicles through which a child's repertoire can be developed. To gain an awareness of how problems arise in a child's environment, you must be able to pose problems from a variety of events and things. It is for this reason that the following list is presented—to develop your sensitivity to vehicles for problem solving.

Vehicle	*Example*
Role playing	Two children are playing store. One child has to make change for the other child.
Current events	A 300-bed hosiptal was just constructed in Maintown. What is the ratio of potential patients to beds? How would you go about determining if this ratio is an adequate ratio for Maintown?
Advertisements	Brand X tire sells for $8.70 and has an 18-month guarantee. Brand Y sells for $9.20 and has a 24-month guarantee. Find the factors that should influence your decision on which tire to purchase.
Science	Derive a hardness test for a set of rocks.
Graphs	Given a graph depicting traffic densities in each of the school's hallways during the noon hour, devise a traffic pattern that will minimize congestion.
Data	Find an equation to fit the following data:

$\bigcirc$	3	1	8	4	5
$\triangle$	10	3	65	17	26

Maps	Determine a round-trip route between City A and City B such that the traveler will never be on the same road twice and such that he would travel the fewest number of miles by taking this round-trip route.
Constructions	Using a compass and a straight edge, construct a hexagon.
Patterns	What would be the next number in the sequence: 1, 2, 3, 5, 8, 13?

Although the story "problems" found in elementary school texts may occasionally be genuine problems for the children, their chief function is to develop the skills and concepts prerequisite to problem solving. These story problems permit application of computational skills and help the child learn the skill of translating problem situations into mathematical equations, but they rarely permit the possibility of many alternative paths to the goal.

The set of story problems found in elementary texts is neither extensive enough nor varied enough to give the child an adequate repertoire of solved problems. It will be your responsibility to supplement these problems with those of your own creation. Therefore, you should begin making your own repertoire as extensive and as varied as possible in order to be prepared to challenge your students with both creative and real problem situations.

2.4. *Types of Problem Situations*

When a child learns to translate a problem situation into an open sentence and then finds one or more numbers that make this sentence true, he has mastered only one aspect of problem solving. Not all mathematical problems have as one of their goals a numerical answer, and even when a numerical answer is obtained, it is often an intermediate point in the problem-solving process and an interpretation or value judgment must still be made with regard to it. Sometimes the problem is simply one of developing a system for organizing the data into a usable format. Or the problem may involve breaking down a mathematical model into machine language in such a manner that an efficient translation is effected. Or the problem may involve creating a unit of measurement or developing a measuring instrument that will give better precision than is possible with the measuring instruments currently available.

Because of the variety of guises in which we can find problem situations, it will be necessary for you to acquaint yourself with the broad area of applied mathematics. You should acquaint yourself with the problems that arise in the sciences and social sciences and in business, economics, government, and daily social activities. At the end of this chapter exercises are given designed to acquaint you with a variety of sources for story problems.

2.5. *Guidelines for Developing Problem-Solving Skills*

If everyone faced the same problems in life or we could readily categorize all of the problems people would face or there existed only a limited number of possible problems, then we could teach children to solve problems by mastering set response patterns that could then be applied rationally to problems. However, not only is the number of problems to which the child can now be faced almost unlimited, but in our rapidly expanding technological society the problems of tomorrow have not yet been identified. It is for these reasons that we must pursue a program that will foster flexibility in the child's ability to solve problems.

In order to foster such flexibility in problem solving the following principles are suggested:

1. Not only should the child be given the skills necessary to solve problems, but he should also be taught how to identify and delimit problems.

2. Not only should the child be taught how to translate a problem into a mathematical sentence, but he should also be taught how to translate the problem into a simpler model of the problem.
3. Not only should the child be taught how to find alternative paths to his goal, but he should also be taught how to decide which of these is the most efficient path.
4. Not only should the child be taught how to derive a numerical answer, but he should also be taught how to interpret and use the information practically.
5. Not only should a child be taught to check his results, but he should also be taught to modify his solution as new data becomes available to him. In other words, he should be made aware of the fact that the answer for today may not be the answer for tomorrow.
6. Not only should a child be taught to solve problems, but he should also be taught to create problems.

   Throughout the remainder of this text we shall discuss techniques for providing the child with the skills necessary for problem solving. We shall also suggest classes of various types of problems that should be added to the child's repertoire.

EXERCISES

1. Identify two situations you might find yourself in that represent real problems.
2. Identify two situations that permit the routine application of habitual responses.
3. Give an example of a problem situation involving mathematics that could be posed using each of the following vehicles.
   a. A field trip to a zoo
   b. A field trip to a service station
   c. A game
   d. A geometry lesson
   e. A social studies lesson
   f. A music lesson
   g. A language lesson
4. Pose a problem that has at least three alternate solutions.
5. Identify some of the skills and concepts that might be prerequisites for the solution of each of the following types of problems:
   a. Estimating the cost of a trip
   b. Estimating how much paint will be needed to paint a house
   c. Estimating how much time will be required to make a given trip
   d. Estimating the amount of organic matter in a truckload of sand
   e. Determining the area of a circle

REFERENCES

D'AUGUSTINE, CHARLES H., "Developing Generalizations with Topological Net Problems," *The Arithmetic Teacher*, vol. 12, February, 1965, pp. 109–112.

DORRIE, HEINRICH, *100 Great Problems of Elementary Mathematics*, New York: Dover Publications, 1965.

HENDERSON, KENNETH B., and ROBERT E. PINGRY, "Problem-Solving in Mathematics," *Twenty-first Yearbook*, National Council of Teachers of Mathematics, Washington, D.C.: National Council of Teachers of Mathematics, 1953, chap. 8.

KOENKER, ROBERT H., "Twenty Methods for Improving Problem Solving," *The Arithmetic Teacher*, vol. 5, March, 1958, pp. 74–78.

LUCHINS, ABRAHAM S., "Mechanization in Problem Solving: The Effect of Einstellung," *Psychological Monographs*, vol. 54, no. 248, 1948.

POLYA, GEORGE, *Mathematical Discovery: On Understanding and Teaching Problem Solving*, New York: John Wiley & Sons, Inc., 1962.

THORNDIKE, ROBERT L., "How Children Learn the Principles and Techniques of Problem Solving," *Learning and Instruction, Forty-ninth Yearbook, Part 1*, National Society for the Study of Education, Chicago: University of Chicago Press, 1950.

TIETZ, HEINRICH, *Famous Problems of Mathematics*, New York: Graylock Press, 1965.

A child's preschool experience can motivate him to learn mathematics.

3

Teaching the Whole Numbers

3.1. *Introduction*

SUPPOSE a child entering school for the first time were to ask you, "What is the number four?" You might be tempted to say, "Why, it's a whole number." Although it is true that the number four can be an element of the set of whole numbers, this explanation would not convey to the child what the number four is. You might tell the child that it is a positive number. Even though it is true that the child will eventually learn about directed numbers, these numbers are not the first numbers he encounters in the elementary school. You might be tempted to tell him that the number four is a symbol. The number four is not a symbol. A symbol, 4, which we call the numeral, is merely a name for the number, in much the same sense that the word *box* is the name for the object, box. Then what is the number four? It is the property of all the sets in the world that can be put into a one-to-one correspondence with the set {one, two, three, four} or the set {apple, orange, pin, car}.

31

3.2. *Techniques of Presenting Sets*

Before we undertake the presentation techniques of teaching specific number properties, and because this presentation will involve, to a large extent, the concept of sets, we shall first investigate techniques of identifying sets. There are essentially four basic ways of identifying sets for children. One way is to use braces. See Figure 3.1.

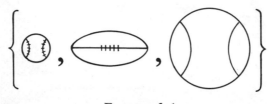

FIGURE 3.1

Each member of the set is separated from the other members by a comma. If we were to leave out one comma, say between the baseball and the football, the number property of the set would be two instead of three.

A second method presenting a set is to list the members of the set. For example, you could write down the words *baseball*, *football*, and *basketball*. This would be a method of listing the set. A class roll is another example of listing a set. Sometimes the listing of a set is referred to as a roster.

Another technique for presenting sets is to loop them. This method is used extensively at the elementary school level. For example, if you had occasion to be talking to your children about a set of pictures on the board, you would draw a loop around the set. The students thus could identify the set about which you were speaking.

The fourth method of presenting sets is to place the objects you want designated to one set proximate to each other. If you use this technique, be careful that the children can easily discriminate the different sets. Figure 3.2 shows these four basic techniques.

3.3. *Sets and Their Properties*

In Figure 3.3, we have a picture of a set of fruit. Each element has the property of sweetness and roundness.

In Figure 3.4, we have a set of animals. One of the properties of each element of the set is the property of animalness. Each element has a property of two-eyedness. Does each element of the set have the property of hairiness? No, because the chicken does not have hair. Does each element have the

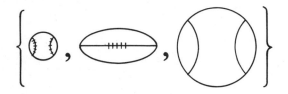

baseball, football, basketball

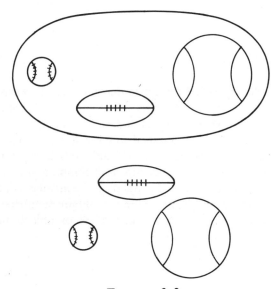

FIGURE 3.2

property of teethness? No, because a chicken does not have teeth. Does each element have the property of leggedness?

The set in Figure 3.4 has a number property. It has the number property of four. How is it possible to talk about a set having properties, when we normally assign a property to an element of a set? We can assign a property to a set by considering the set an element of a superset. For example, the set of all sets having the property of fourness might be designated as follows: $\{\{1, 2, 3, 4\}, \{a, c, d, f\}, \{\Box, \bigcirc, \triangle, O\}, \{ \backslash, C, \Box, \mathcal{R} \}, \ldots\}$ (The three

$$\{ \bigcirc, \, \sigma, \, \bigcirc \}$$

FIGURE 3.3

FIGURE 3.4

dots indicate that there exists an infinite set of sets with the number property of four.)

It is important that a teacher recognize that there are two aspects of every discrete set. One is a description of the set (for example, a set of dogs, a set of trash, a set of coins). The other aspect is that each element of a discrete set has certain properties that can be identified. You will want your children not only to be able to describe sets, but also to be able to talk about the properties of each of the elements. Some elements may have common properties, but they do not have to have a single common property to be members of the same set.

Sets that can be described do not have to contain members of the same class. For example, in Figure 3.5 we have a set of objects taken from a 10-year-old boy's pocket.

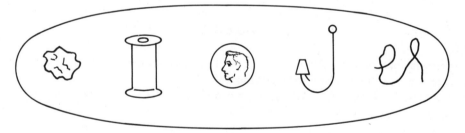

FIGURE 3.5

In describing this set, we could simply say, "This is a set of objects from a 10-year-old boy's pocket." We see that the elements of this set consist of a rock, a spool, a coin, a fishhook with a cork stuck on it, and a string.

Any collection of objects can be described as a set. For example, we could put pictures of a fishhook, a girl's face, and a comb together and call them a set. This set would have the number property of three. A set can be any collection of objects capable of description. We must be able to ascertain when a given element is or is not a member of the set, either from the description or from viewing the set. When a set is discrete, it is possible to talk about its number property. For example, we could say that the set in Figure 3.5 has a number property of five, provided it is understood that the cork and the fishhook represent one thing. Or we could say that this set has the number property of six, if we wanted to view the cork and the fishhook as two distinct things.

Another example of this idea is represented by a set that contains a cup and a saucer. We could say that this cup and saucer represent one thing. Or we could say that the saucer is one thing and the cup is another, so that the number property of the cup and the saucer represents two things. It is important in presenting sets to the students to make it quite clear which elements of the sets can be viewed as distinct elements. (When using brace notation, you can accomplish this by separating each distinct item from another item with a comma. Where brace notation is not used, spacing is the proper technique for distinguishing distinct elements of a set.)

One of the most important ideas you are going to be interested in investigating is which sets have the same number property. The following statement defines which sets have the same number property.

> *Definition:* Two sets have the same number property if, and only if, they can be matched one-to-one.

It is important that this concept be taught before specific number properties of sets are taught. For example, before you teach a child that a particular set has a number property of three, you must get the child to understand that all of the sets that will match a given set one-to-one are equal in number. This concept is developed by giving the child many opportunities to match sets one-to-one. For example, is the number of mice equal to the number of pieces of cheese in Figure 3.6? (Yes.) The child could establish this simply by matching each picture of a mouse with each picture of a piece of cheese.

FIGURE 3.6

In Figure 3.7, we see that after each bee has been matched with one flower, there is one flower that has no bee on it. We can assert that there are fewer bees than there are flowers, or that there are more flowers than there are bees; therefore, the number of bees is not the same as the number of flowers.

After a child understands the one-to-one relationship of matched sets and, thus, that the number properties of such sets are equal, he is ready to learn specific number properties.

FIGURE 3.7

3.4. *Defining Specific Whole Numbers*

Most children come to the first grade with the skill of being able to identify the number property of a set when that property is the number one. How did they learn this concept? It was learned by looking repeatedly at sets of one and hearing someone say, "This is one, and that is one, and there is one," and so on. After a while, the child intuitively grasped the concept of oneness, even though he could not verbalize why a certain set had the property of oneness. He mentally matched a set he knew had the number property of one with his new set in order to determine if the new set was also a set of one.

The whole numbers are defined in much the same way that the child views the number one. For example, we can tell everyone formally what the number one is by the following definition:

> *Definition:* All sets will be said to have the number property of one if they can be matched one-to-one with the set { }. (Any set with the number property of one could have been chosen as our master set against which all other sets will be matched.)

We define the number two in a similar manner:

> *Definition:* All sets will be said to have the number property of two if they can be matched one-to-one with the set { , }. (Again, any set with the number property of two could have been chosen as our master set against which all other sets will be matched.)

In general, our method of defining a specific whole number for a child will consist of our selecting a set with this number property and then telling the child that it has this number property. Then we shall tell the child that all sets matching this set one-to-one also have this number property. The child should be given many opportunities to discover sets with the number property of the teacher's master set by searching his environment for sets that can be put into one-to-one correspondence with the master set.

EXERCISES (1)

1. Describe a set whose elements have all of the following properties: shininess, smoothness.
2. Draw a picture of a set of plants, and list three properties common to each element of this set.
3. Present one set by each of the following techniques: braces, listing, looping, proximity.
4. Define the number four.
5. Define the number zero, using { } as the master set.
6. What is incorrect about the following sentence? "The teacher wrote the number three on the board."
7. Look up the meaning of the word *discrete* in an unabridged dictionary.

3.5. *Cardinal Number as Distinguished from Ordinal Number*

If you were asked the number property of the set in Figure 3.8, you would say that it is the number two.

FIGURE 3.8

You would be giving the cardinal number of this set. Cardinal numbers answer such questions as how many or how much. For example, if you say, "The boy had three apples," you are talking about *how many* apples are in the set. Or if you make the statement, "I bought three pounds of meat," you are talking about *how much* meat was bought. Such statements as, "I saw three birds," "I got six right on the test," "I weigh one hundred twenty pounds," all contain words that identify the cardinal number of a set.

It is also possible to refer to an ordinal number with respect to a set. Numbers that identify *which* object in a set you are talking about are called ordinal numbers. If you say, "This is a set of three boys," you are speaking of the cardinal number of a set, but if you say, "This is the third boy," you are referring to an ordinal aspect of the set.

When you identify the *which one* within a set, you are focusing on some specific *ordered* arrangement of the set and, more specifically, on an element within the ordering. A number used to identify which one within an ordered set is called an ordinal number. When you identify the number property of the whole set, however, you are giving an answer to the question how many or how much, and you are thus talking about a cardinal number.

There are certain things that you, as a teacher, need to do before you can teach the idea of an ordinal number. First, you must establish where a person is supposed to *start* counting the elements of the set. You must also give directions concerning which object is the next one, and the next one, and so on.

For example, assume that you have a series of pictures scattered on the board and you ask the question, "Which is the second one?" Your students can't answer this question until they have been told how they are to determine which is the first one, and then how they are to find the next, and the next. Notice in Figure 3.9 that it is possible to find the second element or the fourth element because a picture of a path has been superimposed upon the pictures.

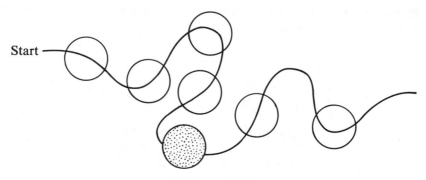

Start

FIGURE 3.9

If you follow the path, it not only will tell you where to start, but it will also tell you how to find each succeeding element. If you were to start at the other end of the path, the third picture would be the one that was shaded. Sometimes a situation is already prestructured. For example, children lined up at a drinking fountain can tell automatically who is the first and how to find the next one simply by counting down the line one person at a time. But if a set is scrambled, then you, as the teacher, have the task of devising some scheme whereby the children can determine the starting point, and then how to find the next, and the next, and so on.

The child will learn that he determines the name of the ordinal number identifying an element within an ordered set by counting the elements in the set and then modifying the last number name stated in counting. For example, the child might count, " One, two, three, four, five, six." He would then say that the last object he counted was the six*th*.

Generally, a person can identify whether a number is being used in an ordinal sense or in a cardinal sense from the word or the symbol that is being used to name the number. For example, the *th* in the word *fourth*, or *th* in the symbol *4th* establishes that four is being used in an ordinal sense. However, there are instances when the th is omitted, and then we must interpret a number's usage from context. For example, " I live at 302 North McKinley." The 302 identifies *which* house I live in. Although it is true that there may not be a 301 North McKinley, the number 302 still conveys the idea of which house. If a person were looking for 308 North McKinley and came from the 200 block to 302 North McKinley, he would know that he must continue in that direction to find 308 North McKinley.

Suppose a student is assigned the number 4602. What does this number mean? The number 4602 indentifies him in terms of when he came into the school system. We can be sure that 4601 students were assigned numbers before him. This number doesn't tell us that there are only 4602 students enrolled in school, however. The number 4602 determines *which one* of the students he is in terms of the total set of students.

Sometimes we use names for numbers when we have no desire either to talk about the number of a set or about a particular ordered element of the set. In these cases, we simply use the numeral to label elements of a set. For example, when a football player has the numeral 14 on the back of his shirt, does the 14 mean that he is the fourteenth player? Does the 14 mean that there are 14 players? Obviously, the 14 is not related to order and thus is not an ordinal number. The 14 is not related to the number property of a set, and thus it is not a cardinal number. The 14 is only a label. Other examples of this type of symbolic usage are 7-Up, Boeing 707, Club 21, and so on.

What kind of a number is the three when one talks of a three-cent stamp? Does the three tell a person how much money the stamp is worth? Does it tell which one it is? Does it tell you that it is the third stamp in a sequence of stamps, beginning with a one-cent stamp and going to a two-cent stamp, a three-cent stamp, and so on (assuming that there aren't any half-cent stamps issued)? Obviously, the answers to the last three questions are "yes," and we see that some numbers can be both cardinal and ordinal.

Another example of this dual usage is found in the sentence: " He is 21 years old today." Does the statement tell us how old he is? Does it also tell " which " year of his life he has completed?

3.6. *Teaching the Concept of Number*

Because we have reviewed the mathematical concepts underlying our presentation of the idea of number, we are ready to investigate how the number concept is presented to the child.

One of the first things to teach a child in the elementary school is to distinguish when one set has more objects, fewer objects, or the same number of objects as another set. Even before you teach him specific cardinal numbers, you must teach him to make these distinctions. You must be able to say and to demonstrate, "This set has more (or fewer or the same number of) objects than another set." You do this by teaching a child to pair the elements of two sets. This pairing can take the form of physically attempting to put each item of one set with each item of a second set, or, when working with pictures of objects, by pairing via connecting marks. (See Figure 3.10.)

FIGURE 3.10

When the child finds elements in one set that he cannot pair in the second set because every item in the second set has been matched, he learns to say that the first set has more objects than the second set. If the sets match one-to-one, he learns to say that the sets are equal in number.

When children enter the first grade, they sometimes think that length or size is related to the cardinality of a set. Because length has absolutely nothing to do with the cardinality of a set, experiences should be provided that will correct this misconception. Give the children exercises where one set of objects arranged linearly, whose number is less than another, is actually the longer of two sets. You might use a set of large box cars from a toy train and a set of small box cars. If the child says that the longer set has more objects than the shorter set, he is thinking of "more" in terms of length rather than in terms of number. Ask him to prove that the longer set has more objects than the shorter set by trying to match the elements of the two sets one-to-one. In this way, you will lead the child to see the "moreness" in terms of the set's number property rather than in terms of its length.

After the child has paired the sets, ask him which set has more. It is important for him to understand that if two sets match one-to-one, they have the same number property; if they do not match one-to-one, they do not have the same number property, and the set with unpaired members has more objects than the other set. When a child discriminates in this manner, we say he understands the concept of "one-to-one correspondence."

Another way you can develop this concept is to proceed as follows: After the first few days of school, put away all the chairs that will not have children sitting in them when everyone is in attendance. In other words, have one chair under each desk for every child that you have on your roll. Have the children check attendance for you simply by looking around the room and seeing if any of the chairs are empty. The children determine whether the number of chairs is the same as the number of children in attendance by establishing one-to-one correspondence.

A second activity promoting the concept of one-to-one correspondence is that of having a child pass out a set of things to the class. (Always precount the set to insure that the number of objects will correspond to the number of children in the room.)

A third activity involves having everyone bring a bottle cap or small pebble to school. Place an empty box by the door. As the children go out to the playground, have each child put his bottle cap or pebble in the box. When they come back in from the playground, have each child reach in and pick up one bottle cap or pebble and take it back to his seat. When the children are seated, pass the box among the children to see if everyone came back in from the playground. If there are any objects left in the box, the children know that someone did not come back to the classroom or that a child forgot to pick up a bottle cap when he came back into the classroom. You cannot discount this possibility.

A fourth activity in which the children can participate is that of lining up in pairs. Each child will be matched with one other child. Ask the questions: "Does everyone have a partner? Are there the same number of people in each line?" (If there is an odd number of children, the teacher may participate.)

3.7. *Oral Number Vocabulary*

Concurrently with the development of specific numbers—in other words, when you start teaching a child that this is a set of three and this is a set of five—you will want to provide the child with experiences that will help make the number-word names a part of his oral vocabulary. (You should begin to develop the meaning of number before the number words are introduced, by using such statements as, "You have as many pennies as fingers on your hand," or "You have as many eyes as ears, because they match one-to-one," and so on.)

A child has to be able to say the word *five* concurrently with attaching meaning to this sound, although he can comprehend fiveness without knowing the word five. In order to get children to make these words a part of their oral vocabulary, you may have them engage in such activities as singing number songs and saying number poems. Such songs as "Ten Little Indians," "Hickory, Dickory, Dock," and "One to Ten," as well as poems such as "Baa, Baa, Black Sheep," "Rub-a-Dub-Dub," and "Ten Little Pennies," help establish these number words in the child's oral vocabulary. They can be used in conjunction with the meaningful activities described in the next section.

3.8. *Teaching the Number Properties of Sets*

We are now in a position to investigate how we teach children the number properties of sets. A first activity might involve your going around the room to show the children sets of one and simultaneously telling them that each of the sets is one. (It is a rare event when a teacher finds a child entering the first grade who cannot identify the number properties of sets of one, two, and three.)

After you have identified sets of one, you identify sets of two for them in a similar manner. As you identify sets of two, have your students find other sets with this number property by matching these sets one-to-one with your master sets. Students should be encouraged to discover many sets with the given number property.

Use care in conveying the number properties of these master sets to a child. When you attempt to teach the cardinal concept, it is wise to choose examples that reflect only cardinal numbers. It is also wise to restrict your examples to situations involving only ordinal numbers when teaching that concept. For example, when the teacher says, "This is one, this is two, this is three, and this is four. Can everybody see that we have four?" she is using an ordinal technique to teach the cardinal concept. (See Figure 3.11.)

Not only is it important to use care in the selection of examples in teaching cardinality and ordinality, but it is important also to be careful in selecting the visual aids for teaching these concepts. A more appropriate teaching aid for conveying the cardinality of a set can be seen in Figure 3.12.

Now when the teacher says, "This is one, this is two, this is three, and this is four," referring to Figure 3.12, it is quite clear that she is referring to the

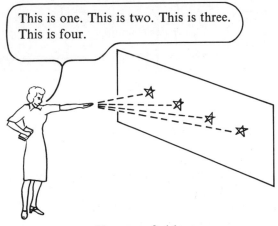

FIGURE 3.11

cardinal number of a set. Do not use a set of objects as a visual aid in teaching the cardinal number of a set unless it really conveys the number property of the whole set.

A flannel board or a magnetic board will be useful aids in teaching the number properties of various sets. Figure 3.13 depicts how a flannel board

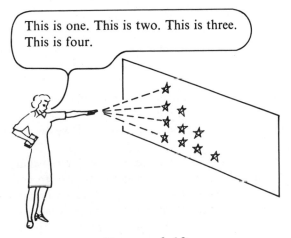

FIGURE 3.12

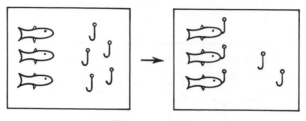

FIGURE 3.13

might be arranged to teach the number three. An accompanying dialogue might be as follows:

"Here we have a set of three fish. Are there more than three fishhooks on the board?" (Yes.)

"Johnny, show that there are more than three fishhooks on the board by pairing a fish with a fishhook until all the fish have been paired. Mary, how do we know there are more fishhooks than there are fish?" (Because we have some fishhooks left over.)

"How would we know if there were just three fishhooks on the board?" (The fishhooks would match the fish one-to-one.)

"Mary, remove some fishhooks from the board so that we have only three fishhooks on the board."

As an alternate method for teaching number, you might use a counting approach, or an $n + 1$ approach.

To develop the concept of number, start with 1 as being a number concept possessed by all entering students. Then proceed to establish 2 as 1 and 1 more, 3 as 2 and 1 more, 4 as 3 and 1 more, and so on. The following dialogue might be used to convey the number property of six: (Six objects are displayed on a flannel board.)

"Would someone volunteer to count out five of these objects?" (Mary counts out five of the objects.)

"How many more than five objects do we have on the board?" (One.)

At this point, you can tell the children that 1 more than 5 is 6, or you might have a child who can count six count the set to determine that the number property is six. You also could have a child who knows already that the number of objects is six volunteer the answer. You would at this point begin matching and patterning experiences such as those discussed in the preceding paragraphs using the fish and fishhook illustrations.

3.9. *Teaching Common Number Patterns*

After you have identified for the children various sets with the number properties of one through ten, you will want to teach the children the skill of identifying the number property of a set through common patterns. This is especially important, of course, if you begin developing pattern recognition before the development of extensive counting experiences. You can accomplish this by working with pattern cards. It is important to present more than one pattern for sets with a number property of two or greater. In Figure 3.14, several sets of different usable patterns are shown.

```
 0    0     0     0      0 0    0 0    0 0    0 0    0 0
0 0    0 0    0 0    0 0 0   0 0 0   0 0 0   0 0 0   0 0 0 0   0 0 0 0 0
               0     0 0    0 0 0   0 0 0 0   0 0 0   0 0 0
                                                     0 0 0   0 0 0 0
                     0     00    000    0000    000     000
 00    000    0000    0000    0000    0000    0000    000     000  0
                                                     000     000


 0     0     0     0 0    0 0    0 0    0 0      0 0 0    0 0
 0     0     0     0 0    0 0    0 0 0    0 0  0   0 0 0    0 0
       0     0     0 0    0 0    0 0    0 0  0   0 0     0 0
             0     0                                0       0 0
                                                            0 0


 0    0 0    0 0    0 0    0 0    0000    0000    0 0    0 0
 0    0 0    0 0    0 0    0 0     0 0    0000    0 0    0 0
                   0 0     0 0                    0000    0000
                   0 0                                     0
```

FIGURE 3.14

There are many commercial and noncommercial aids that can be used for this purpose. You can use dominos, playing cards, or patterns found in the environment. Children need the opportunity to develop the skill of sight recognition of patterns of sets with the number properties of one, two, three, four, and five; then, when you begin teaching a common pattern for six, seven, eight, nine, and ten, you can employ combinations of the previously learned patterns.

For example, you can teach children to recognize a set of six as a set of two and a set of four ([: : :]). Some educators feel that it is important for the child to attain some proficiency with the skill of recognizing the number property of common patterns before he masters completely the skill of determining the number property of a set by counting. This proficiency may vary, depending on the child, from one or two patterns for each number two through five, to as many as seven or eight patterns for the more competent child. You may find that some children have mastered the skill of determining the number of a set by counting prior to being introduced to pattern recognition. Some educators feel that the child will see little sense in learning the new skill when he already has a way to determine the number property of a set, inefficient as this method may be.

Still other educators argue that counting leads to a more natural development of the concept of number and that the child progresses just as rapidly when counting is stressed first. They maintain that counting will be stressed in the child's preschool learning experiences and that it is thus impractical to precede counting experiences with pattern recognition.

3.10. *Teaching Counting*

Counting is a necessary skill for the child, because he will need it to find the number property of sets with many elements. When introducing counting, you should encourage the students to try to tell you the number property of the set to be counted by having them use the pattern-recognition technique (provided you have taught this prior to the counting). You then follow this with the technique of reestablishing the number of the set through counting. For example, you might ask them,

"How many is this?" ⬭ They would say five (or three and two). (If, however, the counting has preceded the pattern recognition, you should have the students try to find patterns of five after they have determined the number property by counting.)

Then say, "Let's see how we can find out that we have five by counting. One, two, three, four, five." (Place your finger on a new dot as you say a new word.)

"Which of these words told us how many there were? The last word we said was five, and that word also names the number of items in this set. Let's see if this method will work again. How many dots have we here?" ⬚⬚ The children would say eight (or four and four).

"Let's see if we can find out the number of dots by counting. One, two, three, four, five, six, seven, eight." Ask which of these words told how many dots there were.

There are two skills involved in the act of counting. It requires one skill to count a set of five, and quite a different skill to count five from a set containing more than five. These are two very distinct ideas. It is important that you teach both of these skills. In the first skill, the child knows that when he associates a number word with the last object, this word tells him how many objects are in the set.

It is a far more difficult task to give a child a set of more than five objects and to have him count five of these. He has to listen for the word five as he is performing the act of counting. In the first skill, he stops automatically when his hand reaches the last one. But in the second skill, he has to be aware constantly of the fact that when he hears the word five this is his cue to stop. In order to help a child acquire both of these skills, it is essential that he be given experiences that require him not only to count a set, but also to create a set of a specified number by counting.

3.11. *Teaching the Concept Zero*

The number concept of zero is extremely important and requires a presentation technique quite different from the techniques used to teach the numbers one through 10. For example, the number of three-legged pink elephants in your room right now is zero. The number of purple-haired fish in the world is zero. Typical statements to first-graders might be: "John got zero problems wrong; there are zero people absent today; Mary had zero papers left after she gave everyone a paper." Statements like these, which call the child's attention to sets with the number property of zero, are necessary for teaching this concept.

3.12. *Teaching the Child to Read Numerals 0 Through 9*

You have now seen techniques for giving children some of the basic ideas about the number property of sets whose numbers range from zero to nine. Let us now discuss helping the child go from the concept to the symbolism for the concept.

First, you need to teach the children to read the symbol, and later to write the symbol. In the beginning, always display the numeral together with the set whose number property is named by that numeral. (0, 1, 2, 3, 4, 5, 6, 7, 8, and 9 are referred to as digits. This basic set of 10 digits is used to write all numerals in the decimal system.) For example, 2 names the number property of the set $\{\triangle\ \bigcirc\}$.

After you have had several days of "reading" the numerals 0 through 9 and relating them to their associated sets, give the children discrimination exercises consisting of matching sets with the numerals that name the number property of these sets.

An example of this type of matching exercise can be seen in Figure 3.15.

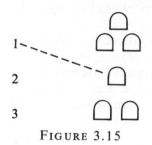

FIGURE 3.15

A teacher should guard against giving the child a matching exercise such as the one pictured in Figure 3.16 if he is attempting to teach the cardinal concept.

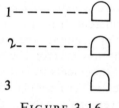

FIGURE 3.16

When you are attempting to teach the cardinality of a set—in other words, the number property of the whole set—you should refrain from exercises that relate to the ordinal concept, such as the one depicted by Figure 3.16, where the 2 obviously refers to the second element of the set and not to two things.*

EXERCISES (2)

1. Write two sentences that contain cardinal-number expressions.
2. Write two sentences that contain ordinal-number expressions.
3. Find the names of two children's songs that contain the word names for the numbers one through 10.
4. Find one poem that could be used to introduce the word names for numbers into the child's vocabulary.
5. Write a description of three sets that you might use to introduce the concept of four.
6. Make up five patterns that could be used to teach a child common patterns of four.

* See a manual on handwriting for a specific guide to teaching the writing of the numerals.

7. Write a description of two activities that would give a child the concept of counting six.
8. Write two sentences that contain the description of a set with the number property of zero.
9. Make up a matching exercise that would test a child's ability to distinguish the numeral 3 from the numeral 4.
10. Select a first-grade teacher's edition from a recently published arithmetic series. Find and report on each of the following:
   a. A game activity that could be useful in developing the concept of number
   b. Types of practice activities suggested by the text
   c. How the concept of order is developed in terms of the whole numbers and the symbols' place according to this ordering

3.13. *Teaching the Concept of Place Value*

As a readiness experience for place value, the child needs activities that will enable him by counting to determine the number of a set whose property is greater than 10.

Some elementary series teach the child the number concepts up to and including 20 before any extension to numbers larger than 20. This author, however, has chosen to look at how place value can be taught in the larger context, working with numbers from one to 100.

After the child can count from one through 10, you can start to teach him to count sets by tens to 100. These sets may consist of boxes of 10 things, sticks tied into bundles of 10, or sets of 10 fingers. Learning to count by tens before beginning to learn to count sets not grouped in tens will facilitate the child's bridging the tens in counting. For example, when he is counting by ones and gets to 29, he will know that the thirties follow the twenties because he has earlier counted sets of 10 to 100.

In order to illustrate the idea that grouping will help in finding the number property of a set, you might use the following introductory activity: Place an ungrouped pile of 63 sticks or straws on a desk. Place 63 sticks or straws that have been grouped into six sets of ten and three ungrouped sticks or straws on another desk. Let one child count the ungrouped straws at the same time that another child is counting the grouped straws (ten, twenty, thirty, forty, fifty, sixty, sixty-one, sixty-two, sixty-three). Ask the class who had the easier job of counting and then ask why. This activity will quickly demonstrate the efficiency gained by grouping.

In order to illustrate the idea of grouping by tens and the recording of this information, the following activity is suggested: Ask a child to come to the front of the room and count the children in the class. Ask him to raise one finger for every child that he counts. (After the child has counted ten children, he will be unable to raise any more fingers to record how many he has counted.) Stop him if he says " Eleven," and ask him how he will record the fact that he has counted 11 children.

Ask the class for suggestions for how the child might go on counting the children in the room. (They will offer such suggestions as, " He could re- member that he has counted 10." " He could put a mark on the board.") After suggestions are offered, ask another child to come up and remember for the first child that he has counted 10. (Place this student on the left of the first child.) Have this second child remember the counting of the one set of 10 by raising one finger. State that this finger will tell us that he is remembering *one set of 10*. Instruct the first child to continue counting, starting at 11. When he gets to 20, ask the class what the second child should do. (Raise another finger.) Remind the class that each of the second child's fingers stands for one set of 10, and ask the class what the first child should do when the second child holds up another finger.

Stop the counting at 24 and ask the child what each of the first child's four fingers stands for. (One child.) Ask what each of the second child's fingers stands for. (One set of 10 children.) Ask how many children we have when we have two sets of 10 and one set of four. (Twenty-four.)

At this point, introduce the child to the words *tens* and *ones*. Place on the board a frame similar to the one in Figure 3.17. Record the 2 tens under the word tens, and the 4 ones under the word ones.

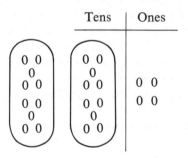

FIGURE 3.17

Give the children many similar experiences. These early experiences should not be of such a nature as to leave 0 ones after counting. It is desirable to establish the need for regrouping through exercises that force this regrouping, so the child needs to be confronted with the necessity of counting the eleventh or twenty-first object, thus making regrouping imperative.

At some time prior to the introduction of the idea of sets of tens and zero ones, it is desirable to formulate with the child the rule that whenever we get a set of ten ones, we will regroup it into one set of ten. There are many commercial aids that can be used for this grouping process.

An idea that will be referred to continually in this text is the cyclic learning experience. It is essential that the child participate in activities that require him to determine the number of a set and that he record this information using the frame. But also he must be given an opportunity to start with the number of items in a set as indicated by numerals in a frame and then construct a set with this number property. This act of going from a concrete situation to the symbolic record, and then from the symbolic record back to the concrete situation, can be referred to as a "cyclic learning experience."

The next stage in teaching place value is to remove the frame that tells the children in the early stages which numeral names the tens and which numeral names the ones. Children should be given experiences similar to the one pictured in Figure 3.18. It should be pointed out to them that the digit on the right of the numeral will designate how many ones they have and that the next digit to the left will tell how many tens they have.

Tens	Ones
4	6

FIGURE 3.18

Not only should they be given an opportunity to write the numeral naming the number of items in a set, but also they should be given the other phase of the cyclic experience; that is, they should be given a numeral and told to construct a set with the correct number property.

Teaching children place value involving hundreds, thousands, ten thousands, and so on involves exactly the same sequence of activities. In summary, the sequencing of activities that promotes mastery of place value is as follows:

1. Counting
2. Illustration of why we group
3. Illustration of how we group
4. Learning to record specific groupings
5. Learning how to construct sets as indicated by a numeral

EXERCISES (3)

1. Give an illustration that will show how a set of objects must have been grouped to give you the following tally:

Tens	Ones
III	I

2. Convert the tally marks to digits:

Tens	Ones		Tens	Ones
IIII	III	$\rightarrow$		
I	III			
	I			

3. Convert the digits back to tally:

Tens	Ones		Tens	Ones
		$\leftarrow$	3	6

4. Indicate by digits how the objects have been grouped:

00   00   00
000 000 000   000
00   00   00   0000
000 000 000

Tens	Ones

5. Give an illustration that will show how a set of objects must have been grouped to give you the following sets of digits:

Tens	Ones
3	7

6. Write the place-value numeral to indicate the following:

Tens	Ones
3	5

7. Write the digits in the place-value boxes so that 97 is indicated:

Tens	Ones

8. Give an illustration that will show how a set of objects must have been grouped to give the numeral 28.
9. Select a teacher's edition of a recently published third-grade series. Find and report on each of the following:
   a. How word names for numbers are introduced
   b. How provision is made for review of place-value concepts
   c. How the names for numbers greater than 100 are introduced

REFERENCES

BANKS, J. HOUSTON, *Learning and Teaching Arithmetic*, Boston: Allyn & Bacon, 1964, pp. 98–102.

BRUMFIEL, CHARLES, ROBERT EICHOLZ, MERRILL SHANKS, and P. G. O'DAFFER, *Principles of Arithmetic*, Reading, Mass.: Addison-Wesley, 1963, pp. 9–12.

CHURCHILL, EILEEN M., *Counting and Measuring*, Great Britain: Routledge & Kegan Paul, 1962, pp. 131–132.

CROUCH, RALPH, GEORGE BALDWIN, and ROBERT J. WISNER, *Preparatory Mathematics for Elementary Teachers*, New York: John Wiley & Sons, Inc., 1965, pp. 27–58.

ELLISON, A., "That Backward Yllis Math," *The Arithmetic Teacher*, vol. 10, pp. 259–261, May, 1963.

FLOURNOY, FRANCES, *Elementary School Mathematics*, Washington, D.C.: The Center for Applied Research in Education, 1964, pp. 10, 16–18.

HEDDENS, JAMES W., *Today's Mathematics, A Guide to Concepts and Methods in Elementary School Mathematics*, Chicago: Science Research Associates, Inc., 1964, pp. 5–7, 209–210.

HOWARD, CHARLES F., and ENOCH DUMAS, *Basic Procedures in Teaching Arithmetic*, Boston: Heath, 1963, pp. 53–56.

LADEMANN, NATHALIE, "Shapes in Numbers," *The Arithmetic Teacher*, vol. 2, pp. 428–430, October, 1964.

LOVELL, K., *The Growth of Basic Mathematical and Scientific Concepts in Children*, Great Britain: Philosophical Library, Inc., 1961, pp. 31–58.

MORRIS, DENNIS E., and HENRY D. TOPFER, *Advancing in Mathematics*, Chicago: Science Research Associates, 1963, pp. 49–58.

MUELLER, F. J., *Arithmetic: Its Structure and Concepts*, Englewood Cliffs, N.J.: Prentice-Hall, Inc., 1964.

NATIONAL COUNCIL OF TEACHERS OF MATHEMATICS, *Enrichment Mathematics for the Grades, Twenty-seventh Yearbook*, Washington, D.C.: The National Council of Teachers of Mathematics, 1963, pp. 261–266.

NATIONAL COUNCIL OF TEACHERS OF MATHEMATICS, *Instruction in Arithmetic, Twenty-fifth Yearbook*, Washington, D.C.: The National Council of Teachers of Mathematics, 1960, pp. 264–267, 284–289.

NATIONAL COUNCIL OF TEACHERS OF MATHEMATICS, *The Growth of Mathematical Ideas: Grades K–12, Twenty-fourth Yearbook*, Washington, D.C.: The National Council of Teachers of Mathematics, 1959, pp. 11–17.

NATIONAL COUNCIL OF TEACHERS OF MATHEMATICS, *The Learning of Mathematics, Its Theory and Practice, Twenty-sixth Yearbook*, Washington, D.C.: The National Council of Teachers of Mathematics, 1961, pp. 242–244.

PAGE, DAVID A., *Number Lines, Functions, and Fundamental Topics*, New York: The Macmillan Company, 1964, pp. 17–25, 55–57.

PETERSON, JOHN A., and JOSEPH HASHISAKI, *Theory of Arithmetic*, New York: John Wiley & Sons, Inc., 1964, pp. 20–32, 45–51, 97–108.

PIAGET, JEAN, *The Child's Conception of Number*, International Library of Psychology, Philosophy, and Scientific Method, New York: Humanities Press, 1952.

RAPKIN, MINNIE K., and LILLIAN C. HOWITT, *Teaching the Third "R,"* Englewood Cliffs, N.J.: Teachers Practical Press, Inc., 1963, pp. 14–16, 36–37, 47–49.

SCHAAF, WILLIAM L., *Basic Concepts of Elementary Mathematics*, New York: John Wiley & Sons, Inc., 1960, pp. 10–24.

SCHOOL MATHEMATICS STUDY GROUP, *Studies in Mathematics, Vol. IX: A Brief Course in Mathematics for Elementary School Teachers*, Stanford, Calif.: Stanford University Press, 1963, pp. 1–20.

SHIPP, DONALD, and SAM ADAMS, *Developing Arithmetic Concepts and Skills*, Englewood Cliffs, N.J.: Prentice-Hall, Inc., 1964, pp. 53–61.

SMITH, SEATON E., JR., *Exploration in Elementary Mathematics*, Englewood Cliffs, N.J.: Prentice-Hall, Inc., 1966, pp. 7–13, 21–23, 27–29.

SPENCER, PETER LINCOLN, and MARGUERITE BRYDEGAARD, *Building Mathematical Competence in the Elementary School*, New York: Holt, Rinehart and Winston, Inc., 1966, pp. 31–55.

SUPPES, P., and B. A. McKNIGHT, "Sets and Numbers in Grade One, 1959–60," *The Arithmetic Teacher*, vol. 8, pp. 287–290, October, 1961.

SWAIN, ROBERT L., and EUGENE D. NICHOLS, *Understanding Arithmetic*, New York: Holt, Rinehart and Winston, Inc., 1965, pp. 54–67.

SWENSON, ESTHER J., *Teaching Arithmetic to Children*, New York: The Macmillan Company, 1964, pp. 36–40.

VAN ENGEN, HENRY, MAURICE L. HARTUNG, and JAMES E. STOCHL, *Foundations of Elementary School Arithmetic*, Chicago: Scott, Foresman and Co., 1965, pp. 12–38, 277, 300–301.

WARD, MORGAN, and CLARENCE HARDGROVE, *Modern Elementary Mathematics*, Reading, Mass.: Addison-Wesley, 1964, pp. 17–43, 377–379.

WEAVER, J. F., "The School Mathematics Study Group Project on Elementary School Mathematics, Grades K–3," *The Arithmetic Teacher*, vol. 10, pp. 514–516, December, 1963.

WOLLWILL, J. F., and R. C. LOWE, "An Experimental Analysis of the Development of Conservation of Number," *Child Development*, vol. 33, pp. 153–156, 1962.

Scale models motivate a child to learn mathematics.

4

Teaching Addition on the Set of Whole Numbers

4.1. *Introduction*

A CHILD'S experiences with addition lay the foundation for a large proportion of his later work in arithmetic. That is, his early successes and failures with addition problems play a significant role in his future attitude toward mathematics. The concepts mastered when he is working with addition on the set of whole numbers are an integral part of such later learning as the multiplication algorithm, when addition is utilized in going from a series of partial products to the product; the exploration of multiplication facts, when the distributive property is used; and when addition is used to test the correctness of a difference obtained in subtraction.

4.2. *Definition, Terminology, and Symbolism*

Before presenting the methods of teaching addition, we shall take a look at the terminology, symbolism, and definitions that will be an integral part of our methods.

Let us now formulate a working definition for *sum* that we might use when trying to convey the idea of addition to children. (A definition will be called a working definition when it depicts the procedure a teacher might use in conveying an idea. Working definitions are not to be construed as those the child would be taught, although it is hoped that he would extract the essence of the idea from the teacher's presentation.) This working definition might be stated as follows:

Suppose we wanted to find the sum of two whole numbers $\square$ and $\triangle$; we would take the following steps:

    Obtain a set, the number of which is $\square$.

    Obtain a set, the number of which is $\triangle$ and that has no elements in common with the first set.

    Join or combine or unite the two sets.

    Determine the number property of the new set that was obtained by the uniting or combining or joining of the two original sets.

    The number property of the new set is designated the sum of $\square$ and $\triangle$.

There are two notations you will want to teach your students. (See Figure 4.1.)

$$\begin{array}{r} 6 \\ +5 \\ \hline 11 \end{array} \quad \text{Vertical form} \qquad 6 + 5 = 11 \quad \text{Horizontal form}$$

FIGURE 4.1

In the horizontal form, we are assuming a left-to-right reading. In the vertical form, we are assuming a top-to-bottom reading.

There are many ways that the mathematical sentences illustrated in Figure 4.1 can be read. A few of the ways of reading them are as follows:

    The sum of 6 and 5 is 11.

    The sum of 6 and 5 equals 11.

    6 and 5 is 11.

    6 and 5 equals 11.

    5 added to 6 equals 11.

    5 added to 6 is 11.

    The sum of 6 and 5 is equal to 11.

When a person is referring to objects, he uses a plural verb. For example, 3 cats and 4 cats are 7 cats. When a person refers to numbers, the singular verb form is used. For example, 3 and 4 is 7. In Figure 4.2, the terminology applied to the various numerals in the addition sentences is identified. These are the terms we shall use to refer to the various elements of the addition sentence.

Addend	Addend	Sum		4	Addend
4	+ 5	= 9		+5	Addend
				9	Sum

FIGURE 4.2

4.3. *Readiness Experiences for Addition*

When you have the child recognize that a pattern of 4 and 4 is a pattern of 8, you are building readiness for the concept that 4 plus 4 is 8. When you have the child recognize that a pattern of 5 and a pattern of 3 is a pattern of 8, you are building readiness for the concept that 5 plus 3 is 8. These patterns aid the child in developing the concept of the number property of a set, and they also build readiness for addition.

Why is it so easy for you to add five to a number whose name in base ten has a zero or five in the ones position? It is probably because when you were a child you played games like hide-and-go-seek in which you would count 5, 10, 15, and so on. Now, when you encounter a situation in which you are required to add five to 65, you automatically think 70, because of this counting experience when you were a child. Having the child do a limited amount of counting (by twos through tens) beginning at various starting points provides him with excellent readiness experiences. For example, if you count by fives, starting at one, you get 1, 6, 11, 16, 21, and so on. If you start at seven, you get 7, 12, 17, 22, 27, 32, 37, 42, 47. It will be easy for the child later to add five to numbers such as 27 or 16 because of these prior counting experiences.

Some pattern-counting experiences are important not only for counting by fives but also for counting by twos, threes, fours, sixes, sevens, eights, nines, and tens. When the child counts 9, 18, 27, 36, 45, 54, 63, is there a pattern that he can discover? What is the pattern in the tens position and in the ones position? Would this pattern hold if a person were to start counting at seven by nines? How does the pattern change?

Not only is it desirable to develop a child's rote-counting experience, but it is also desirable to have him develop his ability to rational count by twos, threes, fours, fives, sixes, sevens, eights, nines, and tens.

> Rational counting is the process of physically counting a set of objects, whereas rote counting is the process of saying the given number sequence without attempting to relate the counting to objects in a set.

When asking a child to determine the number of a set through counting, encourage him to count by a number other than one. For example, in Figure 4.3 the child could be requested to count the dots in the array by threes or twos.

· · ·

· · ·

FIGURE 4.3

4.4. *Teaching the Basic Addition Facts*

Such aids as a flannel board, a magnetic board, blocks, tongue depressors, buttons, a hundred board, a place-value chart, an abacus, charts, and a peg board are all useful in teaching the concept of addition. The procedure for getting a child to discover sums is essentially the same for all of these aids. Each is designed so that the child is an active participant.

A typical dialogue that might be used with these aids is as follows:*

"Here we have three rabbits (blocks, sticks, strips of paper, cards, buttons, beads, boxes, spools, etc.)."

(Point to the set of five objects.) "We join the set of three and the set of five. Who can tell me how many objects are in our new set?" (Eight.)

"We can tell what has happened by writing $3 + 5 = 8$. We read this as three and five is eight." (Later you will teach the children many other ways to read this mathematical sentence.)

"If I had put a set of three rabbits together with a set of four rabbits, how many objects would have been in our new set?" (Seven.)

"John, come up and show us how we find out what three and four is. Mary, come to the board and write down an addition sentence that tells us that 3 and 4 is 7."

"Let's record the addition facts that we have discovered in our addition table."

An aid to teaching addition of whole numbers, and one that needs special attention, is the number-line segment. Figure 4.4 shows how $3 + 5 = 8$ can be shown on the number-line segment. (The teacher is cautioned against

---

* Normally, a teacher does not write a dialogue and then use it with his class. A good teacher, knowing both the content and organization of his subject, develops his dialogue spontaneously and then modifies his presentation as his students react. The dialogues in this book, which were transcribed from demonstration lessons given by the author and which developed spontaneously, are not suggested as ideal models but are presented to acquaint the prospective teacher with the techniques of getting responses for the skill being taught. If a dialogue at times seems artificial, it is because numerous side trips, incorrect responses, and questions were omitted from the transcription of the tapes for the sake of brevity.

introducing a child to a number line before he has a fairly firm grasp of the idea of the cardinality of a set, because the number line lends itself more to ordinality than to cardinality.)

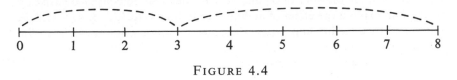

FIGURE 4.4

A dialogue that might be used with the construction of the example in Figure 4.4 follows:

"We take a jump of three." (After making the loop on the number-line segment, write the symbolic expression of this—that is, 3.)

"We keep going the same way." (Write a + to the right of the 3, so that you now have written 3 +.)

"We take a jump of five more." (Write a 5 to the right of the 3, so that you now have written 3 + 5.)

"Where are we after we have taken a jump of three and a jump of five?" (When someone answers eight, write = 8.)

"We have seen that 3 and 5 is 8." (Point to the mathematical sentence.)

During the stage in which the children are discovering the basic addition facts (basic addition facts are all whole numbers x and y, so that x and y are members of the set 0, 1, 2, 3, 4, 5, 6, 7, 8, and 9, and $x + y = z$), you should also have them discovering the identity property and the commutative property of addition.

The child's knowledge of the concept of the identity property (not the name, but the concept) reduces the number of facts that it will be necessary for him to memorize. Because of this, the identity element for addition is one of the earliest properties taught. Soon after a child is taught the meaning of addition, he is presented with situations where one or both of the sets to be joined are empty sets. For example, the teacher might say,

"How many chairs are at Mary's table?" (Two.) "How many chairs are at John's table?" (Two.) "Then together how many chairs are at John's and Mary's tables?" (Four.)

Now the teacher moves the chairs from John's table to Mary's table and again asks the same two questions. Then,

"Together how many chairs are there at Mary's table and at John's table?"

The idea that zero added to a whole number x gives a sum equal to that whole number x is an important concept to be developed. Long before a child can answer the question, "What is the sum of 8 and 9?" he should be able to determine the sum of 65 and 0. This idea can be conveyed easily by having him explore the effect of adding 0 to 0, then 0 to 1, 2, 3, 4, 5, 6, 7, 8, and 9, and then having him extend the pattern to larger numbers. When the commutative property is studied, the concept of the identity element can be extended to include $x + 0 = 0 + x = x$.

A second property of addition that is useful in teaching the basic facts is the commutative property. When we can assign the same unique number regardless of the order of a pair of numbers, we say the commutative property holds for this operation. The fact that $3 + 4 = 4 + 3$ is an instance of the commutative property. It is important that the child make an early discovery of the idea that if we add two whole numbers in either order, we shall always get the same sum. His knowledge of the commutative property will facilitate his discovering some of the basic facts without manipulating concrete objects for every fact explored.

The first step in getting the child to discover the commutative property may consist of your pairing each addition problem with a corresponding commuted problem. For example, when asking a child to find the sum of 3 and 5 by putting a set of three objects together with a set of five objects, and thus finding the number property of the new set, the teacher could ask the child to find the sum of 5 and 3.

When you place the symbolism for this problem on the board, or when the child writes the symbolism, the first request ("Find the sum of 3 and 5.") could be represented as $3 + 5 = \square$; and the second request could be represented by $5 + 3 = \square$. In Figure 4.5 we see examples of pairs of problems that might be presented.

(1a) $3 + 6 = \square$ (2a) $4 + 5 = \square$ (3a) $1 + 8 = \square$
(1b) $6 + 3 = \square$ (2b) $5 + 4 = \square$ (3b) $8 + 1 = \square$

FIGURE 4.5

After the child has discovered the commutative pattern, he can be given problems requiring a knowledge of this pattern for finding a solution. Problems such as $6 + \square = 5 + 6$ and $3 + 8 = \square + 3$ are examples. The only requirement for a child's solving this problem is his recognizing that when we add two numbers in either possible order the sum is the same.

At this point, it should be emphasized that the words "commutative," "identity," and so on, are not as important for the child to acquire as the meaning of the words. As a matter of fact, you probably should make an effort to delay requiring him to verbalize these concepts until he has had some experiences with them.

In general, if an elementary mathematics series does not begin with problems of the discovery stage illustrated in Figure 4.5, it will give problems of the second stage illustrated here. If an elementary series fails to introduce a situation for the child's discovery of the commutative property, you will probably want to structure a situation to promote this discovery.

Problems can be structured for the child that will lead him to a generalization. In this stage, you can present problems with multiple solutions. You can expect and encourage such answers as, "Teacher, any number will work!" Examples of problems in this stage are $3 + \square = \square + 3$, and $\square + 9 = 9 + \square$.

If no student makes the observation that any number could be named, you might single out one person's answer and tell the class that *this* is the correct answer. This designation of one answer as being correct will meet with objections from the class. Someone will say, "Any number would work," which is the generalization you want the children to make. Although no number of such problems will prove the commutative property, it is desirable to get the child to accept the reasonableness of the commutative property by having him work with many instances of it.

In the final stage, the student can be given a pattern such as $\square + \triangle = \triangle + \square$ and be asked to create problems that would be true sentences using it. This type of activity is probably best delayed until the child has reached the intermediate grades at least.

A third property that plays an important role in the child's learning his facts is the associative property for addition—the fact that for all whole numbers $(a + b) + c = a + (b + c)$ is an important idea finding many uses in the development of addition on the set of whole numbers. This fact, identified as the associative property of addition, plays a significant role not only in permitting column addition involving three or more addends from top to bottom or bottom to top, but also in extending a child's concept of addition beyond the basic facts. For example, $8 + 5$ can be renamed $8 + (2 + 3)$, and by making use of the associative property, we get $(8 + 2) + 3$, which names $10 + 3$ or 13.

The first stage in teaching the associative property probably will involve your presenting pairs of problems just as was done in teaching the commutative property. For example, asking the child to find the sum of $(3 + 5) + 7$, finding first the sum of 3 and 5 and then adding the 7 to the 8, could be followed by a request for him to find the sum of $3 + (5 + 7)$, finding first the sum of 5 and 7 and then adding the 12 to the 3. This is an example of a pair of problems being used to show the child that the final sum is not affected by the choice of which pair of numbers is added first. In Figure 4.6, we can see several pairs of problems that could be used to guide the child in discovering the associative property.

(1a) $(4 + 9) + 3 = \square$ (3a) $(3 + 2) + 5 = \square$
(1b) $4 + (9 + 3) = \square$ (3b) $3 + (2 + 5) = \square$

(2a) $6 + (1 + 9) = \square$ (4a) $8 + (3 + 4) = \square$
(2b) $(6 + 1) + 9 = \square$ (4b) $(8 + 3) + 4 = \square$

FIGURE 4.6

After the child has discovered the associative pattern, he can be given problems requiring a knowledge of this pattern for finding solutions. In this stage, he can be asked to identify which numerals are missing in a mathematical sentence. Here his ability to identify the missing numeral is dependent upon his recognizing an instance of the associative property. Notice that this type of experience tests a child's operational ability with a pattern rather than his ability to say "associative pattern." Several examples of problems for this stage can be seen in Figure 4.7.

(a) $(4 + 9) + 6 = 4 + (\square + 6)$

(b) $3 + (\square + 2) = (3 + 5) + 2$

(c) $5 + (6 + 7) = (\square + 6) + 7$

FIGURE 4.7

The chief characteristic of the next stage is that there exists more than one correct solution to any given problem. Typical examples of these multiple-solution problems can be seen in Figure 4.8.

(a) $(3 + 4) + \square = 3 + (4 + \square)$

(b) $(9 + \square) + \triangle = 9 + (\square + \triangle)$

(c) $\square + (7 + 1) = (\square + 7) + 1$

FIGURE 4.8

The final stage in the child's learning the associative property of addition will be that of creating instances of this property. The student can be given a pattern such as $(\square + \triangle) + \bigcirc = \square + (\triangle + \bigcirc)$ and be asked to create problems that would be true sentences using it.

In addition to the structural properties, you have other techniques for developing the basic facts. As an aid to unlocking the facts with sums between 10 and 19, you can teach the child to rename and regroup. For example, $9 + 8 = 9 + (1 + 7) = (9 + 1) + 7 = 17$. Notice the second addend was renamed so that upon regrouping a sum of 10 was obtained. However, we do not have to direct the renaming toward this end.

Suppose your students have just discovered $8 + 8 = 16$. Notice how you can incorporate this information in teaching that $8 + 9 = 17$. $8 + 9 = 8 + (8 + 1) = (8 + 8) + 1 = 16 + 1 = 17$.

The following table summarizes some of the methods a teacher has of getting his children to discover sums:

PROBLEM	METHOD	SOLUTION
$1 + 1 = \square$	Putting sets together. $\{\triangle\} \cup \{\square\} = \{\triangle, \square\}$	$1 + 1 = 2$
$3 + 2 = \square$	Using a number line.	$3 + 2 = 5$
$7 + 6 = \square$	Renaming, regrouping. $7 + 6 = 7 + (3 + 3) = (7 + 3) + 3 = 10 + 3 = 13$	$7 + 6 = 13$
$4 + 5 = \square$	Working from doubles. Because $4 + 4 = 8$ and 5 is one more than 4, then	$4 + 5 = 9$
$9 + 6 = \square$	Using the commutative property. Because $6 + 9 = 15$, then	$9 + 6 = 15$
$6 + 4 = \square$	Using patterns. Because $6 + 1 = 7$ and $6 + 2 = 8$ and $6 + 3 = 9$, then	$6 + 4 = 10$
$9 + 0 = \square$	Generalization. Because $n + 0 = n$, then	$9 + 0 = 9$

4.5. *Memorization of the Basic Facts*

After the child has discovered various sums of whole numbers—for example, after he has discovered all sums up to and including 5—he should be encouraged to memorize these facts. There are many activities in which the child can participate to aid his memorization. The most common of these is to pair him off with another child and use flash cards, one child listening to the responses of the other. Another self-teaching activity involves having the child record the sums of a random set of addition problems. He should be encouraged to check his work and go back and construct concrete situations to rediscover those facts he has missed.

It is important that the teacher use an inventory type of test from time to time in order to discover if there are specific misconceptions being made by a large proportion of the students that would warrant reteaching those concepts. A test administered soon after the children have discovered their sums should not be a timed test. However, after the children develop competence in recalling their facts, they should be encouraged to develop a quick recall ability through activities requiring speed, and through speed tests to motivate them to develop a quick recall ability. One activity that promotes rapid recall is called "Beat the Bounce." The requirement of the game is to give orally the sum of an addition problem before a ball hits the floor. The activity proceeds as follows:

> The teacher, holding a ball in his hand, says, "Five plus four . . . Mary?"
> As he says, "Mary," he drops the ball. Before the ball hits the floor, Mary is to say, "Nine."
> If Mary misses this answer, ask one of the students to help. Record Mary's incorrect answer so that you can check her at some future date to see if she has made up this deficiency.

4.6. *Expanded Notation*

Before teaching a child how to add ones to tens and ones, you will need to teach the child how to express a standard numeral in expanded form and how to express numerals in expanded form as standard numerals. This can be accomplished by having students work exercises similar to the following:

$$
\begin{array}{ll}
\text{a. } 20 + 6 = \square & \text{d. } 22 = 20 + \square \\
\text{b. } 30 + 7 = \square & \text{e. } 82 = \square + 2 \\
\text{c. } 10 + 8 = \square & \text{f. } 99 = 90 + \square
\end{array}
$$

Statement (a) can be read as 2 tens and 6 ones equals 26. Or it can be read as 20 and 6 equals 26.

One of the purposes of teaching the child expanded notation is that he will be forced to focus on the place value inherent in each digit of a standard numeral. A second reason for having him work with expanded notation is that it provides a smooth transition for him to move from the basic facts on to the new skill of adding ones to tens and ones.

4.7. *Addition of Ones to Tens and Ones (Without Regrouping Tens)*

In Figure 4.9, we see a step-by-step symbolic presentation by the teacher depicting the steps used in learning to add ones to tens and ones.

In Step 1, we have renamed the 14, making it (10 + 4). We have done this because the only skills related to this problem that the students know at this point are how to add ones to ones (basic facts) and how to add tens to ones (expanded notation). In Step 2, we make use of the associative property for addition by associating the 4 with the 5. We have done this because we want to add the ones to the ones. In Step 3, we add the 4 and 5 and get 9. In

$$14 + 5$$
$$\downarrow$$
$$\text{Step 1} \_\_\_\_ (10 + 4) + 5$$
$$\downarrow$$
$$\text{Step 2} \_\_\_\_ 10 + (4 + 5)$$
$$\downarrow$$
$$\text{Step 3} \_\_\_\_ 10 + 9$$
$$\downarrow$$
$$\text{Step 4} \_\_\_\_ 19$$

FIGURE 4.9

Step 4, we use the skill we developed working with expanded notation and rewrite $10 + 9$ as 19.

The children need an opportunity to *see* several similar step-by-step explanations. Even though you may not elicit from your students the reasons and/or justifications for each step, student responses should not be discouraged.

After you have developed the justification for adding ones to ones to obtain a sum that is combined with the tens (expanded notation skill), the child is ready to work similar problems using vertical notation. A typical problem in the early stages of this development can be seen in Figure 4.10.

$$\begin{array}{rl} 20 + 1 & \text{Standard} \\ + \quad 8 & \text{numeral} \\ \hline \end{array}$$
$$\square + \triangle = \lozenge$$

FIGURE 4.10

After the students have met success in solving similar problems through the expanded form, they can be given experiences similar to the ones depicted in Figure 4.11. These exercises will provide for a smooth transition to the final stages of mastering the algorithm.

Phase 1	Phase 2
$60 + 4$ 64	64
$+ \quad 3$ $+ 3$	$+ 3$
$\square + \triangle \to \triangleright$	$\square$

FIGURE 4.11

EXERCISES (1)

1. "10, 21, 32, 43, 54, etc." What does the sequence tell us we are counting by? Describe the pattern found in the tens place. Describe the pattern found in the ones place.
2. Describe a purpose for having the child perform a counting exercise such as the example in Problem 1.
3. In the following array, name two numbers greater than one that could be used to count the set of dots.

4. Look in a teachers' edition of an elementary school textbook and find how you use either a place-value chart or a hundred board to teach the basic facts. Draw a series of pictures that would depict the steps for teaching a child that $6 + 9 = 15$, using either a place-value chart or a hundred board.
5. Make up six equations similar to the ones in Section 4.6 that could be used to introduce the child to the concept of expanded notation.
6. Identify the skill or the property for each of the steps in the following presentation.

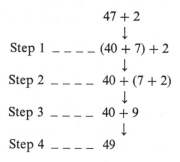

$$47 + 2$$
$$\downarrow$$
$$\text{Step 1} \; \_\,\_\,\_\,\_ \; (40 + 7) + 2$$
$$\downarrow$$
$$\text{Step 2} \; \_\,\_\,\_\,\_ \; 40 + (7 + 2)$$
$$\downarrow$$
$$\text{Step 3} \; \_\,\_\,\_\,\_ \; 40 + 9$$
$$\downarrow$$
$$\text{Step 4} \; \_\,\_\,\_\,\_ \; 49$$

7. Use the definition of sum to illustrate how you would show a child that the sum of 4 and 5 is 9.
8. List five ways you could read $6 + 7 = 13$.
9. Identify the addends and the sum in each of the following problems:

$$3 + 9 = 12 \qquad \begin{array}{r} 7 \\ +4 \\ \hline 11 \end{array}$$

10. Solve the following problem: $6 + \square = 6$. What property for addition does this represent?
11. Make up sample problems for each of the following stages in teaching the commutative property for addition: paired problems for discovering the property; single-solution problems requiring knowledge of the property for solution; multiple-solution problems.
12. Make up sample problems for each of the following stages in teaching the associative property for addition: paired problems for discovering the property; single-solution problems requiring knowledge of the property for solution; multiple-solution problems.

4.8. *Addition of Tens to Tens*

A skill that must be developed before the children are taught addition involving " regrouping the tens" is the skill of adding tens to tens.

The techniques and aids used in teaching the concept of adding tens to tens are quite similar to those used in teaching the addition of ones to ones. One of the techniques used in teaching these sums is to have the child recognize that when he learned the basic facts for ones he was also learning relationships that would help him to learn the addition of tens.

Some activities that will focus the child's attention on the close relationship between the addition of ones and the addition of tens can be seen in Figure 4.12.

A typical dialogue that might be used to talk to children about addition of tens that would focus on the relation between adding ones and adding tens is as follows:

"3 tens and 6 tens is how many tens? 9 tens is correct. What is another name for 3 tens?" (Thirty.)
"What is another name for 6 tens?" (Sixty.)
"What is another name for 9 tens?" (Ninety.)
"What must 30 and 60 be equal to, then?" (Ninety.)

Similar activities can be used to establish the relationship between ones and hundreds, between ones and thousands, and so on.

4.9. *Addition of Tens and Ones to Tens and Ones (Without Regrouping)*

Teaching children to add tens and ones to tens and ones is accomplished best by having the children start out working with problems in vertical expanded notation, as shown in Figure 4.13.

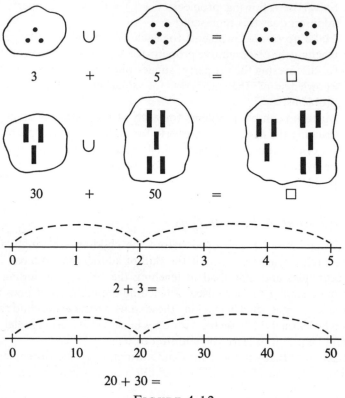

$$2 + 3 =$$

$$20 + 30 =$$

FIGURE 4.12

A dialogue to accompany the vertical notation in Figure 4.13 might be as follows:

"What number is named by 30 + 2?" (Thirty-two.)

"What number is named by 60 + 5?" (Sixty-five.)

"We are going to learn how to add 32 and 65 using vertical notation. We have learned how to add tens to tens, and ones to ones. If we add the 2 and 5, what will we get?" (Seven.)

"If we add the 3 tens and the 6 tens, we will get what?" (9 tens, or ninety.)

"What is named by 9 tens and 7 ones?" (Ninety-seven.)

$$
\begin{array}{r}
30 + 2 \\
+\,60 + 5 \\
\hline
\square + \triangle = \lozenge
\end{array}
$$

FIGURE 4.13

In the early stages of teaching the children to add using this notation, you can use expressions such as "6 tens" and "4 tens." This terminology can then give way to calling the 6 tens "60" and the 4 tens "40."

After the children have met success in solving addition problems in the expanded form, you can phase out the expanded form for the more efficient numeral form. In Figure 4.14, we see examples representing typical exercises that could be used to phase out the expanded notation.

Phase 1		Phase 2
$30 + 8$	38	38
$40 + 1$	41	$+41$
$\square + \triangle \rightarrow \bigcirc$		$\bigcirc$

FIGURE 4.14

4.10. *Addition of Ones to Tens and Ones* (*With Regrouping*)

In Figure 4.15, we see a step-by-step symbolic presentation that might be placed on the board by the teacher. This presentation depicts the steps in learning to add ones to tens and ones when it is necessary to regroup after adding the ones. In Step 1, we have renamed 23, changing it to $(20 + 3)$.

We have done this renaming because the skills the student has at this point to help him find the sum are those of adding ones to ones, tens to tens, and

$$23 + 9$$
$$\downarrow$$
Step 1 _ _ _ _ $(20 + 3) + 9$
$$\downarrow$$
Step 2 _ _ _ _ $20 + (3 + 9)$
$$\downarrow$$
Step 3 _ _ _ _ $20 + 12$
$$\downarrow$$
Step 4 _ _ _ _ $20 + (10 + 2)$
$$\downarrow$$
Step 5 _ _ _ _ $(20 + 10) + 2$
$$\downarrow$$
Step 6 _ _ _ _ $30 + 2$
$$\downarrow$$
Step 7 _ _ _ _ 32

FIGURE 4.15

expanded notation. In Step 2, we make use of the associative property for addition, because we are interested in adding the 3 ones and the 9 ones. In Step 3, we add the 3 and 9 and get 12.

In Step 4, we rename the 12, calling it (10 + 2), because the only skill that the child has enabling him to find the answer is "how to add tens and tens." In Step 5, we *associate* the 20 with the 10. In Step 6, we add the tens and get 30. In Step 7, making use of the expanded-notation skill, we rename 30 + 2, making it the standard numeral name, 32.

After you have developed the justification for regrouping the tens obtained when adding ones to ones, the child is ready to work similar problems using a vertical notation. A typical problem, along with guides showing what to record, is seen in Figure 4.16.

FIGURE 4.16

After the student has met success in solving similar problems, he can be given experiences similar to the ones shown in Figure 4.17. These exercises could serve to phase out the intermediate explanatory stage.

Phase 1		Phase 2
30 + 9	39	39
20 + 8	28	+28
□ + △ = ▷		□

FIGURE 4.17

4.11. *Teaching Column Addition*

Before introducing children to the concept of column addition, you will find it useful to have them discover the associative property. (See Section 4.4.) The first problems of column addition a child should encounter are those in which the final sum is less than 10. A typical problem of this type can be seen in Figure 4.18.

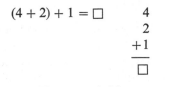

$$(4 + 2) + 1 = \square$$

$$\begin{array}{r} 4 \\ 2 \\ +1 \\ \hline \square \end{array}$$

FIGURE 4.18

A dialogue to accompany the vertical notation in Figure 4.18 might be as follows:

"We have seen how to add $(4 + 2) + 1$." (Have this expression displayed on the board.)

"We are now going to add the same three numbers in vertical form. If we add the 4 and the 2, what sum will we get?" (Six.)

"What did we do with the 6 when we got it here?" (Point to $(4 + 2)$ in the expression on the board.)

"We now add the 6 and 1 and get 7." (Write the numeral 7 in the placc holder.)

The second type of problem the child should encounter is one with three addends arranged so that the first sum obtained is less than 10. Good examples of this type of problem are contrasted with unsatisfactory examples in Figure 4.19.

$$\begin{array}{cc cc} 3 & 4 & 7 & 8 \\ 6 & 5 & 4 & 9 \\ +9 & +6 & +2 & +1 \\ \hline \square & \square & \square & \square \end{array}$$

Acceptablc   Nonacceptable

FIGURE 4.19

After the concept of adding ones to tens and ones has been taught, the students should be ready to perform column addition involving a first sum greater than nine, so that the next addend will not force a regrouping situation.

After the concept of adding ones to tens and ones involving regrouping has been taught, the child is ready for any single-column addition problems.

Teaching two-digit column addition follows essentially the same sequence of steps. They are

1. Column addition with no regrouping
2. Column addition with sums of ones greater than nine
3. Column addition with sums of tens greater than 90
4. Any two-digit column addition

Extension of the skill of regrouping tens, hundreds, thousands, and so on, follows the same basic sequence developed for the ones to tens and ones. Techniques used in the introduction of these concepts follow the same procedure as has been developed up to this point and will be further developed as exercises for you to work.

4.12. *Column Addition with Limited Regrouping*

Most of our emphasis to this point has been on developing the child's understanding of addition. However, if the child is to make addition an effective tool, he must not only understand how the tool functions, but also be able to perform with the tool efficiently. Let us now examine how we might develop this efficiency.

$$
\begin{array}{r}
27 \\
49 \\
68 \\
+83 \\
\hline
\end{array}
$$

In adding from top to bottom in the example at the left, it is necessary, if we desire efficiency, to be able automatically to identify sums associated with $7 + 9$, $16 + 8$, $24 + 3$, $2 + 2$, $4 + 4$, $8 + 6$, and $14 + 8$.

Even more efficiency could be obtained by being able to identify sums associated with the pairs of numbers $(7, 9)$, $(16, 8)$, $(24, 3)$, $(2, 2)$, $(4, 4)$, $(8, 6)$, and $(14, 8)$.

We have already discussed how automatic recall for sums involving the basic facts is developed. Let us now study a possible learning sequence that may help the child acquire the skills necessary for rapid higher-decade addition.

Until now we have had the child reason that $27 + 8 = 20 + 15 = 30 + 5$. However, this type of analysis is not efficient when we begin performing column addition. It is now more important for the child to begin to perform a pattern analysis similar to the following:

$$8 + 7 = 15, 18 + 7 = 25, 28 + 7 = 35, \text{ etc.}$$

This type of analysis points out that the general "effect" of adding 7 to x tens and 8 ones always results in $(x + 1)$ tens and 5 ones.

Once the child has mastered the basic facts, you should extend his skill level to the automatic mastery of adding ones to tens and ones. One way this can be accomplished is through finding sums and then studying their pattern. The following set of exercises might represent such a typical set of problems:

$$
\begin{array}{cccc}
9 & 19 & 29 & 39 \\
+6 & +\ 6 & +\ 6 & +\ 6 \\
\hline
\end{array}
$$

$$
\begin{array}{llll}
5 + 8 = \square & 15 + 8 = \square & 25 + 8 = \square & 35 + 8 = \square \\
7 + 2 = \square & 17 + 2 = \square & 27 + 2 = \square & 37 + 2 = \square
\end{array}
$$

After the children have mastered the skill adding one to tens and ones automatically, they can apply this skill to column-addition problems such as the following:

$$
\begin{array}{cccc}
8 & 35 & 346 & \$7.89 \\
9 & 68 & 288 & .98 \\
7 & 74 & 997 & .64 \\
+4 & +\ 26 & +\ 645 & +\ 8.29 \\
\hline
\end{array}
$$

EXERCISES (2)

1. Illustrate with pictures of sets how you would establish for children the relationship between 7 ones plus 8 ones equals 15 ones, and 7 tens plus 8 tens equals 15 tens.
2. Illustrate on a number-line segment how you would establish for children the relationship between 6 ones plus 7 ones equals 13 ones, and 6 tens plus 7 tens equals 13 tens.
3. Make up a dialogue that could be used to introduce the following vertical notation:

$$
\begin{array}{ll}
40 + 5 & \text{Standard} \\
30 + 1 & \text{numeral} \\
\hline
\square + \triangle = \lozenge &
\end{array}
$$

(Pretend that you have a class and try to anticipate its answers. The purpose of this exercise is to focus your attention on the basic structure of a presentation and not to have you develop "canned" dialogues to use with your students. Remember, the dialogues you will use later will develop spontaneously in a classroom, and the skill of your presentation will depend on your insight into what you are teaching.)

4. Justify or identify the skill involved in each of the following steps:

$$35 + 8 \xrightarrow{\text{Step 1}} (30 + 5) + 8 \xrightarrow{\text{Step 2}} 30 + (5 + 8) \xrightarrow{\text{Step 3}}$$
$$30 + 13 \xrightarrow{\text{Step 4}} 30 + (10 + 3) \xrightarrow{\text{Step 5}} (30 + 10) + 3 \xrightarrow{\text{Step 6}}$$
$$40 + 3 \xrightarrow{\text{Step 7}} 43$$

5. Write a dialogue that could be used to introduce vertical notation with regrouping, through the following example:

$$
\begin{array}{r}
80 + 9 \\
+ \qquad 8 \\
\hline
\Diamond + \square
\end{array}
$$

6. Work out a step-by-step presentation that could be used to justify and identify the skills needed to teach $38 + 47$.

7. Work out a dialogue that could be used to introduce the child to the following problem:

$$
\begin{array}{cc}
\begin{array}{r} 30 + 4 \\ 60 + 5 \\ +60 + 7 \\ \hline \Diamond + \square \end{array}
&
\begin{array}{r} 34 \\ 65 \\ +67 \\ \hline \triangleright \end{array}
\end{array}
$$

8. Sequence the following set of problems from the first taught to the last:

$$
\begin{array}{ccc}
\begin{array}{r} 3 \\ 5 \\ +6 \\ \hline \end{array}
&
\begin{array}{r} 2 \\ 2 \\ +5 \\ \hline \end{array}
&
\begin{array}{r} 1 \\ 9 \\ +4 \\ \hline \end{array}
\end{array}
$$

9. Sequence the following set of problems from the first taught to the last:

$$
\begin{array}{ccc}
\begin{array}{r} 31 \\ 52 \\ +63 \\ \hline \end{array}
&
\begin{array}{r} 21 \\ 32 \\ +45 \\ \hline \end{array}
&
\begin{array}{r} 48 \\ 16 \\ +29 \\ \hline \end{array}
\end{array}
$$

4.13. *Addition " Story" Problems*

Problem solving involving *word problems* or *story problems* can be thought of as the process of extracting the basic information of the problem, translating this basic information into a mathematical sentence, and then applying previously learned concepts to derive a "solution" to the mathematical sentence. Although this is a greatly oversimplified interpretation of problem solving, it will provide us with a base from which to discuss techniques of developing problem-solving skills involving word and story problems.

Some of the basic principles we shall want to have to accompany our techniques of developing problem-solving skills are as follows:

1. A flexible framework should be provided that will facilitate the child's ability to translate and solve new problems. Children should not be discouraged from using novel approaches that are valid to problem solving.
2. Problems should be within the realm of the child's experience. If not, experiences such as field trips, exhibits, visual aids, dramatizations, and speakers should be employed to fill in the experiential gaps.
3. The relationships that exist between various elements of the problem must be a part of the child's repertoire of concepts prior to his attempting to solve the problem.
4. Development of reading skills applicable to problem solving should parallel or precede problem solving involving word problems.
5. Children should be encouraged to create problems from mathematical data. This principle cannot be overstressed. The essence of true mathematical problem solving often involves the accumulation of data via experimentation or compilation, followed by the construction of a mathematical model to fit the data and then the testing of the validity of this model with future events or experiments.
6. Children should be instructed in techniques of estimation and verification.
7. After the children have had extensive experience with certain types of problems, the development of a generalization should be undertaken.

Although the author has chosen to isolate and analyze those techniques of teaching children to solve word problems that apply to specific computational skills—such as addition of whole number, subtraction of whole number, and so on—in the specific chapter in which the operation is discussed, in actual practice, giving the child a large number of problems involving one operation will dull his flexibility for attacking unrelated problems. The inclusion of problem solving within each chapter emphasizes another element of problem solving—that is, computation and problem solving being highly interrelated, computation is not an end in itself, but a facet of the larger goal of problem solving.

The author would like to stress that the problems found in elementary textbook series should represent only a small portion of the types of problem-solving situations to which a child can be exposed. Even though these problems serve as a useful base from which to extend problem-solving skills, the very nature of how these problems came to be included in these texts has eliminated the "unique-now" type of problem. Publishers and authors cannot include problems dealing with recent events, because this type of problem dates a book. As a consequence, problems of an immediate concern are omitted, leaving those problems of a yesterday, today, and tomorrow nature.

It is the specific responsibility of the teacher to provide children with problems of a current-events nature, as well as to solicit such problems from them. It is also important that the development of problem-solving skills be oriented so that even the child with weak reading skills can develop skill in attacking problems of a quantitative nature. Such devices as a taped series of problems, problems displayed as picture situations on film strips, and loop films depicting problems in picture form can serve as good substitutes for textbook problems for the "nonreader," in order to develop his skill for attacking problems.

Although there are many studies in the area of problem solving, there are few, if any, "truths" that can be derived from research in this area. Experimental evidence suggests that requiring a group of children to conform to a particular pattern is not as effective as allowing them some flexibility in attacking problems. This is not to say that some individuals may not actually thrive under the more rigid regime, nor is it to say that we should not search for the basic structure of the problem and attempt to translate it into one or more mathematical sentences. Let us examine an "addition problem."

> John had 3 marbles. Mary gave him 2 more.
> John is 5 years old. How many marbles does John have now?

The child's first step is one of examination. If the problem is communicated in writing, then this examination takes the form of reading the problem until he feels that he understands it. If it is given orally, the examination takes the form of his listening and asking for the problem to be restated until he understands it.

A useful technique at this point is to request the student to restate the problem. Often, failure in problem solving is not due to a lack of problem-solving ability, but to the failure of the teacher to communicate the problem to the child. Requesting a restatement of the problem will help to identify this breakdown in communication.

As the problem is examined, have the child identify what we want to find out. In everyday situations, this often represents a complex skill. Even though in the typical elementary textbook the problem is identified with a question or a missing word or phrase in a sentence, in an everyday situation the problem is identified spontaneously within the context of the quantitative situation. Frequently, the problem precedes the collection of quantitative data that will be used to find a solution to the problem. For the problem given here we are concerned with finding, "How many marbles does John have now?"

Following the identification of the problem, the student has the task of identifying those quantitative aspects of the ideas communicated to him that will relate to the problem to be solved. Obviously, John's age will not relate to the number of marbles he has. The teacher should frequently introduce extraneous information in order to promote the child's ability to identify the structure of a problem within a larger context. This ability to discriminate the essential from the nonessential is an aspect of everyday problem solving that we must interject continually into the problems we present to our students. This interjection of nonessential data into a problem will have the following effects:

1. It will reduce the tendency of a child to interpret automatically a problem as involving addition when he sees several names for numbers in the problem.
2. It will cause the child to examine each problem with greater care, knowing that some data may be extraneous.
3. The problems will be better models of those problems the child meets in everyday situations.

After the child has extracted the basic structure of the problem, he should do the following:

1. If he recognizes how to translate the problem into a mathematical sentence, he does so. The problem about John and Mary translates to $3 + 2 = \square$. (The teacher may want to relate the problem to the mathematical model of putting together sets (union) and the concept of addition.)
2. The child proceeds to derive a solution for the mathematical sentence he has constructed.

Other phases of developing problem-attack skills involving addition will be developed through the exercises.

EXERCISES (3)

1. Using one or more of the following sources, construct five story problems of a current-events nature involving basic addition facts appropriate for a group of students in a second-grade class:
   a. Newspaper   b. *World Almanac*   c. Magazine
2. Using the same sources, construct five story problems of a current-events nature involving column addition appropriate for a group of students in a third-grade class.

3. Using the same sources, construct five story problems of a current-events nature requiring the child to use addition and either subtraction, multiplication, division, or addition again to get the answer. These problems should be appropriate for a group in a fifth-grade class.

4. Using the same sources, construct five story problems of a current-events nature requiring the child to use addition and two other operations. These problems should be appropriate for a group in a fifth-grade class.

5. Make up a word problem for each of the following mathematical sentences:

a. $3 + 0 = \square$ c. $30\cent + 40\cent + 10\cent = \square$
b. $15 + 15 + 15 = \square$ d. $4567 + 3487 = \square$

REFERENCES

BALOW, I. H., "Reading and Computation Ability as Determinants of Problem Solving," *The Arithmetic Teacher*, vol. 11, pp. 18–22, January, 1964.

BANKS, J. HOUSTON, *Learning and Teaching Arithmetic*, Boston: Allyn & Bacon, 1964, pp. 147–163.

CHURCHILL, EILEEN M., *Counting and Measuring*, Great Britain: Routledge & Kegan Paul, 1962, pp. 141–144.

CROUCH, RALPH, GEORGE BALDWIN, and ROBERT J. WISNER, *Preparatory Mathematics for Elementary Teachers*, New York: John Wiley & Sons, Inc., 1965, pp. 67–77.

EVENSON, A. B., *Modern Mathematics: Introductory Concepts and Their Implications*, Chicago: Scott, Foresman and Co., 1962, pp. 33–37, 42–43.

FLOURNOY, FRANCES, "A Consideration of the Ways Children Think when Performing High-Decade Addition," *Elementary School Journal*, vol. 57, pp. 204–208, January, 1957.

FLOURNOY, FRANCES, *Elementary School Mathematics*, Washington, D.C.: The Center for Applied Research in Education, 1964, pp. 32–33.

FOLSOM, M. O., "Have Pupils Generalize Their Way to Mastery of Basic Facts," *Updating Mathematics*, sect. 2, vol. 5, no. 4, 1962.

GROSSNICKLE, F. E., and L. J. BRUECKNER, *Discovering Meanings in Elementary School Mathematics*, New York: Holt, Rinehart and Winston, Inc., 1963.

HACKER, SIDNEY G., WILFRED E. BARNES, and CALVIN T. LONG, *Fundamental Concepts of Arithmetic*, Englewood Cliffs, N.J.: Prentice-Hall, Inc., 1963, pp. 64, 68.

HANNON, H., "Problem Solving—Programming and Processing," *The Arithmetic Teacher*, vol. 9, pp. 17–19, January, 1962.

MARKS, JOHN L., JAMES R. SMART, and IRENE SAUBLE, *Enlarging Mathematical Ideas*, Boston: Ginn and Company, 1961, pp. 1–5.

MOSER, H., "Number Sentences: An Approach to Solving Word Problems," *Updating Mathematics*, sect. 11, vol. 3, no. 2, 1960.

NATIONAL COUNCIL OF TEACHERS OF MATHEMATICS, *Instruction in Arithmetic, Twenty-fifth Yearbook*, Washington, D.C.: The National Council of Teachers of Mathematics, 1960, pp. 71–72, 343–345.

NATIONAL COUNCIL OF TEACHERS OF MATHEMATICS, *The Growth of Mathematical Ideas, Grades K–12, Twenty-fourth Yearbook*, Washington, D.C.: The National Council of Teachers of Mathematics, 1959, pp. 20–22.

PAGE, DAVID A., *Number Lines, Functions, and Fundamental Topics*, New York: The Macmillan Company, 1964, pp. 37–42.

PETERSON, JOHN A., and JOSEPH HASHISAKI, *Theory of Arithmetic*, New York: John Wiley & Sons, Inc., 1963, pp. 86–92.

RAPKIN, MINNIE K., and LILLIAN C. HOWITT, *Teaching the Third " R,"* Englewood Cliffs, N.J.: Teachers Practical Press, Inc., 1963, pp. 22–24, 49–53.

RIEDESEL, C. ALAN, "Verbal Problem Solving: Suggestions for Improving Instruction," *The Arithmetic Teacher*, vol. 11, pp. 312–316, May, 1964.

SCHAAF, WILLIAM L., *Basic Concepts of Elementary Mathematics*, New York: John Wiley & Sons, Inc., 1963, pp. 107–118.

SCHOOL MATHEMATICS STUDY GROUP, *Mathematics for the Elementary School*, Stanford, Calif.: Stanford University Press, 1962.

SCHOOL MATHEMATICS STUDY GROUP, *Studies in Mathematics, vol. IX: A Brief Course in Mathematics for Elementary School Teachers*, Stanford, Calif.: Stanford University Press, 1963, pp. 41–76.

SHIPP, DONALD, and SAM ADAMS, *Developing Arithmetic Concepts and Skills*, Englewood Cliffs, N.J.: Prentice-Hall, Inc., 1964, pp. 162–165, 170–171.

SMITH, SEATON E., JR., *Explorations in Elementary Mathematics*, Englewood Cliffs, N.J.: Prentice-Hall, Inc., 1966, pp. 48–50.

SPENCER, PETER LINCOLN, and MARGUERITE BRYDEGAARD, *Building Mathematical Competence in the Elementary School*, New York: Holt, Rinehart and Winston, Inc., 1966, pp. 140–145.

SPITZER, HERBERT F., and FRANCES FLOURNOY, "Developing Facility in Solving Verbal Problems," *The Arithmetic Teacher*, vol. 3, pp. 177–182, November, 1956.

SUTHERLAND, ETHEL, *One-Step Problem Patterns and Their Relation to Problem Solving in Arithmetic*, Contributions to Education, No. 925, New York: Teachers College, Columbia University, 1947, p. 170. (Summary in *Teachers College Record*, vol. 49, p. 492, April, 1948.)

SWENSON, ESTHER J., *Teaching Arithmetic to Children*, New York: The Macmillan Company, 1964, pp. 81–111, 115–143.

THORPE, C. B., *Teaching Elementary Arithmetic*, New York: Harper & Row, 1962.

VANDERLINE, LOUIS F., "Does the Study of Quantitative Vocabulary Improve Problem Solving?" *The Elementary School Journal*, vol. 65, pp. 143–152, December, 1964.

VAN ENGEN, HENRY, MAURICE L. HARTUNG, and JAMES E. STOCHL, *Foundations of Elementary School Arithmetic*, Chicago: Scott, Foresman and Co., 1965, pp. 84–90, 145–150.

WARD, MORGAN, and CLARENCE HARDGROVE, *Modern Elementary Mathematics*, Reading, Mass.: Addison-Wesley, 1964, pp. 112–113, 136–140.

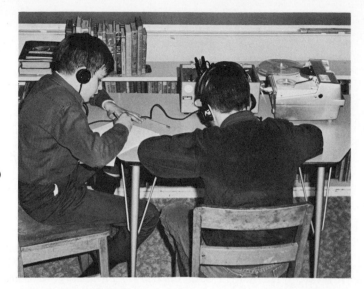

Audio aids can motivate a child to learn mathematics. (Children who lack reading skills are being given story problems to work via an audio recording.)

5

Teaching Subtraction on the Set of Whole Numbers

5.1. *Introduction*

SUBTRACTION presents a more complex teaching situation than does addition. The child must learn to interpret such varying problems as, "John has four marbles and Jim has three. How many more marbles has John than Jim?" or "If John had four marbles and lost three, how many would he have left?" Both situations require subtraction for their solutions.

Subtraction on the set of whole numbers has a set of properties distinctly different from those the child encounters when studying addition. For example, the compensation property for subtraction, which employs the patterns $(\Box + \triangle) - (\bigcirc + \triangle) = \Box - \bigcirc$ and $(\Box - \triangle) - (\bigcirc - \triangle) = \Box - \bigcirc$, utilizes the idea that if the same number is to be added to or subtracted from both the minuend and the subtrahend, the difference will be the same as if no number were added to or subtracted from the minuend and subtrahend.

The closure property does not hold for subtraction on the set of whole numbers. Neither the commutative property nor the associative property holds for subtraction. Although there exists an identity element for subtraction, its employment must be modified due to the noncommutative nature of subtraction. Even though the properties of subtraction will be new to the child, it is important to establish the close relationship existing between addition sentences and subtraction sentences.

5.2. *Definition, Terminology, and Symbolism*

The definition, terminology, and symbolism that we use in communicating the concepts of subtraction play a very significant role in teaching. Whereas faulty language, such as "3 is added to 2," when referring to "3 + 2," causes only minimal interference with the child's ability to master the concepts of addition, similar faulty language usage for subtraction will greatly interfere with his mastery of subtraction. An incorrect statement, such as, "We always subtract the smallest from the largest," will lead the child to develop a misconception, because he later will learn subtraction with the set of integers where it is possible to subtract a larger number from a smaller number. "We can't subtract a larger number from a smaller number" is an incorrect statement that will lead the child to modify a problem so that he can follow directions. For example, in the problem $48 - 19 = \square$, if the child thinks that he cannot subtract 9 ones from 8 ones, he will subtract 8 ones from 9 ones. Careful attention to precise usage of definition, terminology, and symbolism should be given special emphasis when subtraction is being taught.

Let us examine two working definitions of subtraction derived from such interpretations of subtraction as *set separation* and *set comparison*. (We also have a *missing addend* interpretation that is extremely important in relating addition and subtraction. For example, we can say $7 - 3 = 4$ because $4 + 3 = 7$.)

A working definition using the idea of *set separation* might be stated as follows:

Suppose we wanted to find the difference of two whole numbers $\square$ and $\triangle$. We would take the following steps:

Obtain a set, the number of which is $\square$.

Take away $\triangle$ objects from the set.

Determine the number property of the set remaining.

The number property of the set remaining is designated the difference of $\square$ and $\triangle$.

A working definition employing the idea of *set comparison* might be stated as follows:

Suppose we wanted to find the difference of two whole numbers $\square$ and $\triangle$.

We would take the following steps:

Obtain a set, the number of which is □.

Obtain a set, the number of which is △.

Attempt to pair the sets.

Determine the number property of the unmatched subset of the set whose number property was □.

The number property of the unmatched subset is designated the difference of □ and △.

$$6 - 2 = \square \qquad \begin{array}{r} 6 \\ -2 \\ \hline \square \end{array} \qquad \square + 2 = 6$$

FIGURE 5.1

There are three basic notations that you, as the elementary teacher, must teach your students. (See Figure 5.1.) Notice that $\square + 2 = 6$ is identified as a notation for subtraction. It is important that the child learn to think of this as a subtractive situation, because he will be translating some story problems to this mathematical sentence. Viewing this sentence as a subtractive sentence will facilitate his obtaining a solution to this type of problem.

There are many ways the mathematical sentences depicted in Figure 5.1 might be read. Some of these follow:

6 minus 2 is 4.

6 minus 2 equals 4.

6 subtract 2 equals 4.

2 subtracted from 6 equals 4.

2 from 6 is 4.

2 from 6 equals 4.

Minuend*	Subtrahend*	Difference
6 —	2 =	4
Sum	Known addend	Missing addend and sometimes the remainder

Sum   6 Minuend*   Missing Known
Known addend −2 Subtrahend*   addend   addend   Sum

Missing   4 Difference   ↓   ↓   ↓
addend   ↑   4   +   2   =   6
             Sometimes the
             remainder

* Traditional vocabulary

FIGURE 5.2

In Figure 5.2, the terminology applied to the subtraction notations is depicted. The reader will note that there are two sets of terminology for every mathematical sentence except one. A teacher should exercise caution not to mix terms. For example, it would not be proper to say "minuend 6 and known addend 2." When we use the term minuend, we must be consistent and refer to the other numeral as the subtrahend.

5.3. *Readiness Experiences for Subtraction*

When you have your children attempt to pair sets and then ask how many items have not been paired, you are building readiness for subtraction. In the early phase of teaching addition, when you have the child find a missing addend without calling his attention to the fact that he is learning subtraction, you are preparing him for the concept that subtraction is the inverse of addition.

Other readiness activities consist of having the child count backward, starting at various points. For example, counting backward by twos starting at 21 prepares the child for subtracting two from a number whose name in the one's place is either one, three, five, seven, or nine. The child should be given pattern-counting experiences with twos, threes, fours, fives, sixes, sevens, eights, and nines. He should be asked to start at various numbers less than 100 and count backward by twos, threes, and so on. For example, a dialogue for a counting experience involving threes starting with a set of 11 might proceed as follows:

"I have 11 objects and I take away three objects. I now have eight objects. I take away three more objects and I now have five objects. I take away three more objects and I have two objects."

5.4. *Teaching the Basic Subtraction Facts*

Those aids that proved useful in teaching the addition facts will also prove useful in teaching the subtraction facts. Flannel boards, magnetic boards, place-value charts, charts, and peg boards are a few of the aids that will help in teaching the concept of subtraction. Note that all of them are so constructed as to permit the active involvement of the child.

A typical dialogue that might be used with these aids to teach subtraction as the inverse of addition is as follows:

" Here we see eight ducks (blocks, sticks, strips of paper, stones, buttons, beads, spools, pegs, etc.)."

(Point to the set of eight objects.) "I am covering some up." (Cover some of the objects—say five—with a cardboard or your hand.) "How many can we see now?" (Three.)

"When we put these three together with the ones I am covering up, we get eight. How many am I covering up?" (Five.) "Yes, 3 and 5 is 8."

A typical dialogue that might be used to teach subtraction as the comparison of two sets is as follows:

"Here we see some cats and some dishes. How many cats are there?" (Five.) "How many dishes are there?" (Three.)

"Mary, would you try to pair the dishes with the cats? How many cats do not have dishes?" (Two.) "How many more cats than dishes are there?" (Two.)

A typical dialogue that might be used to teach subtraction as the partitioning of a subset from a set might be as follows:

"Here we have seven objects. If I take three objects away, how many do I have left?"

In each case, as the child discovers a subtraction fact, he should record his answer. You should structure his discovery of his basic facts in such a way that he becomes aware of the interrelatedness of certain addition facts and subtraction facts. For example, $4 + 3 = 7, 3 + 4 = 7, 7 - 3 = 4$, and $7 - 4 = 3$ constitute a set of related facts. Discovering the interrelatedness of subtraction facts and addition facts will cause the child not only to anticipate certain relationships, but also to be efficient by reducing the number of facts he must discover physically through the manipulation of sets.

The number-line segment is another useful aid in teaching subtraction. In Figure 5.3 we can see how $8 - 6 = 2$ would be shown on the number-line

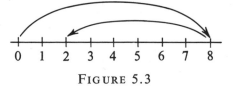

FIGURE 5.3

segment. Notice that we are starting this number line at 0 so that a jump of eight units to the right will put us at 8.

The dialogue that might be used with this example is as follows:

"We take a jump of eight." (After making the loop on the number-line segment, write the symbolic expression of this: 8.)

"We turn around." (Write a — to the right of the 8 so that you have now written 8 —.) "We take a jump of six." (Write 6 to the right of the 8 — so that you now have written 8 — 6.)

"Where are we after we have taken a jump of eight and turned around and jumped six?" (After someone answers two, write = 2.)

"We have seen that 8 less 6 is 2." (Point to the mathematical sentence.)

It will be useful to introduce the child to the "right" identity element for subtraction soon after he has been introduced to the concept of subtraction. (It is called the right identity element because, in the mathematical sentence $\square - \triangle = \square$, the zero is placed to the right of the subtraction symbol, as in $15 - 0 = 15$. This relation does not hold if the zero is placed to the left of the subtraction symbol, as in $0 - 15 \neq 15$.) Working with sets of objects, this concept can be conveyed so that the child can easily understand it. A statement such as the following will be useful in teaching this concept:

"Johnny carried five cents into a store. He didn't spend any money. How much money does he have left?" Or, "Beth has three dolls. Mary has zero dolls. How many more dolls has Beth than Mary?"

The children should be given the opportunity to solve problems similar to this: $5 - \square = 5$; $\square - 0 = 7$; $8 - 0 = \square$; $8 + \square = 8$.

The following table summarizes some of the ways we have of teaching the basic subtraction facts:

PROBLEM	METHOD	SOLUTION
$5 - 2 = \square$	Partitioning sets.	$5 - 2 = 3$
$8 - 6 = \square$	Comparing sets.	$8 - 6 = 2$
$11 - 5 = \square$	Related addition sentence. $5 + 6 = 11$	$11 - 5 = 6$
$14 - 6 = \square$	Related subtraction sentence. $14 - 8 = 6$	$14 - 6 = 8$
$15 - 9 = \square$	Subtraction by parts. $\quad 15 - 5 = 10 \quad 10 - 4 = 6$	$15 - 9 = 6$
$12 - 3 = \square$	By patterns. $12 - 1 = 11 \quad 12 - 2 = 10$	$12 - 3 = 9$
$15 - 7 = \square$	By compensation. $\quad 15 - 7 - (15 + 3) - (7 + 3) = 18 - 10$	$15 - 7 = 8$
$7 - 4 = \square$	By the number line.	$7 - 4 = 3$
$9 - 6 = \square$	By relating to other facts. $8 - 6 = 2$	$9 - 6 = 3$

5.5. *Memorization of the Basic Facts*

At predesignated places in the child's discovery of the basic subtraction facts (such as after the subtraction facts with minuends through five have been discovered), the student should be encouraged to memorize the facts discovered.

Such activities as "show and tell," using flash cards, nonspeed and speed tests, and "Beat the Bounce" (see Section 4.5) are useful ones that will motivate the child to memorize the subtraction facts. Experiences with patterns of interrelated facts will facilitate memory and mastery of the basic facts. The exercises depicted in Figure 5.4 have been designed to promote recall through the exploration of familiar patterns.

(a) $6 - 4 = \square$ (e) $8 - \square = 2$
(b) $6 - \square = 4$ (f) $8 - \square = 6$
(c) $5 - 3 = \square$ (g) $\square - 5 = 3$
(d) $5 - 2 = \square$ (h) $\square - 3 = 5$

FIGURE 5.4

5.6. *Subtraction of Ones from Tens and Ones* (*Without Regrouping Tens*)

Teaching the child the concept of subtracting ones from tens and ones should presuppose that the child is familiar with expanded notation. (See Section 4.6.) In Figure 5.5, we see a step-by-step symbolic presentation by the teacher depicting the steps used in learning to subtract ones from tens and ones.

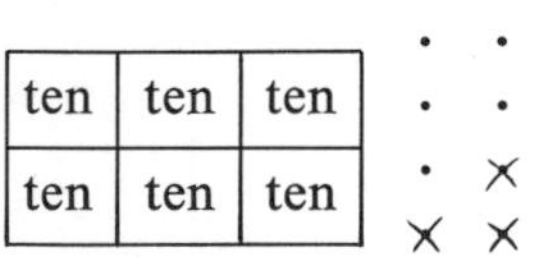

					Stage 1	Stage 2	Stage 3
			.	.			
ten	ten	ten	.	.	$6 \text{ tens} + 8 \text{ ones} \rightarrow$	$60 + 8 \rightarrow$	68
ten	ten	ten	.	×	$- \qquad\qquad 3 \text{ ones}$	$- \quad 3$	-3
			×	×			
					$\_\_ \text{ tens} + \_ \text{ ones}$	$\_\_ + \_$	

FIGURE 5.5

A dialogue to accompany this presentation might be as follows:

"Here we have 6 tens and 8 ones. If we take away 3 ones (mark out three of the dots), how many ones do we have left?" (Five. Write the 5 in the blank next to the word "ones.") "If we do not take away any tens, how many tens do we have left?" (Six.)

Repeat this type of questioning with the expanded notation form and the standard subtraction algorithm.

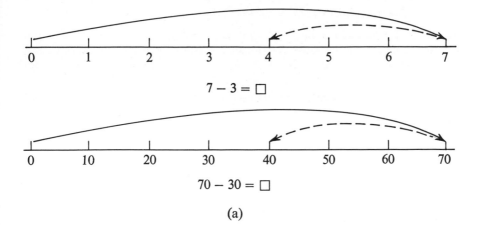

$$7 - 3 = \square$$

$$70 - 30 = \square$$

(a)

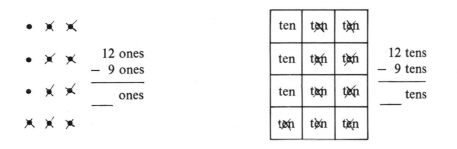

(b)

Place-value chart

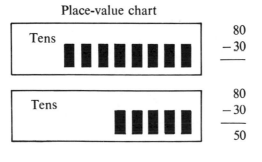

$$
\begin{array}{r}
80 \\
-30 \\
\hline
\end{array}
$$

$$
\begin{array}{r}
80 \\
-30 \\
\hline
50
\end{array}
$$

(c)

FIGURE 5.6

5.7. *Subtraction of Tens from Tens*

It is important in teaching subtraction of tens from tens that the children be made aware of the close relationship existing between subtracting ones from ones and tens from tens. Figure 5.6 depicts several teaching aids and activities that will be useful in conveying this idea.

A typical dialogue that might be used to tell children about subtraction of tens in example (c), Figure 5.6, is as follows:

> "3 tens from 8 tens is how many tens?" (Five tens.) "What is another name for 3 tens?" (Thirty.) "What is another name for 8 tens?" (Eighty.)
> "What is another name for 5 tens?" (Fifty.) "What must 30 from 80 be equal to, then?" (Fifty.)

Similar activities can be used to establish the relationship between ones and hundreds, between ones and thousands, and so on.

5.8. *Subtraction of Tens and Ones from Tens and Ones (Without Regrouping)*

Teaching the students to subtract tens and ones from tens and ones is best accomplished by having them work their problems in the vertical, expanded form. This form allows them to focus on the nature of place value and its role in the subtraction algorithm. Figure 5.7 depicts the use of the place-value chart as an aid to teaching this concept.

Place-value chart

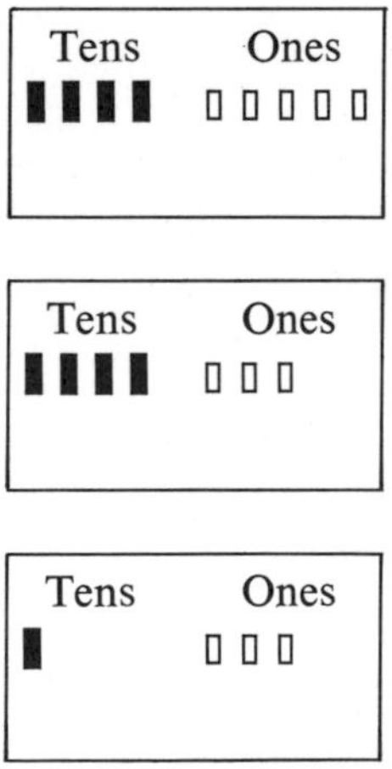

FIGURE 5.7

A dialogue to accompany this presentation might be as follows:

" How many ten tabs are on our place-value chart?" (Four.) "What is another name for 4 tens?" (Forty.) "How many one tabs are on our chart?" (Five.)

"What number is named by 4 tens and 5 ones?" (Forty-five.) "Let's write our 45 in expanded notation." (Write 40 + 5.) "Suppose we had four sets of 10 objects and five sets of one object, and someone took away three sets of 10 and two sets of one. How could we show that three sets of 10 and two sets of one were being taken away, by using expanded notation?" (We could write $-(30 + 2)$, which means that 30 and 2 are being subtracted from 40 and 5.)

"How many ones are we supposed to subtract?" (Two.) Have a student come up and remove two of the one tabs.

"Let's record that we have 3 left after we have subtracted 2 from 5. How many tens are we supposed to subtract?" (Three tens.) Remove three of the ten tabs.

"Let's record that we have 1 ten left after we have subtracted 3 tens from 4 tens, or 30 from 40."

When teaching subtraction of tens and ones from tens and ones, you should teach the child that by convention we subtract the ones first, and then the tens. You can use teaching aids that will help the child reach this conclusion. As each child is practicing his subtraction algorithm, you will want to check to see that he follows this right-to-left procedure.

Figure 5.8 depicts the notation that may be used to phase in the standard subtraction algorithm.

$$\begin{array}{cc} 80 + 9 & 89 \\ -(30 + 6) \rightarrow & -36 \\ \hline \_ + \_ & \end{array}$$

FIGURE 5.8

A typical dialogue to accompany this phasing-in process might be as follows:

"What number does 80 + 9 name?" (Eighty-nine.) "What number does 30 + 6 name?" (Thirty-six.) "What does the 9 in the numeral 89 stand for?" (Nine ones.) "What does the 8 in the numeral 89 stand for?" (Eight tens.)

"Here we see the standard way to write 36 subtracted from 89. In the expanded form, do we subtract the ones first, or the tens?" (The ones.) "We subtract the ones first in the standard form, also. What is the difference of 9 and 6?" (Three.)

(Write 3 in both ones positions.) "What is the difference of 8 tens and 3 tens?" (Five tens. Write the 50 in the blank of the expanded form and the 5 in the tens column place in the standard algorithm.)

5.9. *Subtraction Involving Regrouping*

A crucial stage in the child's mastering of subtraction concepts is his learning how to regroup prior to proceeding with the subtraction algorithm. There are many activities that will help him master this skill of regrouping the minuend in subtraction. One of them is to involve the child in situations such as the following:

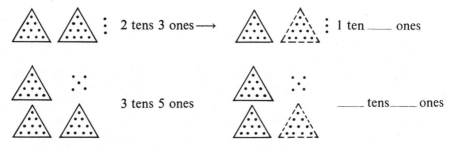

You might have the child work with expanded-notation activities such as the following:

$$70 + 5 = 60 + \underline{} \qquad \underline{} + 8 = 40 + 18$$
$$30 + 9 = \underline{} + 19 \qquad 60 + \underline{} = 50 + 15$$

It is important that the child learn to view names for numbers in many ways. For example, in the equation $356 - 192$, it is desirable for him to think

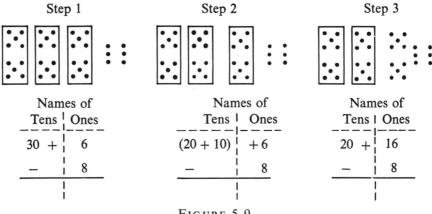

FIGURE 5.9

of 356 as 2 hundreds, 15 tens, and 6 ones; but when the problem is 356 − 92, it may be more desirable to view 356 as 35 tens and 6 ones.

A common regrouping or *decomposition method* is seen in Figure 5.9.

A typical dialogue that might be used to accompany the visual aids and notations in Figure 5.9 might be as follows:

> (Employing sets arranged similarly to those depicted in Step 1, Figure 5.9, display the notation used in Step 1.) "What are we asked to subtract from 3 tens and 6 ones?" (Eight ones.)
>
> "If I sent someone to the board and asked him to mark out eight dots, could he do it without marking out any of the dots in the sets of 10?" (No.) "Why not?" (Because there are only six dots not grouped by tens.)
>
> "Then we can see that in order to subtract, we are going to have to get some more ones. Where did we see that we could get some more ones?" (From the sets of 10.)
>
> "What is the smallest number of sets of ten that we need to get 8 ones?" (One set of 10.)
>
> (Display Step 2.) "How many tens do we have left when we remove this one set of 10 from the 3 tens?" (Two tens.) "If we add this 10 to our 6 ones, how many ones will we have?" (Sixteen.)
>
> (Display Step 3.) "What will we get when we subtract 8 ones from 16 ones?" (Eight ones.) "How many tens will we have if we don't subtract any tens?" (Two tens, or twenty.)
>
> "We have seen that when we subtract 8 ones from 3 tens and 6 ones, we get a difference of 2 tens and 8 ones. What number is named by 30 + 6?" (Thirty-six.) "When we subtract 8 from 36, our difference is what?" (Twenty-eight.)

After the children have become familiar with and competent in this process of regrouping using the expanded notation, you should introduce them to the method of decomposing using the standard algorithm.

In the matter of teaching the standard subtraction algorithm involving regrouping, there are basically two approaches that can be taken. The first is sometimes called the "crutch" method and involves having the child cross out the numeral naming the type of set decomposed and renaming selected digits as shown in Figure 5.10.

$$\begin{array}{r} 3 \\ 3\cancel{4}2 \\ -215 \\ \hline \end{array} \qquad \begin{array}{r} 59 \\ \cancel{6}\cancel{0}4 \\ -177 \\ \hline \end{array}$$

FIGURE 5.10. "Crutch."

The second method is sometimes called the "mental" method and involves having the child remember what has been decomposed and what the new groups are. Extension of this algorithm will be reserved for the exercises.

5.10. *An Alternate Subtraction Algorithm*

This author is making the following assumptions in this presentation:

1. The pattern to be discussed will be new to you.
2. You will best understand a discovery technique if you are involved in a discovery technique.
3. This is just one of many approaches that might be used to get a student to discover this number pattern.

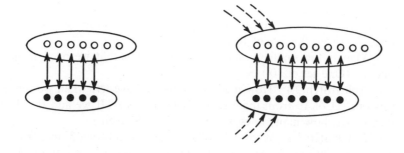

John has 7 marbles. Bill has 5 marbles. How many more marbles has John than Bill?

Write the equation that could be used to solve this problem. If you wrote $7 - 5 = \Box$, you are correct.

Now suppose John and Bill each got 3 more marbles. How many more marbles does John have than Bill?

Does the equation $(7 + 3) - (5 + 3) = \Box$ describe the situation where John and Bill have each received 3 marbles and the marbles are again compared to see how many more marbles John has than Bill?

Does John now have more marbles than he did before?

Notice how we have constructed a pair of problems to explore this pattern: $7 - 5 = \Box$
$$(7 + 3) - (5 + 3) = \Box$$

Would John have more marbles than Bill if we added 8 marbles to both sets, or 10 to both, 64 to both, etc.?

Find the differences of the following problems. Study the pairs of problems that yield the same differences. Make up other problems that seem to follow the pattern you have discovered.

1a. $65 - 37 = \Box$ 2a. $10 - 7 = \Box$ 3a. $16 - 5 = \Box$
1b. $68 - 40 = \Box$ 2b. $9 - 6 = \Box$ 3b. $16 - 7 = \Box$

4a. $29 - 15 = \square$ 5a. $187 - 29 = \square$ 6a. $347 - 296 = \square$
4b. $30 - 14 = \square$ 5b. $207 - 49 = \square$ 6b. $341 - 290 = \square$

The pattern $a - b = (a + c) - (b + c) = (a - d) - (b - d)$ is called the compensation property for subtraction.

The compensation property for subtraction finds a useful application in the modification of subtraction problems requiring some type of regrouping before use of the subtraction algorithm. The following sequence of steps shows how we might use the compensation property to restructure the problem so as to permit subtraction of tens from tens:

$$
\begin{array}{ccc}
234 & (237 + 40) & 277 \\
-164 & -(164 + 40) & -204 \\
\hline
\end{array}
$$

The first stage in teaching the compensation property for subtraction is to construct pairs of problems from which the child can discover a pattern similar to the one just illustrated in the discussion of the marbles. Figure 5.11 shows several representative problems from this stage.

(1a) $13 - 7 = \square$ (2a) $14 - 5 = \square$
(1b) $(13 - 2) - (7 - 2) = \square$ (2b) $(14 + 3) - (5 + 3) = \square$
(3a) $35 - 17 = \square$
(3b) $(35 - 7) - (17 - 7) = \square$

FIGURE 5.11

In the second stage, you may want to give the child problems similar to those shown in Figure 5.12. These problems will require him to make use of the recently discovered pattern.

(a) $25 - 12 = (25 - 2) - (12 - \square)$
(b) $27 - 8 = (27 + \square) - (8 + 3)$
(c) $15 - 6 = 12 - \square$
(d) $26 - 12 = 28 - \square$

FIGURE 5.12

The third stage in teaching the compensation property for subtraction is to present problems having multiple solutions. It is a good idea to display some of the many solutions for each of these problems so that the students can begin to be guided toward a generalization. Representative problems from this stage are shown in Figure 5.13.

(a) $30 - 6 = (30 + \square) - (6 + \square)$
(b) $27 - 13 = (27 - \square) - (13 - \square)$
(c) $15 - 3 = (15 + \square) - (3 + \square)$
(d) $45 - \square = (45 - 2) - (\square - 2)$

FIGURE 5.13

In the last stage, you can give the students patterns such as $\square - \triangle = (\square - \bigcirc) - (\triangle - \bigcirc)$, and $\square - \triangle = (\square + \bigcirc) = (\triangle + \bigcirc)$, and ask them to create true sentences using them.

A subtraction algorithm involving an approach quite different from the previously discussed techniques of regrouping the minuend is the compensation algorithm. In this algorithm, when the child encounters a situation that would otherwise require regrouping, he adds a number to both the minuend and subtrahend. For example, in $305 - 132$, he could add 70 or 80 or 90 to both the minuend and the subtrahend, restructuring the problem to $375 - 202$, or $385 - 212$, or $395 - 222$. However, for this example, 70 would probably be selected, because it would result in a zero in the subtrahend's tens position, and subtraction by zero is the easiest type of subtraction problem, due to zeros being the identity element. In Figure 5.14, we can see how several problems are restructured using the compensation property. Notice in those instances having more than one situation requiring regrouping that the compensation property is used to alleviate each need for regrouping.

$$
\begin{array}{rrrr}
400 & (400 + 1) & (401 + 90) & 491 \\
-209 & -(209 + 1) & -(210 + 90) & -300 \\
\hline
 & & & 191 \\
\end{array}
$$

$$
\begin{array}{rrr}
1645 & (1645 + 200) & 1845 \\
-842 & -(842 + 200) & -1042 \\
\hline
 & & 803 \\
\end{array}
$$

$$
\begin{array}{rrr}
384 & (384 + 4) & 388 \\
-196 & -(196 + 4) & -200 \\
\hline
 & & 188 \\
\end{array}
$$

FIGURE 5.14

Most elementary textbook series concentrate on developing the regrouping method as an integral part of the algorithm development. However, whichever method the series you use employs, it is probably best to give each child a wide variety of algorithms after he has mastered one.

EXERCISES (1)

1. By using pictures of sets, illustrate how you would make use of the definition of difference from Section 5.2 called set separation to teach the child that $9 - 4 = 5$.

2. Using the definition of difference from Section 5.2 called set comparison, illustrate how you would teach a child that $9 - 4 = 5$.

3. Write five ways that one could read $6 - 5 = 1$.

4. For each of the following notations, when possible, identify the minuend, subtrahend, difference, sum, known addend, and unknown addend:

$$\begin{array}{c} 7 \\ -3 \\ \hline \boxed{4} \end{array} \qquad 8 - 2 = \boxed{6} \qquad 3 + 4 = \boxed{7}$$

5. Count backward by nines, starting at 53. What pattern develops that will help the child learn to subtract nine from a number?

6. Make up a specific matching activity that could be used to teach some fact giving a difference of three.

7. Illustrate $8 - 5 = 3$ on a number-line segment.

8. Using the partitioning-out interpretation of subtraction, illustrate how you would teach $11 - 2 = 9$.

9. What are two related addition sentences and one related subtraction sentence for the sentence $13 - 7 = 6$?

10. Make up a dialogue to explain the following problem. Illustrate your dialogue with an aid similar to the one in Figure 5.4.

$$\begin{array}{ccc} 8 \text{ tens} + 9 \text{ ones} & 80 + 9 & 89 \\ - \qquad\quad 6 \text{ ones} & - \quad 6 & -\ 6 \\ \hline \end{array}$$

11. Using number-line segments, illustrate the relation between subtracting six from 14 and 60 from 140.

12. Make up a dialogue to explain the following problem. Illustrate your dialogue with a sequence of pictures of a place-value chart as in Figure 5.7.

$$\begin{array}{ccc} 9 \text{ tens} + 8 \text{ ones} & 90 + 8 & 98 \\ -(3 \text{ tens} + 6 \text{ ones}) & -(30 + 6) & -36 \\ \hline \end{array}$$

13. Make up a dialogue that will explain how to handle the need for regrouping in each of the following problems. Use a decomposition algorithm.

$$\begin{array}{lll} \text{a.} \quad 372 & \text{b.} \quad 2004 & \text{c.} \quad 1240 \\ \quad\ -246 & \quad\ -913 & \quad\ -330 \\ \quad\ \overline{} & \quad\ \overline{} & \quad\ \overline{} \end{array}$$

14. Make up a dialogue that will explain how to handle the need for regrouping in each of the following problems. Use the compensation algorithm.

$$
\text{a.} \quad
\begin{array}{r} 372 \\ -246 \\ \hline \end{array}
\qquad
\text{b.} \quad
\begin{array}{r} 2004 \\ -913 \\ \hline \end{array}
\qquad
\text{c.} \quad
\begin{array}{r} 1240 \\ -330 \\ \hline \end{array}
$$

15. A student mentally works the following problem in the described manner:

    $32 - 14$. (4 from 2 equals a negative 2. A negative 2 and 30 is 28. 10 from 28 is 18.)

    a. Did he get the right answer?

    b. Would this method always give him the correct answer?

    c. Would you discourage the child from working problems in this manner, or would you compliment him on his ingenuity?

    d. Would his algorithm be one you could teach all third-graders? Why, or why not?

16. Give an example that will show that the associative property does not hold for subtraction.

17. Make up a set of problems for each of the first three stages in teaching the compensation property for subtraction.

18. Given the following pattern, $\Box - (\triangle + \bigcirc) = (\Box - \triangle) - \bigcirc$, make up sample problems for the first three stages of teaching this property.

19. Given the following pattern, $(\Box + \triangle) - (\bigcirc + \bigcirc) = (\Box - \bigcirc) + (\triangle - \bigcirc)$, make up sample problems for each of the first three stages in teaching this property.

20. Given the following pattern, $(\Box + \triangle) - \bigcirc = \Box + (\triangle - \bigcirc)$, make up sample problems for each of the first three stages in teaching this property.

21. Identify which of the patterns depicted in Exercises 18, 19, and 20 are employed in each of the following algorithms:

$$
\begin{array}{r} 35 \\ -7 \\ \hline \end{array}
\qquad
\begin{array}{r} 30 \\ -2 \\ \hline \end{array}
\qquad
\begin{array}{r} 30+4 \\ -2 \\ \hline \end{array}
\qquad
\begin{array}{r} 20+8 \\ -(10+6) \\ \hline \end{array}
$$

5.11. Subtraction "Story" Problems

Teaching a child to become proficient in solving subtraction story problems is complicated by the fact that the subtraction situation has many guises. The three most common ways of viewing subtraction in a social situation are as partitioning out, or "take away" (given a set, after part of the set is removed, the child determines the number property of the remaining subset); as comparison (given two sets, after the attempt to pair the sets, the child derives the number property of the unpaired subset); and as a missing addend (in which the union of two sets is taken and the number property of the resultant set and one of the original sets is known, after which the number property of the other original set is determined).

Generally, the first type of subtraction story that a child encounters is the take-away form. Let us first study some techniques of presenting this type of problem. Early work with it should concern stories that are easily depicted with concrete materials. For example, take the following problem:

John has 11 pencils.
He gives Mary 7 of his pencils.
How many pencils does he have then?

One technique that might be used to present this problem to children is to allow a child to take the part of John and another child to take the part of Mary. (Whenever possible, make the problems ones with which the children can identify.) A possible dialogue that might be used to accompany the action is as follows:

"How many pencils does John have?" (Eleven. Write an 11 on the board.)

"What is he doing?" (He is giving some pencils to Mary. Write the $-$ to the right of the 11.)

"How many does he give to Mary?" (Seven. Write a 7 to the right of the $11 -$.)

"What are we asked to find?" (How many John has left now. Write $= \square$ to the right of $11 - 7$.)

"We have learned that 11 less 7 is what?" (Four.)

"How many pencils do you have left?" (Four.)

"As you see, we can find the answer to our problem by acting it out, or by working it mathematically."

You will want to contrast the take-away subtraction problems with the previously studied addition problems. A useful technique at this point is to start with John having four pencils and to have Mary return the seven pencils, thus establishing the equation $4 + 7 = \square$.

Viewing subtraction in its social situation as comparison is more complex than the take-away situation. Whereas physical action is generally characteristic of the take-away situation, the comparison situation may or may not involve a physical action. Comparison involves two sets that may or may not be equivalent in number. For example, note the following problem:

John has 6 marbles.
Mary has 2 marbles.
How many more marbles does John have than Mary?

Let us discuss how we might use a flannel board to present the essential aspects of this problem. A possible dialogue that could be used to accompany this action is as follows:

"Let's use these red disks as the marbles that John has. How many marbles does the problem tell us John had?" (Six. Write a 6 on the board. Place six disks on the flannel board. See Figure 5.15.)

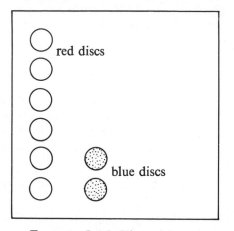

FIGURE 5.15. Flannel board.

"Let's use these blue disks for the marbles that Mary has. How many marbles does the problem tell us Mary has?" (Two. Write a 2 to the right of the 6.)

"If we pair Mary's two marbles with two of John's, how many are not paired?" (Four. Do this pairing with the disks.)

"Do the four unpaired disks tell us how many more marbles John has than Mary?" (Yes. Write = 4 to the right of 6   2.)

"What operation symbol should I put between the 6 and the 2?" (The subtraction symbol.)

"As we have seen, when we are interested in finding out how many more members one set has than another, we can attempt to pair the sets to find out the answer, or we can find the answer using subtraction."

Children should be given many opportunities to translate problems involving set comparison into subtraction equations. In Figure 5.16, we see the three variations of problems of a comparative nature.

Problems that can be translated into an equation with a missing addend can be referred to as missing addend problems. By the time the student reaches the point of analyzing missing addend story problems, he has already learned to retranslate problems such as $3 + \square = 8$ into $8 - 3 = \square$.

Number of set A Number of set B Number of unmatched subset	Known Known Unknown	Known Unknown Known	Unknown Known Known
Some possible translations	$a - b = \square$ or $a = \square + b$	$a - \square = c$ or $a - c = \square$ or $a = \square + c$	$\square - b = c$ or $\square = c + b$ or $\square - c = b$

FIGURE 5.16

Let us discuss a direct approach that could be used to lead the students to translate the problem into an equation.

John has 5 marbles.
Mary gives him some more.
He now has 9 marbles.
How many marbles did Mary give him?

A possible dialogue that could accompany this problem is as follows:

"How many marbles does the problem tell us John started with?" (Five. Write a 5 on the board.)
"What happened next?" (Mary gave him some marbles.)
"What symbol do you think we could use to translate the 'giving to John'?" (The addition symbol.) "Does the sentence tell us how many she gave him?" (No.)
"How can we show that we don't know this yet?" (Draw a square. The children may sometimes refer to this square as a box.)
"How can we show 'he now has nine marbles'?" (Write $= 9$ to the right of $5 + \square$.)
"What is another mathematical sentence that would ask the same question?" ($9 - 5 = \square$.)

Some children may immediately recognize the subtractive nature of the preceding problem and translate it directly to $9 - 5 = \square$. Others may translate it first to $5 + \square = 9$ and then to $9 - 5 = \square$ before solving. Some children may solve the problem directly from the $5 + \square - 9$ translation. You probably will not want to discourage this flexibility in their methods of arriving at a solution to problems.

In summary, subtraction takes many forms. You will want to give each child a broad perspective of the many ways he may encounter subtractive situations in his environment. You also will need to contrast subtraction problems with addition problems by reconstructing subtraction problems into addition problems.

EXERCISES (2)

1. Using one or more of the following sources, construct five story problems of a current-events nature involving take-away situations appropriate for a third-grade class:
   a. Newspaper   b. *World Almanac*   c. Magazine
2. Using the same sources, construct five story problems of a current-events nature involving comparison situations appropriate for a third-grade class.
3. Using the same sources, construct five story problems of a current-events nature involving missing addend situations appropriate for a third-grade class.
4. Using the same sources, construct five story problems of a current-events nature involving subtraction and another operation, for a third-grade class.
5. Make up a word problem for each of the following mathematical sentences:

   a. $27 - 9 = \square$ d. $88 - \square = 34$
   b. $32 - 25 = \square$ e. $\square + 45 = 68$
   c. $35\cent - \square = 28\cent$ f. $91 + \square = 165$

REFERENCES

BANKS, J. HOUSTON, *Learning and Teaching Arithmetic*, Boston: Allyn & Bacon, 1964, pp. 163–178.

BELL, CLIFFORD, CLELA D. HAMMOND, and ROBERT B. HERRERA, *Fundamentals of Arithmetic for Teachers*, New York: John Wiley & Sons, Inc., 1962, pp. 78–90.

CHURCHILL, EILEEN M., *Counting and Measuring*, Great Britain: Routledge & Kegan Paul, 1962, pp. 144–145.

CROUCH, RALPH, GEORGE BALDWIN, and ROBERT J. WISNER, *Preparatory Mathematics for Elementary Teachers*, New York: John Wiley & Sons, Inc., 1965, pp. 169–181.

EDUCATION RESEARCH COUNCIL OF GREATER CLEVELAND, *Key Topics in Mathematics for the Primary Teacher*, Chicago: Science Research Associates, Inc., 1962, pp. 45–47.

FLOURNOY, FRANCES, *Elementary School Mathematics*, Washington, D.C.: The Center for Applied Research in Education, 1964, pp. 33–34.

GIBB, E. GLENADINE, "Children's Thinking in the Process of Subtracting," *Journal of Experimental Education*, vol. 25, pp. 71–80, September, 1956.

GIBB, E. GLENADINE, "Take-Away Is Not Enough!" *The Arithmetic Teacher*, vol. 1, pp. 7–10, April, 1964.

HACKER, SIDNEY G., WILFRED E. BARNES, and CALVIN T. LONG, *Fundamental Concepts of Arithmetic*, Englewood Cliffs, N.J.: Prentice-Hall, Inc., 1963, p. 172.

MARKS, JOHN L., JAMES R. SMART, and IRENE SAUBLE, *Enlarging Mathematical Ideas*, Boston: Ginn and Company, 1961, pp. 28–29.

NATIONAL COUNCIL OF TEACHERS OF MATHEMATICS, *The Growth of Mathematical Ideas, Grades K–12, Twenty-fourth Yearbook*, Washington, D.C.: The National Council of Teachers of Mathematics, 1959, p. 22.

NATIONAL COUNCIL OF TEACHERS OF MATHEMATICS, *Instruction in Arithmetic, Twenty-fifth Yearbook*, Washington, D.C.: The National Council of Teachers of Mathematics, 1960, pp. 42–44, 343–345.

OSBORN, ROGER, M. VERE DeVAULT, CLAUDE BOYD, and ROBERT HOUSTON, *Extending Mathematics Understanding*, Columbus, Ohio: Charles E. Merrill Books, Inc., 1961, pp. 50–58.

RAPKIN, MINNIE K., and LILLIAN C. HOWITT, *Teaching the Third " R,"* Englewood Cliffs, N.J.: Teachers Practical Press, Inc., 1963, pp. 24–25, 53–54.

RHEINS, GLADYS B., and JOEL J. RHEINS, "A Comparison of Two Methods of Compound Subtraction: The Decomposition Method and the Equal Additions Method," *The Arithmetic Teacher*, vol. 2, pp. 63–69, October, 1955.

SAUSJORD, G., "What Is the Complementary Method of Subtraction?" *The Arithmetic Teacher*, vol. 10, pp. 262–267, May, 1963.

SHIPP, DONALD, and SAM ADAMS, *Developing Arithmetic Concepts and Skills*, Englewood Cliffs, N.J.: Prentice-Hall, Inc., 1964, pp. 168–169.

SMITH, SEATON E., JR., *Explorations in Elementary Mathematics*, Englewood Cliffs, N.J.: Prentice-Hall, Inc., 1966, pp. 60–62.

SPENCER, PETER LINCOLN, and MARGUERITE BRYDEGAARD, *Building Mathematical Competence in the Elementary School*, New York: Holt, Rinehart and Winston, Inc., 1966, pp. 136–138, 140–145.

SWAIN, ROBERT L., and EUGENE D. NICHOLS, *Understanding Arithmetic*, New York: Holt, Rinehart and Winston, Inc., 1965, pp. 81–83, 98–105.

SWENSON, ESTHER J., *Teaching Arithmetic to Children*, New York: The Macmillan Company, 1964, pp. 144–160, 173–188.

VAN ENGEN, HENRY, MAURICE L. HARTUNG, and JAMES E. STOCHL, *Foundations of Elementary School Arithmetic*, Chicago: Scott, Foresman and Co., 1965, pp. 102–103, 152–156.

WARD, MORGAN, and CLARENCE HARDGROVE, *Modern Elementary Mathematics*, Reading, Mass.: Addison-Wesley, 1964, pp. 140–143.

Puzzles can motivate a child to learn mathematics.

6

Teaching Multiplication on the Set of Whole Numbers

6.1. *Introduction*

THE CONCEPTS relating to multiplication, like the concepts of addition, are closely intertwined with many concepts in arithmetic. It is important, therefore, for the teacher to build a sound foundation of understanding multiplication before other processes and concepts can be understood.

Mastery of such concepts as the division algorithm, "reduction of fractions," least common denominator, and the compensation property for division have as a prerequisite the mastery of multiplication concepts.

6.2. *Definition, Terminology, and Symbolism*

There are three definitions of multiplication being used in elementary school textbooks. They are identified as *set, array,* and *cross-product* definitions. We will now illustrate how each of these definitions could be used to teach a child that the product of the factors 3 and 2 is 6.

In using the set definition, we would present three disjoint sets to the child, in which each set contains two objects. Then we would have him determine the number of items in the three sets. (In many instances, before the child is asked to determine the number of objects in the three sets, the union of the sets would be made.) The number he obtains, namely 6, would then be designated the product of 3 and 2.

In using the array definition, we would present the child with an array consisting of three rows of dots with two dots in each row. (See Figure 6.1.)

$$3 \times 2 = \square \qquad 3 \quad \begin{matrix} \cdot & \cdot \\ \cdot & \cdot \\ \cdot & \cdot \end{matrix}$$

$$2$$

FIGURE 6.1

He would then be asked to determine the number property of the array. The 6 that he would obtain would then be designated the product of 3 and 2.

There are several approaches that might be taken in presenting the cross-product definition. One of these is to describe a natural pairing situation. For example, if a girl had three blouses and two skirts, how many different ways could she dress? (See Figure 6.2.) The number 6 would be designated the product of 3 and 2.

A similar approach is to use a frame and colored sticks. To find the product of three and two, the child would select three sticks of one color (say black) and two sticks of a different color (gray). The child would lay one color

FIGURE 6.2

horizontally in his frame and the other color vertically. (See Figure 6.3.) He would then be asked to determine the number of cross points. Because there are six points where the gray sticks cross the black sticks, we say the product of 3 and 2 is 6.

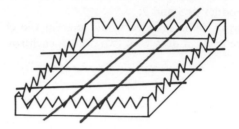

FIGURE 6.3

There are two notations you must teach your students. In the horizontal form, we are assuming a left-to-right reading. In the vertical form, we are assuming a bottom-to-top reading.

$$\begin{array}{r} 5 \\ \times\ 6 \\ \hline 30 \end{array}$$ Vertical form $6 \times 5 = 30$ Horizontal form

FIGURE 6.4

There are many ways that the mathematical sentences illustrated in Figure 6.4 can be read. A few of them follow:

    6 sets of balls are 30 balls.
    6 times 5 equals 30.
    6 times 5 is 30.
    6 fives equal 30.
    The product of the factors 6 and 5 is 30.
    The product of the factors 6 and 5 equals 30.
    5 multiplied by 6 is 30.
    5 multiplied by 6 equals 30.

In Figure 6.5, the terminology applied to the various numerals in multiplication sentences is identified. Note that there are two sets of terms for each mathematical sentence. As a teacher, you should use care not to mix these terms in an explanation. For example, it would not be proper to say, "factor 6 and multiplicand 5." When using the word *factor*, be consistent and use factor for the other number.

Factor		Factor	Product	Multiplicand*	5 Factor
6	×	5	= 30	Multiplier*	×6 Factor
Multiplier*	Multiplicand*		Product	Product	30 Product

* Traditional vocabulary.

FIGURE 6.5

6.3. *Readiness Experiences for Multiplication*

One of the earliest readiness exercises for multiplication is the counting activity conducted to develop readiness for addition. These counting activities build readiness for multiplication when the child starts counting at a multiple of the number he is counting by. For example, he might start counting by twos, starting at eight.

Another readiness exercise consists of having a child find the sums of doubles, triples, quadruples, and so on, by working with equal sets. For example, $4 + 4, 6 + 6 + 6, 3 + 3 + 3 + 3$.

The teacher can provide activities, even at the first-grade level, that will prepare the child for multiplication. Such questions as, "How many shoes do we have if we have two pairs of shoes?" and "How many people do we have if we have two sets of twins?" represent readiness questions.

6.4. *Teaching the Basic Multiplication Facts*

The flannel board, magnetic board, stick frame with sticks, place-value chart, blocks for arrays, buttons, bottle tops, disks, spool board, and peg board are all useful aids in teaching the concept of multiplication.

Three sets of four equal 12

FIGURE 6.6

The flannel board and magnetic board, along with accompanying objects, will be useful when the set definition is used for teaching multiplication facts. Figure 6.6 shows one arrangement a teacher might use in preparing to teach that three sets of four are equal to 12.

An accompanying dialogue might be as follows:

"Here we have three sets of birds. How many birds in each set? Let's count by fours and find out the total number of birds." (Four, eight, twelve.)

"We can record that we found three sets of four to be equal to 12 by writing $3 \times 4 = 12$." (Write the sentence $3 \times 4 = 12$ on the board.)

A similar technique can be used with the magnetic board. The peg board, spool board, and blocks will be useful when the array definition is used for teaching the multiplication facts. Figure 6.7 shows the arrangement a teacher might use on a spool board in preparing to teach that three rows of four are equal to 12.

$3 \times 4 = 12$

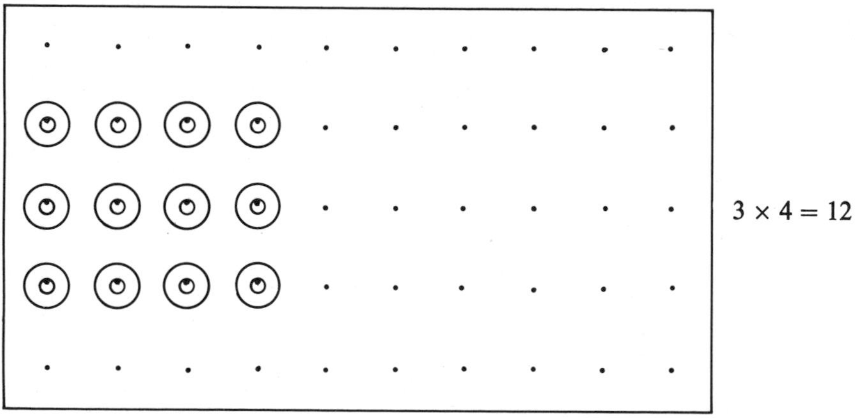

FIGURE 6.7

An accompanying dialogue might be as follows:

"Here we have three rows of spools. How many spools in each row? Let's count by fours and find out how many spools there are." (Four, eight, twelve.)

"We can tell that three rows of four are equal to 12 by writing the sentence $3 \times 4 = 12$." (Write this on the board.)

We can use a similar technique when using the peg board or blocks. The stick frame will be a useful aid to the teacher who is employing the cross-product definition to teach the multiplication facts. Figure 6.8 depicts the stages a child would go through in discovering that $3 \times 4 = 12$.

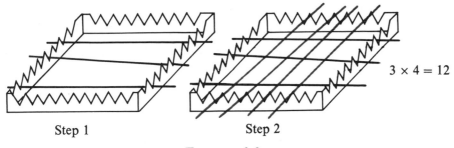

$3 \times 4 = 12$

Step 1   Step 2

FIGURE 6.8

An accompanying dialogue might be as follows:

"Place three black sticks in your stick frame." (Be demonstrating this on a large stick frame so that the children can see how you want the sticks placed. See Step 1, Figure 6.8.)

"Place four gray sticks in the frame so that they cross the black sticks." (Be demonstrating this. See Step 2, Figure 6.8.)

"Let's find out how many places the black sticks cross the gray sticks by counting by fours." (Four, eight, twelve.)

"We can show that there are three sets of four crosspoints by writing the sentence $3 \times 4 = 12$."

Although the number line is not especially useful in introducing the basic facts, it will prove to be a very useful aid in teaching later multiplication skills; therefore, it may be advantageous to introduce it occasionally in teaching some basic multiplication facts, to familiarize the students with it. Figure 6.9 represents $3 \times 4 = 12$ on a number line.

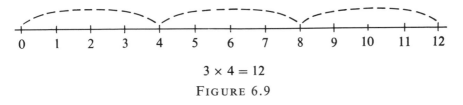

$3 \times 4 = 12$

FIGURE 6.9

An accompanying dialogue might be as follows:

"Let's take a jump of four, and another jump of four, and another jump of four. How many jumps of four did we take?" (Three.)

"Where did we begin our jumping?" (At zero.)

"Where did we end our jumping?" (At twelve.)

"We could tell this by writing the sentence $3 \times 4 = 12$." (Write this on the board.)

The identity property for multiplication is taught soon after the child begins to discover the multiplication facts, because it will eliminate the need for memorizing the facts in isolation. One way to teach this property is to structure several learning situations in which one of the factors is one, and to ask the child to find the products. He will soon discover that $1 \times n = n \times 1 = n$. You should extend this concept beyond numbers for which n is less than 10. For example, 23 times one is equal to what, or one times a million is equal to what?

The commutative property for multiplication is also introduced early in the child's experience with multiplication. If you will have the child discover this property (the fact that $a \times b = b \times a$) early in his work with multiplication, it will reduce the number of facts that he will have to discover. (This is not to be construed as meaning that the child will not have to memorize all of the facts.) In this first stage, you should present pairs of problems that will lead to the discovery. Figure 6.10 shows how we might use an array to

FIGURE 6.10

get the child to discover the commutative property. (The rows running left-to-right are identified with the first factor.)

As the array technique is used, the teacher should focus the child's mind on the fact that the number in the array is not changed by switching the number of rows and the number in each row. He can do this by asking, "Did the number of stars change when I put the array on its side? How did the multiplication sentence change?"

In Figure 6.11, we can see several pairs of problems that can be used to guide the child in discovering the commutative property of multiplication.

(1a) $3 \times 4 = \square$ (2a) $6 \times 9 = \square$ (3a) $2 \times 5 = \square$
(1b) $4 \times 3 = \square$ (2b) $9 \times 6 = \square$ (3b) $5 \times 2 = \square$

FIGURE 6.11

In the second stage, the child should be given an opportunity to use this newly discovered concept in problems requiring single solutions. Before presenting students with examples from this stage, the teacher should be sure that they have discovered the commutative property in stage one. Problems such as $7 \times \square = 9 \times 7$, and $3 \times 4 = \square \times 3$ are examples. The only requirement for a child's solving problems in this second stage is his recognizing that when we multiply two numbers in either order the product will be the same.

In general, if an elementary mathematics series does not begin with the discovery stage, it will pick up the teaching of the commutative property at this stage. If the discovery stage is not the first one presented, it is the teacher's responsibility to provide exercises to guide the child in discovering the commutative property of multiplication.

You should begin now to extend the child's concept toward a generalization. Problems having multiple solutions will help you. In this stage, you should expect and encourage such answers as, "Teacher, any number will work!" Examples of problems in this stage are as follows: $3 \times \square = \square \times 3$ and $\square \times 8 = 8 \times \square$.

One technique for eliciting the response that any number could be a factor is to ask for some of the solutions to these problems. Writing the various correct responses on the board will prompt someone to *say* that any number could be a factor. If this response is not forthcoming, you might say, "Have I listed all the correct answers on the board?"

In the last stage for getting the children to generalize, you can give patterns such as $\square \times \triangle = \triangle \times \square$ and ask them to create problems that could be true sentences using this pattern. This stage is often postponed until the intermediate or junior high level.

Another useful property in teaching children their basic facts is the *associative property*. For example, the product of the factors 4 and 5 can be discovered by renaming 4 as 2×2 and then using the associative property to obtain $2 \times (2 \times 5) = 2$ sets of 10, or 20.

In Figure 6.12, we can see how the associative property for multiplication [the fact that $(a \times b) \times c = a \times (b \times c)$] can also be used in teaching the child how to multiply ones times a multiple of 10.

$$3 \times 40 = 3 \times (4 \times 10) \xleftrightarrow[\text{property}]{\text{Associative}} (3 \times 4) \times 10 = 12 \times 10 = 120$$

FIGURE 6.12

In the first stage of teaching the associative property, you can give pairs of problems that will lead to the discovery. Figure 6.13 shows how we might use a block array to guide a child in discovering the associative property.

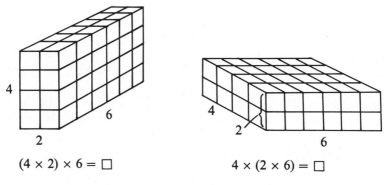

$(4 \times 2) \times 6 = \square$ $4 \times (2 \times 6) = \square$

FIGURE 6.13

As the array technique is used, the teacher should focus the child's mind on the fact that the number property is not changed by changing the position of the array. He can do this by asking, "Did we change the number of blocks by changing the position of the array? How did the multiplication sentence change?" It is also possible to change the viewing position to form a new mathematical sentence.

In Figure 6.14, we can see several pairs of problems that can be used to guide the child in discovering the associative property for multiplication.

(1a) $(3 \times 7) \times 6 = \square$ (2a) $4 \times (5 \times 6) = \square$ (3a) $(2 \times 3) \times 2 = \square$
(1b) $3 \times (7 \times 6) = \square$ (2b) $(4 \times 5) \times 6 = \square$ (3b) $2 \times (3 \times 2) = \square$

FIGURE 6.14

In the second stage, presented after the associative property has been discovered, you can give problems that require the use of this new concept to find a single solution. The child can be asked to identify which numeral is missing in a mathematical sentence. His ability to work these problems is dependent on his recognizing instances of the associative property. Several problems in this stage can be seen in Figure 6.15.

(a) $3 \times (5 \times 4) = (3 \times \Box) \times 4$
(b) $(8 \times \Box) \times 6 = 8 \times (11 \times 6)$
(c) $5 \times (1 \times 2) = (5 \times 1) \times \Box$

FIGURE 6.15

The third stage in teaching the associative property of multiplication can be one in which you lead the child toward a generalization. One of the purposes of this stage is to develop the child's awareness that any factor he chooses will be correct. This awareness can be developed by asking for solutions to each of the problems and then by listing them on the board. Typical examples can be seen in Figure 6.16.

(a) $(3 \times 8) \times \Box = 3 \times (8 \times \Box)$
(b) $6 \times (\Box \times \triangle) = (6 \times \Box) \times \triangle$
(c) $(\Box \times 1) \times 9 = \Box \times (1 \times 9)$

FIGURE 6.16

In the final stage of learning the associative property of multiplication, you can give your students patterns such as $(\Box \times \triangle) \times \bigcirc = \Box \times (\triangle \times \bigcirc)$ and ask them to create problems that are true sentences using this pattern.

A third property bridging the concept of multiplication and addition is the distributive property of multiplication over addition [the fact that $a \times (b + c) = (a \times b) + (a \times c)$]. It is one of the most useful of the structural properties. It provides flexibility in teaching the basic multiplication facts and plays a significant role in the teaching of the multiplication algorithm.

Let us look at how this property provides flexibility in discovering the basic facts. Let us assume that a student knows $7 \times 1 = 7$, $7 \times 2 = 14$, $7 \times 3 = 21$, $7 \times 4 = 28$, and $7 \times 5 = 35$. Assume also that he knows the distributive property of multiplication over addition. When he is faced with the problem of determining the product of the factors 7 and 7, he could find the product in any one of the following ways:

$$7 \times (5 + 2) = (7 \times 5) + (7 \times 2) = 35 + 14 = 49$$
or
$$7 \times (3 + 4) = (7 \times 3) + (7 \times 4) = 21 + 28 = 49$$
or
$$7 \times (2 + 2 + 2 + 1) = (7 \times 2) + (7 \times 2) + (7 \times 2) + (7 \times 1)$$
$$= 14 + 14 + 14 + 7 = 49$$
etc.

In working the problem shown in Figure 6.17, we make use of the distributive property in multiplying the 3 and 2 ones, and then the 3 and 1 ten, and then by adding the 30 and 6 to get 36.

$$12 \rightarrow \quad 12 \rightarrow \quad 12$$
$$\underline{\times\ 3} \qquad \underline{\times\ 3} \qquad \underline{\times\ 3}$$
$$\qquad\qquad 6 \qquad\quad 36$$

FIGURE 6.17

The first stage in teaching the distributive property leads the child to discover it and can be taught using pairs of problems. It is important to have the child discover this distributive property early in his work with multiplication, so that he can use it to discover new facts.

In Figure 6.18, we have depicted an array in various stages of teaching the distributive property. In the left picture, the rows are united to form a single array before the product is determined. In the right picture, the child is instructed to find the product of each array and then to determine the sum.

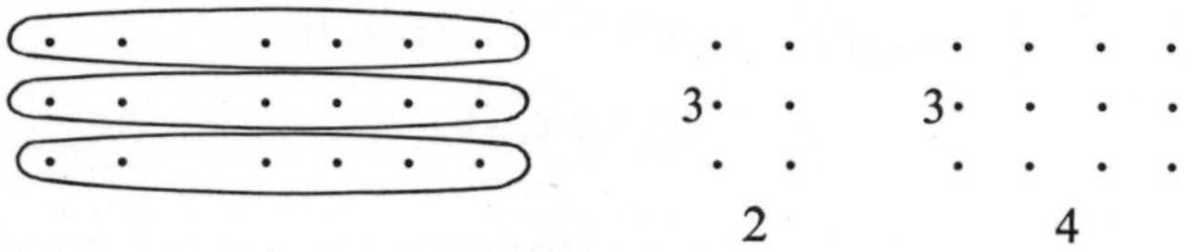

$$3 \times (2 + 4) = \square$$

$$(3 \times 2) + (3 \times 4) = \square$$

FIGURE 6.18

In Figure 6.19, we can see several pairs of problems that can be used to guide the child in discovering the distributive property of multiplication over addition.

(1a) $2 \times (1 + 2) = \square$ (2a) $3 \times (4 + 2) = \square$
(1b) $(2 \times 1) + (2 \times 2) = \square$ (2b) $(3 \times 4) + (3 \times 2) = \square$

(3a) $4 \times (4 + 1) = \square$
(3b) $(4 \times 4) + (4 \times 1) = \square$

FIGURE 6.19

In the second stage, the child is expected to identify the missing factor or missing addend, based on the previously learned pattern of the distributive property. In Figure 6.20, we can see representative problems of this stage.

(a) $3 \times (\square + 8) = (3 \times 5) + (3 \times 8)$
(b) $4 \times (8 + 7) = (\square \times 8) + (\square \times 7)$
(c) $3 \times (2 + 5) = (3 \times \square) + (3 \times 5)$

FIGURE 6.20

In the third stage, the child is pointed toward the generalization that "any three whole numbers can be used in the distributive pattern." Examples of problems in this stage are depicted in Figure 6.21.

(a) $\square \times (4 + 8) = (\square \times 4) + (\square \times 8)$
(b) $7 \times (\square + 2) = (7 \times \square) + (7 \times 2)$
(c) $3 \times (\square + \triangle) = (3 \times \square) + (3 \times \triangle)$

FIGURE 6.21

In the final stage of teaching the distributive property of multiplication over addition, the student is asked to create true mathematical sentences using the pattern $\square \times (\triangle + \bigcirc) = (\square \times \triangle) + (\square \times \bigcirc)$.

The distributive property of multiplication over subtraction can be developed in a similar manner. This property also has several useful applications in elementary school mathematics because it is useful in discovering the multiplication facts. For example, if a child knows this property and his fives facts and ones facts, he could discover all of the fours facts as follows:

$$1 \times (5 - 1) = (1 \times 5) - (1 \times 1) = 4$$
$$2 \times (5 - 1) = (2 \times 5) - (2 \times 1) = 8$$
$$9 \times (5 - 1) = (9 \times 5) - (9 \times 1) = 36$$

This property is also useful for developing multiplication-speed skills. For example, to multiply 8×19, the child thinks, "$8 \times 20 = 160$, and $8 \times 1 = 8$, and $160 - 8 = 152$." Thus, he finds the product of 8×19 by making use of this distributive property. In Figure 6.22, we can see several pairs of problems that can be used to guide the child in making his initial discovery of this distributive property.

(1a) $3 \times (7 - 2) = \square$ (2a) $2 \times (9 - 5) = \square$
(1b) $(3 \times 7) - (3 \times 2) = \square$ (2b) $(2 \times 9) - (2 \times 5) = \square$

(3a) $5 \times (3 - 1) = \square$
(3b) $(5 \times 3) - (5 \times 1) = \square$

FIGURE 6.22

After the child has discovered the pattern, he should be given an opportunity to use this concept in problems requiring single solutions. A short review of problems from the paired-problem stage should probably be undertaken before presenting problems from this stage. Figure 6.23 depicts several typical problems from this stage.

(a) $3 \times (5 - 2) = (3 \times \square) - (3 \times 2)$
(b) $4 \times (\square - 6) = (4 \times 9) - (4 \times 6)$
(c) $3 \times (6 - 4) = (\square \times 6) - (\square \times 4)$
(d) $\square \times (3 - 1) = (8 \times 3) - (8 \times 1)$

FIGURE 6.23

You should gradually extend the child's concepts toward the generalization. Problems having multiple solutions will help you toward this goal. Figure 6.24 shows typical problems from this stage.

(a) $\square \times (8 - 6) = (\square \times 8) - (\square \times 6)$
(b) $4 \times (9 - \square) = (4 \times 9) - (4 \times \square)$
(c) $8 \times (\square - 1) = (8 \times \square) - (8 \times 1)$
(d) $3 \times (\square - \square) = (3 \times \square) - (3 \times \square)$

FIGURE 6.24

In the final stage of getting the child to generalize this property, you can give him a pattern such as $\bigcirc \times (\square - \triangle) = (\bigcirc \times \square) - (\bigcirc \times \triangle)$ and ask him to create problems that are true sentences using this pattern.

The following table summarizes some methods for teaching the basic multiplication facts:

PROBLEM	METHOD	SOLUTION
$2 \times 3 = \square$	Using arrays. · · · · · ·	$2 \times 3 = 6$
$3 \times 2 = \square$	Using sets.	$3 \times 2 = 6$
$2 \times 4 = \square$	Using a number line. 0 1 2 3 4 5 6 7 8 9	$2 \times 4 = 8$
$7 \times 5 = \square$	Using the commutative property. Because $5 \times 7 = 35$, then	$7 \times 5 = 35$
$8 \times 9 = \square$	Using the distributive property. $8 \times (4 + 5) = (8 \times 4) + (8 \times 5) = 32 + 40$	$8 \times 9 = 72$
$7 \times 1 = \square$	Using the identity property. Because $n \times 1 = n$, then	$7 \times 1 = 7$

PROBLEM	METHOD	SOLUTION
$4 \times 2 = \square$	Cross product.	$4 \times 2 = 8$
$9 \times 5 = \square$	Using patterns. $9 \times 1 = 9$, $9 \times 2 = 18$, 9×3 $= 27$, $9 \times 4 = 36$	$9 \times 5 = 45$
$7 \times 9 = \square$	Using generalizations. Because $(n - 1) \times (n + 1)$ $= n^2 - 1$, $8 \times 8 = 64$, then	$7 \times 9 = 63$
$3 \times 5 = \square$	Repeated addition. $5 + 5 + 5 = 15$	$3 \times 5 = 15$

6.5. *Memorization of the Basic Facts*

After the child has discovered various products—for example, after he has discovered all the products 25 or less—he should be encouraged to memorize these facts. Some previously mentioned activities (see Section 4.5) are teaming up to use flash cards; nontimed and timed tests followed by practice on or rediscovery of missed facts; and "Beat the Bounce."

6.6. *The Product of Ones and Tens*

Before teaching a child how to multiply ones and tens and ones, it is necessary to establish the skill of finding the product of ones and tens. There are essentially two approaches that can be used to help the child establish the relationship between "ones times ones" and "ones times tens."

The first of these approaches, we shall call the "skip-counting" method. It involves having the child establish the product through counting by multiples of 10 on a "tens number line." Figure 6.25 depicts how to discover that $3 \times 40 = 120$ by using the tens number line.

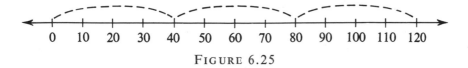

FIGURE 6.25

A dialogue to accompany this presentation might be as follows:

"How many tens are named by 40?" (Four.) "If we take three jumps of 4 tens, we have jumped how far?" (Either 120 or 12 tens. Stress the 12 tens aspect, because you want the child to establish the relationship between multiplying ones and ones, and ones and tens.)

"We could record this by writing the sentence 3 × 40 = 120." (Write this on the board.)

The second approach to teaching ones times tens we shall call the "re-naming-associative technique." In teaching the child to multiply 3 × 40, you might first teach him to multiply ones times 10 by skip counting. He would then learn to rename 40 as 4 × 10. His problem would thus appear 3 × (4 × 10), the name 4 × 10 having been substituted for the name 40. The associative property is used to associate the 3 and the 4 and this product is determined. The final step consists of renaming 12 × 10, making it 120.

After a child has mastered the basic facts and the skill of multiplying ones and tens, he is ready to learn the one-digit-two-digit multiplication algorithm.

6.7. *Multiplication of Ones Times Tens and Ones*

In Figure 6.26, we see a step-by-step symbolic presentation by the teacher depicting the steps used in learning to multiply ones times tens and ones.

$$5 \times 17$$
$$\downarrow$$
Step 1 – – – – $5 \times (10 + 7)$
$$\downarrow$$
Step 2 – – – – $(5 \times 10) + (5 \times 7)$
$$\downarrow$$
Step 3 – – – – $50 + 35$
$$\downarrow$$
Step 4 – – – – $50 + (30 + 5)$
$$\downarrow$$
Step 5 – – – – $(50 + 30) + 5$
$$\downarrow$$
Step 6 – – – – $80 + 5$
$$\downarrow$$
Step 7 – – – – 85

FIGURE 6.26

In Step 1, we have renamed 17, making it (10 + 7). We have done this because the only multiplication skills the student has are how to multiply ones and ones, and ones and tens. In Step 2, the distributive property has been used. In Step 3, the teacher has used the two multiplication skills the children have been taught. In Step 4, the 35 has been renamed (30 + 5) because of the need to add the 3 tens to the 5 tens. In Step 5, the associative property of addition has been applied. Addition of tens to tens has been made in Step 6. In Step 7, (80 + 5) has been renamed 85.

The teacher should give special attention in his explanation to Step 5. At the end, he should go back to this step and ask, "What did we do with the 3 tens that we got by multiplying 5 and 7?"

After you have developed the idea that the tens, obtained by multiplying the ones and ones, is added to the tens obtained by multiplying the ones and tens, the child is ready to learn to use vertical notation for multiplication. A typical problem in the early stages of this development can be seen in Figure 6.27.

$$
\begin{array}{r}
30 + 8 \\
\times \quad\quad 9 \\
\hline
\square + \triangle = \Diamond
\end{array}
$$

FIGURE 6.27

A typical dialogue that could be used to introduce this algorithm might be as follows:

"9 times 8 is equal to what?" (Seventy-two.)

"We will record the 72 in the triangular region. 9 times 3 tens is equal to what?" (27 tens or 270.)

"We will record the 270 in the square region. In the horizontal form, what did we do with the 7 tens in 72?" (We added it to the tens we got when we multiplied ones and tens.)

"If we add the 7 tens to the 27 tens, how many tens will we have?" (Thirty-four.) "If we then rename our 34 tens and 2 ones, what will our standard numeral be?" (342.) "We write 342 in the hexagonal region."

EXERCISES (1)

1. Name a readiness activity that would prepare a child for multiplication by nine.
2. Explain how you would use a magnetic board to teach 5 × 7 = 35. Use illustrations. Make up a dialogue.

3. Explain how you would use a peg board to teach $8 \times 6 = 48$. Use illustrations. Make up a dialogue.

4. Explain how you would use a stick frame to teach $8 \times 7 = 56$. Use illustrations. Make up a dialogue.

5. Explain, using a number line, how you would teach $3 \times 5 = 15$. Use illustrations. Make up a dialogue.

6. Explain how you would use a number line to teach $9 \times 20 = 180$. Use illustrations. Make up a dialogue.

7. Explain how you would teach 8×90 by the "renaming-associative technique."

8. Make up a step-by-step presentation, with dialogue, explaining how you would introduce 8×28, using horizontal notation.

9. Make up a dialogue that could be used to introduce the following problem:

$$\begin{array}{r} 50 + 6 \\ \times \qquad 3 \\ \hline \square + \triangle = \bigcirc \end{array}$$

10. Use the set definition of product and illustrate how you would show a child that the product of the factors 4 and 5 is 20.

11. Use the array definition of product and illustrate how you would show a child that the product of the factors 3 and 7 is 21.

12. Use the cross-product definition and illustrate how you would show a child that the product of the factors 1 and 1 is 1.

13. List six ways you could read $5 \times 9 = 45$.

14. Identify each of the following in the mathematical sentences: factor, product.

$$\text{a. } 8 \times 9 = 72 \qquad \text{b.} \begin{array}{r} 6 \\ \times 3 \\ \hline 18 \end{array}$$

15. Solve the following problem: $88 \times \square = 88$. What property for multiplication is illustrated?

16. Make up sample problems for each of the first three stages in teaching the commutative property for multiplication.

17. Make up sample problems for each of the first three stages in teaching the associative property for multiplication.

18. Make up sample problems for each of the first three stages in teaching the distributive property of multiplication over addition.

19. Make up sample problems for each of the first three stages in teaching the distributive property of multiplication over subtraction.

6.8. *Introducing a Standard Vertical Form for Multiplying Ones and Tens and Ones*

After the student has developed his ability to multiply ones and tens and ones using expanded notation and understands that the tens obtained by multiplying ones and ones are added to the tens obtained by multiplying ones and tens, he is ready to learn the standard form of the multiplication algorithm. Figure 6.28 depicts the sequencing for introducing the standard form:

Phase 1	Phase 2	Phase 3
$20 + 8$	28	28
$\times \qquad 7$	$\times \quad 7$	$\times \quad 7$
$140 + 56$	56	196
	140	
	196	

FIGURE 6.28

Dialogue to accompany this presentation might be as follows:

"When we multiplied 7 and $(20 + 8)$, we obtained 140 and 56. What did we do with these two numbers then?" (We added them together.)

"What is the most convenient way to write 56 and 140 in order to add the 56 and the 140?" (In vertical notation.)

"Let's now learn a new way to work this problem." (Write $\begin{array}{r} 28 \\ \times \ 7 \\ \hline \end{array}$ on the board.)

"When we multiply 7 and 8, what product do we get?" (Fifty-six.)

"Place the 56 here." (Place as shown in Phase 2.)

"What does the 2 stand for in 28?" (Two tens.)

"If we multiply 7 and 2 tens, what will the product be?" (Fourteen tens, or 140.)

"Place the 140 here." (Place as shown in Phase 2.)

"Can anyone tell me why we have placed the 140 directly below the 56?" (Because it will be easy for us to add the 140 and the 56 in this form.)

"We now add the 140 and the 56 and obtain 196."

Some of your students of minimal ability may never progress to the next phase. It is possible that these children would have been the same students who, without the simplified algorithm depicted in Phase 2, would remain at the basic facts stage of development.

In Phase 3, the child is directed to write down the numeral for the 6 ones he obtains when he multiplies 7 and 8, and to mentally retain the 5 tens, which will be added to the tens obtained when he multiplies 7 and 20.

6.9. *Multiplication of Tens and Tens*

The first activity in developing the skill of multiplying tens and tens is that of having a student learn that 10 times 10 is equal to one hundred. This can be done either through the previously discussed skip-counting technique, or by relating the concept of $10 \times 10 = 100$ to the concept of 10 dimes is as much as 100 pennies.

Many textbooks employ the renaming-associative technique to teach the product of tens and tens. Figure 6.29 gives a step-by-step presentation using this technique.

$$40 \times 50$$
$$\downarrow$$
Step 1 – – – – $\quad (4 \times 10) \times (5 \times 10)$
$$\downarrow$$
Step 2 – – – – $\quad 4 \times (10 \times 5) \times 10$
$$\downarrow$$
Step 3 – – – – $\quad 4 \times (5 \times 10) \times 10$
$$\downarrow$$
Step 4 – – – – $\quad (4 \times 5) \times (10 \times 10)$
$$\downarrow$$
Step 5 – – – – $\quad 20 \times 100$
$$\downarrow$$
Step 6 – – – – $\quad 2000$

FIGURE 6.29

In Step 1, the 40 and 50 have been renamed 4×10 and 5×10, respectively. Step 2 makes use of the associative property, because the desire is to multiply the ones and ones, and the tens and tens. Step 5 makes use of the basic multiplication facts skill and the skill of multiplying 10 and 10. In Step 6, 20×100 has been renamed 2000.

This technique will be extended to include multiplication of ones and hundreds, ones and thousands, tens and hundreds, tens and thousands, and so on. Further development of this concept is reserved for the exercises.

6.10. *Multiplication of Tens and Ones by Tens and Ones*

Although you will employ a detailed step-by-step presentation for introducing the skill of multiplying tens and ones by tens and ones, the student will start at a stage comparable to Phase 2 (see Section 6.8). Figure 6.30 shows such a step-by-step presentation by the teacher. The justification or skill required for the steps is given above each one.

27×35
    renaming
$(20 + 7) \times 35$
    distributive property of multiplication over addition
$(20 \times 35) + (7 \times 35)$
    renaming
$[20 \times (30 + 5)] + [7 \times (30 + 5)]$
    distributive property of multiplication over addition
$[(20 \times 30) + (20 \times 5)] + [(7 \times 30) + (7 \times 5)]$
    multiplication skills
$600 + 100 + 210 + 35$
    renaming
$600 + 100 + 200 + 10 + 30 + 5$
    addition skills
$900 + 40 + 5$
    renaming
945

FIGURE 6.30

The teacher should give special emphasis to the step $(20 \times 30) + (20 \times 5) + (7 \times 30) + (7 \times 5)$. He should focus the child's attention on what is being multiplied by the 7 in 27 and what is being multiplied by the 20 in 27.

In introducing the standard algorithm, the phasing-in starts at Phase 2 (see Section 6.8). Figure 6.31 depicts the phasing-in stages.

Phase 1	Phase 2
35	35
× 27	× 27
35	245
210	700
100	945
600	
945	

FIGURE 6.31

An accompanying dialogue might be as follows:

> "We have seen that in order to find the product of 27 and 35, we multiply the 7 and 5, and the 7 and 3 tens, the 2 tens and 5, and finally the 2 tens and 3 tens. We then find the sum of these four products. Notice where I have placed these four products."
>
> "Why have I placed the numerals like this?" (Because we wish to find the sum, and this is the most convenient form for adding these numbers.)
>
> "We add and find the product of the factors 27 and 35, which is 945."

You may have some students of low aptitude who will stay at this phase in the development of the multiplication algorithm. Do not be overly concerned that they do not progress beyond it, be pleased that they at least have mastered a means of finding the product of two whole numbers. This phase is slightly less efficient than the next phase, but we occasionally must sacrifice the more efficient algorithm for one that is simpler to understand.

In the next phase, the child is taught to remember those numbers that will go into the regrouping upon the next multiplication. The teacher should show the child that the sum of the partial products, 35 and 210 in the first form, is the partial product 245 in the second phase. Also, it should be pointed out that the sum of the partial products, 100 and 600 in the first phase, forms the partial product 700 in the second phase.

In essence, the child has all the essential background at this point to extend the algorithm with a minimum of new technique. Further development of the multiplication algorithm is left for the exercises. In summary, the following are prerequisites for the mastery of the previously discussed multiplication algorithm:

1. The child must know the basic multiplication facts.
2. He needs to understand his decimal system to the extent that he knows $1 \times 1 = 1$, $1 \times 10 = 10$, $10 \times 10 = 100$, $10 \times 100 = 1000$.
3. He needs also to know that

	Example:
ones times ones = ones	7 ones $\times$ 8 ones = 56 ones
ones times tens = tens	7 ones $\times$ 8 tens = 56 tens or 560
tens times tens = hundreds, etc.	7 tens $\times$ 8 tens = 56 hundreds or 5600

4. He needs to know and be able to use the distributive property of multiplication over addition.

EXERCISES (2)

1. Make up a dialogue that could be used to introduce

$$
\begin{array}{r}
92 \\
\times\ 8 \\
\hline
16 \\
720 \\
\hline
736
\end{array}
$$

2. Make up a dialogue that could be used to introduce

$$
\begin{array}{r}
92 \\
\times\ 8 \\
\hline
736
\end{array}
$$

3. Give a step-by-step explanation using the renaming-associative technique to explain $300 \times 4000 = 1,200,000$.

4. Give a step-by-step explanation in horizontal form on how the product of 35 and 182 is determined.

5. Work the following problem by using partial products requiring no mental regrouping. (Phase 1, Section 7.14.)

$$
\begin{array}{r}
237 \\
\times\ 46 \\
\hline
\end{array}
$$

6. Make up a dialogue that will explain how each of the partial products is obtained in the following problem:

$$
\begin{array}{r}
237 \\
\times\ 46 \\
\hline
1422 \\
9480 \\
\hline
10902
\end{array}
$$

6.11. *Multiplication "Story" Problems*

One of the first awarenesses that a child needs to acquire is that the request to determine the number of a set formed by the unions of a number of sets equal in number signals a multiplicative operation. He also has to recognize that these sets, equal in number, can occur in an array, in a measurement situation (such as a set of four nickels), or in a situation where he is expected to extract the equal sets. For example, if items are bought costing five cents, twelve cents, five cents, twelve cents, and twelve cents, the total cost is obtained by "$(2 \times 5) + (3 \times 12)$."

Let us examine some problems that involve translation into multiplication sentences.

John bought 3 pencils.
Each pencil cost 5 cents.
What was the total cost of the pencils?

Let us examine how a chart might be employed to broaden the child's problem-solving skills. Let us assume that you have constructed a chart similar to the one shown in Figure 6.32.

NUMBER OF PENCILS	COST OF EACH PENCIL	TOTAL COST
1	5¢	
2	5¢	
3	5¢	
4	5¢	
5	5¢	

FIGURE 6.32

The following dialogue might be used to accompany this chart:

"If we bought one pencil for five cents, we would pay five cents for the pencil." (Record five cents in the total-cost column.)

"If we bought two pencils, how much would we have to pay?" (Ten cents. Discuss the different ways we could have found the total cost. Add five cents and five cents, or say that $2 \times 5 = 10$.)

"If we bought three pencils, how much would we have to pay?" (Fifteen cents. Discuss the different ways we could have found this total cost. Add ten cents and five cents.) "Knowing that two pencils cost ten cents helps us find the cost of three pencils." ($5 + 5 + 5 = 15$ and $3 \times 5 = 15$.)

After completing the table, place the following equations on the board:

$$1 \square 5 = 5$$
$$2 \square 5 = 10$$
$$3 \square 5 = 15$$
$$4 \square 5 = 20$$
$$5 \square 5 = 25$$

"What operation are we using if the pair of numbers 1, 5 gives us 5, the pair of 2, 5 gives us 10, and so on?" (Multiplication.)

Analyze other similar problems, always pointing out the fact that when we find that we have many sets equal in number, the operation of multiplication will help us find the total number of members of the sets.

The child should be given some activities in solving problems that involve nothing other than the experience of translating a story problem into a mathematical sentence. When multiplication is involved, we can request the child to see how many ways he could translate a given problem. For example, the following problem can be translated in several ways:

Mary has 5 bags of cookies.
Each bag contains 6 cookies.
How many cookies does Mary have?

Translations are $5 \times 6 = \square$; $6 + 6 + 6 + 6 + 6 = \square$; $(2 \times 6) + (3 \times 6) = \square$; $(1 \times 6) + (4 \times 6) = \square$; and so on.

EXERCISES (3)

1. Using one of the following sources, construct five story problems of a current-events nature involving basic multiplication facts appropriate for a group of students in a third-grade class.

   a. Newspaper   b. *World Almanac*   c. Magazine

2. Using the same sources, construct five story problems of a current-events nature involving a factor using one digit and a factor using two digits appropriate for fourth-grade students.

3. Using the same sources, construct five story problems of a current-events nature involving two steps in which one of the operations is multiplication. These problems should be appropriate for fourth-grade students.

4. Using the same sources, construct five story problems of a current-events nature requiring the children to use multiplication and two other operations appropriate for sixth-grade students.

5. Make up a word problem for each of the following mathematical sentences:

a. $3 \times .17 = \square$ c. $(2 \times 5) + (3 \times 6) = \square$

b. $3 \times 17 = \square$ d. $34 \times 67 = \square$

REFERENCES

BANKS, J. HOUSTON, *Learning and Teaching Arithmetic*, Boston: Allyn & Bacon, 1964, pp. 181–206.

BELL, CLIFFORD, CLELA D. HAMMOND, and ROBERT B. HERRERA, *Fundamentals of Arithmetic for Teachers*, New York: John Wiley & Sons, Inc., 1962, pp. 59–73.

BRUMFIEL, CHARLES, ROBERT EICHOLZ, and MERRILL SHANKS, *Fundamental Concepts of Elementary Mathematics*, Reading, Mass.: Addison-Wesley, 1962, pp. 29–49.

CHURCHILL, EILEEN M., *Counting and Measuring*, Great Britain: Routledge & Kegan Paul, 1962, pp. 146–149.

CROUCH, RALPH, GEORGE BALDWIN, and ROBERT J. WISNER, *Preparatory Mathematics for Elementary Teachers*, New York: John Wiley & Sons, Inc., 1965, pp. 77–91.

EDUCATION RESEARCH COUNCIL OF GREATER CLEVELAND, *Key Topics in Mathematics for the Primary Teacher*, Chicago: Science Research Associates, Inc., 1962, pp. 48–61.

FLOURNOY, FRANCES, *Elementary School Mathematics*, Washington, D.C.: The Center for Applied Research in Education, 1964, pp. 10, 35.

HACKER, SIDNEY G., WILFRED E. BARNES, and CALVIN T. LONG, *Fundamental Concepts of Arithmetic*, Englewood Cliffs, N.J.: Prentice-Hall, Inc., 1963, pp. 70–71.

JOHNSON, DONOVAN A., and WILLIAM H. GLENN, *Understanding Numeration Systems*, St. Louis, Mo.: Webster, 1960, pp. 6–44.

MARKS, JOHN L., JAMES R. SMART, and IRENE SAUBLE, *Enlarging Mathematical Ideas*, Boston: Ginn and Company, 1961, pp. 28–34, 41–45.

MESERVE, BRUCE E., and MAX A. SOBEL, *Mathematics for Secondary School Teachers*, Englewood Cliffs, N.J.: Prentice-Hall, Inc., 1962, pp. 11–31.

MORRIS, DENNIS E., and HENRY D. TOPFER, *Advancing in Mathematics*, Chicago: Science Research Associates, Inc., 1963, pp. 19–45.

NATIONAL COUNCIL OF TEACHERS OF MATHEMATICS, *Instruction in Arithmetic, Twenty-fifth Yearbook*, Washington, D.C.: The National Council of Teachers of Mathematics, 1960, pp. 50–52, 345–348.

NATIONAL COUNCIL OF TEACHERS OF MATHEMATICS, *The Growth of Mathematical Ideas*, *Grades K–12, Twenty-fourth Yearbook*, Washington, D.C.: The National Council of Teachers of Mathematics, 1959, pp. 23–24.

PAGE, DAVID A., *Number Lines, Functions, and Fundamental Topics*, New York: The Macmillan Company, 1964, pp. 26–36.

PAGE, DAVID A., *Number Lines, Functions and Fundamental Topics*, Urbana, Ill.: University of Illinois, Arithmetic Project, 1961.

PETERSON, JOHN A., and JOSEPH HASHISAKI, *Theory of Arithmetic*, New York: John Wiley & Sons, Inc., 1964, pp. 92–98.

RAPKIN, MINNIE K., and LILLIAN C. HOWITT, *Teaching the Third " R,"* Englewood Cliffs, N.J.: Teachers Practical Press, Inc., 1963, pp. 26–29.

SCHAAF, WILLIAM L., *Basic Concepts of Elementary Mathematics*, New York: John Wiley & Sons, Inc., 1960, pp. 173–183.

SMITH, SEATON E., JR., *Explorations in Elementary Mathematics*, Englewood Cliffs, N.J.: Prentice-Hall, Inc., 1966, pp. 79–81.

SPENCER, PETER LINCOLN, and MARGUERITE BRYDEGAARD, *Building Mathematical Competence in the Elementary School*, New York: Holt, Rinehart and Winston, Inc., 1966, pp. 145–151.

SPITZER, HERBERT F., *The Teaching of Arithmetic*, 3rd ed., Boston: Houghton Mifflin Company, 1961, pp. 121–142.

SWAIN, ROBERT L., and EUGENE D. NICHOLS, *Understanding Arithmetic*, New York: Holt, Rinehart and Winston, Inc., 1965, pp. 107–117.

SWENSON, ESTHER J., *Teaching Arithmetic to Children*, New York: The Macmillan Company, 1964, pp. 191–214.

VAN ENGEN, HARRY, MAURICE L. HARTUNG, and JAMES E. STOCHL, *Foundations of Elementary School Arithmetic*, Chicago: Scott, Foresman and Co., 1965, pp. 90–95, 156–158.

WARD, MORGAN, and CLARENCE HARDGROVE, *Modern Elementary Mathematics*, Reading, Mass.: Addison-Wesley, 1964, pp. 145–149.

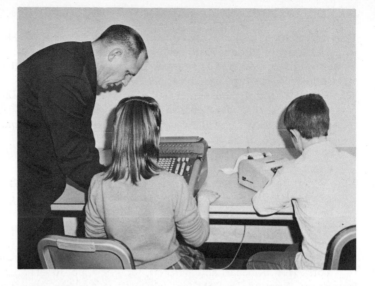

Games can motivate a child to learn mathematics.

7

Teaching Division on the Set of Whole Numbers

7.1. *Introduction*

THE CONCEPTS related to division on the set of whole numbers play a crucial role in the concepts that are developed after division concepts—the concepts of the fractional numbers and the concepts relative to the set of rational numbers.

The compensation property for division will not only facilitate the mastery of the decimal division algorithm, but will also serve as a basis for determining equivalence classes for fractional numbers. It also will be an integral part of the development of and justification for the division algorithm for fractional numbers.

The right identity element for division of whole numbers will also play a leading role in the development of division on the set of fractional numbers. The right distributive properties of division over addition, and division over subtraction, will provide the bridging concepts for a smooth transition into addition and subtraction of fractional numbers. Careful development of these distributive properties will explain away much of the mystery of why we do not add the *denominators*, or why it is important that the denominators name the same number.

7.2. *Definition, Terminology, and Symbolism*

Before exploring the techniques of teaching division, it will perhaps be advantageous to review the symbolism, terminology, and definitions which will be used to communicate our ideas. A definition of quotient follows:

> The quotient of two whole numbers x and y ($y \neq 0$) will be the whole number z if y times $z = x$.

For example, the quotient of 8 and 2 is 4, because $4 \times 2 = 8$ (or because $2 \times 4 = 8$). This definition of quotient will suffice if the first whole number is divisible by the second whole number. [*Definition of divisible:* A whole number x is said to be divisible by a whole number y ($y \neq 0$) if there exists a whole number z such that $x = z$ times y.] This definition of quotient is not adequate when we are concerned with division situations accompanied by remainders. In these cases, the quotient and remainder are defined as follows:

> Let x and y be whole numbers such that y is not equal to zero. The quotient and remainder of x and y are w and z respectively, if $x = (y$ times $w) + z$.

An example of the use of this definition is as follows: The quotient of 14 and 3 is 4 with a remainder of 2, because $14 = (3 \times 4) + 2$.

Although we use the previous definitions for quotients, when we are interested in an efficient process to find this quotient, we "interpret" division in terms of repeated subtraction. A generalized form of this interpretation follows:

> The quotient of two whole numbers x and y ($y \neq 0$) is the number of times y must be subtracted from x in order to get a remainder r, and $0 \leq r < y$.

An algorithm that uses this interpretation is called a *repeated-subtraction division algorithm*. There are four basic notations that represent division. (See Figure 7.1.)

An elementary teacher often has the tendency to stress the notation in Figure 7.1(d) at the expense of the other notations. Notation (a) is an important form permitting natural left-to-right reading that also is a useful method of recording the basic division facts. It is important that students also become familiar with notation (c), as it points out the fact that fractions can be thought of as denoting the quotient of two whole numbers.

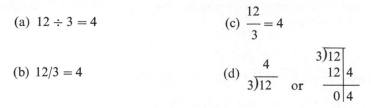

(a) $12 \div 3 = 4$

(b) $12/3 = 4$

(c) $\dfrac{12}{3} = 4$

(d) $\begin{array}{r} 4 \\ 3\overline{)12} \end{array}$ or ...

FIGURE 7.1

There are many ways that the mathematical sentences illustrated in Figure 7.1 can be read. A few of them follow:

The quotient of 12 and 3 is 4.
The quotient of 12 and 3 equals 4.
12 divided by 3 is equal to 4.
12 divided by 3 is 4.

In Figure 7.2, the terminology applied to the division notation and sentences relative to the definitions is identified. Note that there are two sets of terminology for every division sentence except one. You should exercise care not to mix your terms in an explanation. For example, it would not be best to say "product 12 and divisor 3." When you use the term product, you should be consistent and refer to the other numbers as "known factor," "unknown factor," and "remainder."

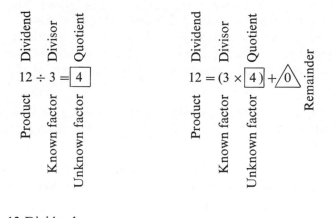

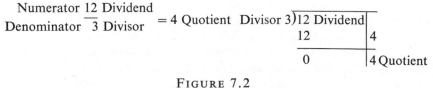

FIGURE 7.2

7.3. *Teaching the Basic Division Facts*

A readiness activity for division at the first-grade level involves having the children actually construct sets, equal in number, from a given set. For example, given a set of eight objects, see how many sets of two can be constructed. Another example might consist of having the children distribute 12 cards or buttons to the four corners of their desks so that they have the same number of cards in each corner. When the children are ready, the teacher asks, "How many are in each corner of your desk?" Then he says, "You have four sets. How many are in each set?"

A child encounters division when he is asked to find a missing factor in a multiplication sentence. For example, in presenting the equation $\square \times 3 = 12$, the teacher asks, "What number is 3 multiplied by in order to get a product of 12?" The child's first encounter with the division symbol probably occurs in conjunction with the related mathematical sentence. For example, $\square \times 5 = 15$ is shown together with the problem $15 \div 5 = \square$. The teacher will tell the class that these mathematical sentences are asking exactly the same question, and that this second sentence is just another way of writing the first sentence.

After moving from multiplication to division via the missing-factor sentence, you can set aside this bridging technique and concentrate on developing division with the standard division notations. There are several useful teaching aids that will facilitate the mastery of the division facts. For example, blank cards can be used. Suppose that we want to have the children explore the 36 dividend "family"—facts such that the dividend is 36. Give each child 36 cards. The following dialogue illustrates how the teacher might proceed to have the children discover certain division facts:

"Everyone deal out cards into nine piles. How many cards do you find in each pile?" (Four.) "We have, therefore, found that 36 divided by 9 is what?" (Four.)

Repeat this process, exploring the partitioning* of 36 into four piles and then into six piles. It may be desirable, also, to explore partitioning into five piles, or eight piles. Then ask, "How many more cards do we need so that each pile will have the same number of cards?"

A second useful teaching aid for exploring the division facts is the number line. This gives the teacher a good device for interpreting division as repeated subtraction. In Figure 7.3, we see a cartoon depicting a child finding out how many jumps of three it takes to go from 12 to 0.

* In this text, *partitioning* will be used in the sense of forming sets equal in number. It is also possible to form sets unequal in number by partitioning.

FIGURE 7.3

Even though the number of jumps of a given length will correspond to the quotient, the numbers corresponding to the various stopping points will be the remainders obtained when the student is using the repeated-subtraction interpretation of division. For example, when finding the number of sets of three that can be partitioned out of a set of 12, we will have nine left when we have partitioned out one set of three, six of the 12 left when we have partitioned out two sets of three, and so on.

A third useful device for exploring division facts is the flannel board (the magnetic board is used in exactly the same manner). An example is as follows:

> "Let's discover what 28 divided by four is equal to." (Place 28 objects on a flannel board.) "Johnny, come up and take some sets of four, and if there are any left over when you are through, you can call on someone to get some more sets of four." (This type of direction will guide the children in seeing the arbitrariness of how many sets of four can be removed initially from the set of 28.)
>
> "How many sets of four did Johnny remove? How many objects did Johnny remove?" (The latter question will be important when the repeated-subtraction algorithm is developed.)

Repeat this type of questioning until all sets of four have been removed and the total number of sets of four in a set of 28 has been determined.

After a set of facts has been discovered, it is important that the child be encouraged to memorize these facts. Although early tests of mastery should not be speed tests, the child should be encouraged to develop speed of recall as he develops competence in the recall of the division facts.

The right identity element for division is taught soon after the child begins to learn his division facts. (It is called the "right" identity element because, in the mathematical sentence $\square \div \triangle = \square$, the 1 is placed to the right of the division symbol, as in $16 \div 1 = 16$, and this relation does not hold if the one is placed to the left of the division symbol, because $1 \div 16 \neq 16$.)

This is a comparatively easy concept to teach. If you present a few examples in which the divisor refers to the number of sets you have, and the dividend refers to the total number of objects that will be distributed to the one set, it is relatively easy to see that the resulting set contains the same number as represented by the dividend. You should extend this concept beyond numbers for which the n (in $n \div 1 = n$) is greater than 10. For example, if we had 354 apples and put them in one set, how many apples would be in the one set, or $354 \div 1 = \square$?

Another property you may want to have your students discover in their early experiences with basic division facts is the right distributive property of division over addition. This property will permit them to explore and discover division facts based on facts they already know. For example, suppose a child knows $30 \div 5 = 6$, and $15 \div 5 = 3$. He could be asked to discover what $45 \div 5$ is equal to as follows:

"$(30 + 15) \div 5 = \square$. What number is named by $(30 + 15)$?" (Forty-five.) "Let us discover what $45 \div 5$ is equal to by using our right distributive property. We rewrite the equation as $(30 \div 5) + (15 \div 5) = \square$. Find each of the quotients and add them. Who has discovered what $45 \div 5$ is equal to?"

Now we can give the students problems in which they are asked to discover some facts. For example:

$$36 \div 9 \quad (18 + 18) \div 9 = \square$$
$$63 \div 9 \quad (27 + 36) \div 9 = \square$$
$$40 \div 5 \quad (20 + 20) \div 5 = \square$$

The first step in getting children to discover the right distributive property of division over addition is to give them paired problems that will lead them to the discovery. In Figure 7.4, we can see several pairs of problems that can be used to guide them in discovering the right distributive property of division.

(1a) $(12 + 6) \div 3 = \square$ (2a) $(6 \div 2) + (4 \div 2) = \square$
(1b) $(12 \div 3) + (6 \div 3) = \square$ (2b) $(6 + 4) \div 2 = \square$
         (3a) $(8 + 4) \div 2 = \square$
         (3b) $(8 \div 2) + (4 \div 2) = \square$

FIGURE 7.4

Before presenting students with examples for the second stage, the teacher should be certain that the students have discovered the property. Then problems such as those shown in Figure 7.5 could be given. These problems require only a single solution.

(a) $(30 + 10) \div 5 = (\Box \div 5) + (10 \div 5)$
(b) $(10 + 4) \div 2 = (10 \div \Box) + (4 \div \Box)$
(c) $(\Box + 15) \div 3 = (6 \div 3) + (15 \div 3)$

FIGURE 7.5

In the third stage, the teacher can elicit multiple correct responses so that the children can see many solutions. Figure 7.6 shows typical problems.

(a) $(12 + 24) \div \Box = (12 \div \Box) + (24 \div \Box)$
(b) $(30 + 15) \div \Box = (30 \div \Box) + (15 \div \Box)$
(c) $(12 + \Box) \div 2 = (12 \div 2) + (\Box \div 2)$

FIGURE 7.6

The last stage is usually taught at the junior high level and should guide the students to make a generalization. They are given a pattern such as $(\Box + \triangle) \div \bigcirc = (\Box \div \bigcirc) + (\Box \div \bigcirc)$ and asked to create problems that would be true sentences using this pattern.

Teaching the right distributive property of division over subtraction uses exactly the same techniques as the right distributive property of division over addition. Development of this property will be treated as an exercise. A child's acquaintance with the right distributive property of division over addition also will be useful to him in phasing in addition of fractional numbers.

A third property you may want to introduce concurrently with the teaching of the basic division facts is the compensation property of division. It is one of the most useful division properties. It has application in establishing equivalent classes of fractions, simplifying division problems and simplifying division of fractional numbers using decimal notation, and in exploring the fractional-number division algorithm. (See Figure 7.7.)

Finding equivalent names:

$$\frac{1}{2} = \frac{1 \times 3}{2 \times 3} = \frac{3}{6}$$

Simplification of division problems:

$$.17\overline{)16.4} \qquad .17 \times 100\overline{)16.4 \times 100} \qquad 17\overline{)1640}$$

$$24\overline{)216} \rightarrow 24 \div 4\overline{)216 \div 4} \rightarrow 6\overline{)54}$$

Obtaining a common divisor for addition and subtraction of fractional numbers:

$$\frac{2}{3} + \frac{2}{4} = \frac{2 \times 4}{3 \times 4} + \frac{2 \times 3}{4 \times 3} \qquad \frac{3}{5} - \frac{1}{7} = \frac{3 \times 7}{5 \times 7} - \frac{1 \times 5}{7 \times 5}$$

Obtaining a divisor of 1 when dividing by fractional numbers:

$$\frac{3}{4} \div \frac{2}{7} = \left(\frac{3}{4} \times \frac{7}{2} \right) \div \left(\frac{2}{7} \times \frac{7}{2} \right)$$

FIGURE 7.7

The method of teaching this property proceeds a little differently from methods previously discussed. It is not begun by using the pairs of problems to lead to the discovery. It is better to start with a series of problems such as those shown in Figure 7.8.

Column A	Column B
$5 \div 1 = \square$	$60 \div 30 = \square$
$10 \div 2 = \square$	$30 \div 15 = \square$
$15 \div 3 = \square$	$10 \div 5 = \square$
$30 \div 6 = \square$	$2 \div 1 = \square$

FIGURE 7.8

A typical dialogue to accompany the problems in Figure 7.8 (after the students have solved the equations) might be as follows:

(Column A) "Did we get the same quotient as a solution for each equation in Column A?" (Yes.) "What must we have done to the 5 and 1 in $5 \div 1$ to get the equation $10 \div 2 = \square$?" (Multiplied the dividend and divisor by 2.) "What must we have done to the 5 and 1 in $5 \div 1$ to get the equation $30 \div 6 = \square$?" (Multiplied the dividend and divisor by 6.) "When we multiplied the divisor and dividend by the same nonzero number, did our quotient change?" (No.)

(Column B) "Did we get the same quotient as a solution for each equation in Column B?" (Yes.) "What must we have done to the 60 and 30 in $60 \div 30$ to get the equation $30 \div 15 = \square$?" (Divided the divisor and dividend by 2.) "What must we have done to the 60 and 30 in $60 \div 30$ to get the equation $10 \div 5 = \square$?" (Divided the 60 and 30 by 6.) "When we divided the divisor and dividend by the same nonzero number, did our quotient remain the same?" (Yes.)

After focusing the child's attention on the results of multiplying the dividend and divisor by a nonzero number, and of dividing the dividend and divisor by a nonzero number, the child is ready to explore this concept further by working with pairs of problems. Figure 7.9 depicts problems typical of this stage.

(1a) $16 \div 8 = \Box$ (2a) $14 \div 2 = \Box$ (3a) $28 \div 14 = \Box$

(1b) $32 \div 16 = \Box$ (2b) $42 \div 6 = \Box$ (3b) $4 \div 2 = \Box$

FIGURE 7.9

In the third stage, problems requiring single solutions are given. Representative problems for this stage are $30 \div 10 = (30 \div \Box) \div (10 \div 5)$; $6 \div 3 = (6 \times 4) \div (3 \times \Box)$; and $12 \div 4 = (\Box \div 2) \div (4 \div 2)$.

Then problems requiring multiple solutions are given to the children. Typical problems for this stage are $24 \div 6 = (24 \div \Box) \div (6 \div \Box)$; $8 \div 4 = (8 \times \Box) \div (4 \times \Box)$; and $49 \div \Box = (49 \times 3) \div (\Box \times 3)$.

In the fifth and last stage, the students are given two patterns, such as $\Box \div \triangle = (\Box \times \bigcirc) \div (\triangle \times \bigcirc)$, and $\Box \div \triangle = (\Box \div \bigcirc) \div (\triangle \div \bigcirc)$. They are then asked to create sentences for each of the patterns that would be true sentences using these patterns.

Some of the many methods we have of teaching the basic division facts are summarized in the following table:

PROBLEM	METHOD	SOLUTION
$6 \div 2 = \Box$	Using sets. (Partition) 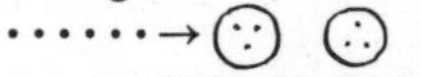 $\cdots\cdots \rightarrow$ ⊙ ⊙ (Measurement) 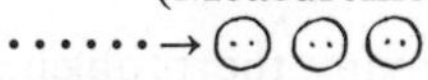 $\cdots\cdots \rightarrow$ ⊙ ⊙ ⊙	$6 \div 2 = 3$
$4 \div 2 = \Box$	Using arrays. 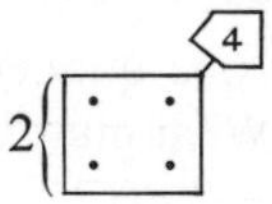	$4 \div 2 = 2$
$8 \div 2 = \Box$	Using a number line. 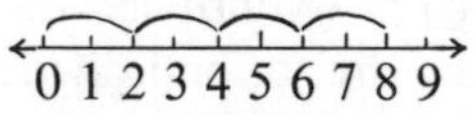	$8 \div 2 = 4$
$36 \div 6 = \Box$	Using the right distributive property. $(30 + 6) \div 6 = (30 \div 6) +$ $(6 \div 6) = 5 + 1$	$36 \div 6 = 6$
$8 \div 1 = \Box$	Using properties. Because $n \div 1 = n$, then	$8 \div 1 = 8$
$8 \div 8 = \Box$	Because $n \div n = 1$, then	$8 \div 8 = 1$
$12 \div 3 = \Box$	Using repeated subtraction. $12 - 3 = 9, 9 - 3 = 6,$ $6 - 3 = 3, 3 - 3 = 0$	$12 \div 3 = 4$

EXERCISES (1)

1. Using the definition of quotient (without remainder), show that the quotient of 144 and 6 is 24.
2. Explain why 72 is divisible by 9.
3. Using the definition of quotient and remainder, show that the quotient of 16 and 5 is 3 with a remainder of 1.
4. Write four basic division notations for: The quotient of 15 and 3 is 5.
5. List four ways of reading the following: $6 \div 2 = 3$.
6. Where possible, identify each of the following: dividend, divisor, quotient, remainder, product, known factor, unknown factor.

$$20 = (4 \times 5) + 0 \qquad 16 \div 2 = 8 \qquad 3\overline{)15} \atop \underline{15} \atop 0$$

7. Make up sample problems for each of the first three stages in teaching the right distributive property of division over subtraction.
8. Make up sample problems for the second, third, and fourth stages for teaching the compensation property for division.

7.4. *A Repeated-Subtraction Division Algorithm*

The first stage in teaching the repeated-subtraction division algorithm involves introducing the child to the notation he will use. The mechanics of using this notation should be introduced by using some basic fact for which the child already knows the quotient. This known fact can be used so that he can focus on the mechanics of handling the notation without the distraction of also searching for the quotient of two numbers involving new division situations. For example:

"We have discovered that the quotient of 15 and 3 is 5. Let's learn a new method of finding the quotient of two whole numbers." (Place on the board the notation depicted in Stage 1 of Figure 7.10.)

"This is another way of asking, '5 divided by 3 equals what number?'" (Place a set of 15 objects on a flannel board.) "Johnny, will you come up and get some sets of 3?" (He may get 1, 2, 3, 4, or 5 sets of 3.) "How many sets of 3 did you take?" (Let us assume that he took 4 sets of 3.)

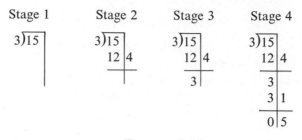

FIGURE 7.10

"How do we find out how many objects Johnny took, if we know that he took 4 sets of 3?" (We multiply 4 and 3.)

"Let's put our 4 here (see Stage 2) to show that Johnny took 4 sets, and let's put our 12 here (see Stage 2) to show how many objects Johnny took. How do we find out how many objects are left on the board, if we use arithmetic to find our answer?" (We subtract the 12 from the 15. See Stage 3.)

"How many sets of 3 are left on the board?" (One.) "Mary, will you take this one set of 3 from the board? Let's put our 1 here (see Stage 4) to show that Mary took one set of 3, and let's put our 3 here (see Stage 4) to show how many objects Mary took from the board."

"How do we find, by using arithmetic, how many we have left on the board?" (We subtract the 3 from the 3.) "We have taken 4 sets of 3 and 1 set of 3 from the board. How do we find, by using arithmetic, the total number of sets of 3 taken from the board?" (Add the 4 and the 1, as in Stage 4.)

Use this problem again considering other possible ways of removing the sets of 3. For example, consider the case in which the sets of 3 are removed one set at a time. Call the children's attention to the fact that there are many ways in which we can arrive at the answer. Emphasize the fact that in spite of the different approaches we might take in arriving at the answer, in each case the quotient is the same.

Write on the board all of the possible ways of finding that the quotient of 15 and 3 is 5. Ask what specific numerals in the algorithms mean. Check each stage of the development of the algorithm to see that the children understand the mechanics of recording the number of sets removed, the total number of objects removed, and the number of objects remaining on the board. After the children have developed a familiarity with the mechanics of the repeated-subtraction algorithm using familiar facts, they are ready to attack complex division situations. Let's explore a typical complex situation with an example and accompanying dialogue.

"In the problem $72 \div 4 = \square$, we are asked to find how many sets of 4 are in 72." (In Stage 1, Figure 7.11, we see how we will write the symbols so that we can compute the answer.)

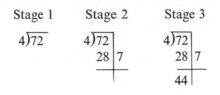

Stage 1   Stage 2   Stage 3

FIGURE 7.11

"Will someone take a guess at how many sets of 4 can be taken from the 72?" (Assume that someone says 7, although any number less than or equal to 18 will be correct.)

"How do we find out how many we are taking if we take 7 sets of 4?" (Multiply 7 and 4 to get 28.) "Let's put the 28 here (see Stage 2) to show how many have been taken from 72. How do we find out how many are left after we take 28 from 72?" (We subtract.) "We now have 44 left." (See Stage 3.)

Repeat this process until all of the sets of 4 have been removed from the set of 72. Each time sets of 4 are removed, call the children's attention to how we find out how many objects are left.

When all sets of 4 have been removed, ask,

"How do we find the total number of sets of 4 which have been removed?" (By adding.)

Have the children rework this problem in a different way. Call their attention to the fact that although there are many ways to work the problem, some of the ways are faster than others.

After they have mastered the basic idea that we can find the quotient of two whole numbers by the technique of using repeated subtraction, the teacher should guide each child in the refinement of this algorithm. The child should constantly be asked to improve his solution of current problems in the light of his experience with previous problems. He should constantly examine and compare the effects of removing various numbers of sets of a given number.

Questions similar to the following are appropriate for guiding the child in refining his division algorithm:

"Did taking 6 sets of 6 from 354 reduce 354 very much?" See (a), Figure 7.12. (No.) "Why don't you try removing a larger number of sets of 6?"

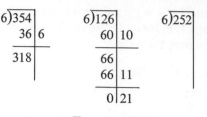

FIGURE 7.12

"We have seen that there are 21 sets of 6 in 126." (See (b), Figure 7.12.) "Will 252 have more or less sets of 6 than 126?" (More.) "Can we use this information to help us find how many sets of 6 there are in 252?"

7.5. *Activities to Promote Efficiency*

There are certain activities the teacher can structure for the child that will promote efficiency with the repeated-subtraction algorithm. The first of these involves having the child discover the relationship existing between multiplication of multiples of 10 and division of multiples of 10. For example, notice how the following problems would promote the child's discovery of this relationship:

If	*then*	*and*
$6 \times 4 = 24$	$6 \times 40 = \underline{\hspace{1cm}}$	$6 \times 400 = \underline{\hspace{1cm}}$
$24 \div 6 = 4$	$240 \div 6 = \underline{\hspace{1cm}}$	$2400 \div 6 = \underline{\hspace{1cm}}$

A second activity to promote the child's efficiency is to have him find sets of factors that can serve as a replacement in making a true sentence in an inequality. Problems of this type can be seen in Figure 7.13, along with the sets of factors.

A third activity involves having the child develop skill in ascertaining the largest multiple of 1000, 100, 10, or 1 that can be subtracted each time. A typical dialogue to develop this concept might be as follows:

"Could we subtract 1000 sets of 16 in this problem?" (See Figure 7.14. The answer is "yes," because $1000 \times 16 = 16,000$, and 16,000 can be subtracted from 42,645.) "Can we subtract 3000 sets of 16?" (No, because $3000 \times 16 = 48,000$, and we do not have 48,000 things.)

This process is repeated, asking how many hundred sets of 16 can be removed, and then tens, and then ones.

Replacement set: counting numbers

Set of factors

$8 \times \square < 100$ {1, 2, 3, 4, 5, 6, 7, 8, 9, 10, 11, 12}
$11 \times \square < 100$ {1, 2, 3, 4, 5, 6, 7, 8, 9}

Replacement set: multiples of ten

Set of factors

$8 \times \square < 1000$ {10, 20, 30, 40, 50, 60, 70, 80, 90, 100, 110, 120}
$11 \times \square < 1000$ {10, 20, 30, 40, 50, 60, 70, 80, 90}

Replacement set: multiples of one hundred

Set of factors

$8 \times \square < 10,000$ {100, 200, 300, 400, 500, 600, 700, 800, 900, 1000, 1100,
1200}

$11 \times \square < 10,000$ {100, 200, 300, 400, 500, 600, 700, 800, 900}

Replacement set: counting numbers

Set of factors

$82 \times \square < 384$ {1, 2, 3, 4}
$147 \times \square < 1874$ {1, 2, 3, 4, 5, 6, 7, 8, 9, 10, 11, 12}

FIGURE 7.13

The child should be given the opportunity to see that the removal of sets by multiples of thousands, hundreds, tens, and ones offers a distinct advantage in terms of efficiency and ease of subtraction over removal of multiples of sets representing intermediate numbers, such as the removal of 137 sets of 16 and then 228 sets of 16, and so on. He should be given the opportunity to discover that a knowledge of the place-value system aids in deciding how many of a given set can be removed. For example, in the preceding problem we were just concerned with how many sets of 16 were in 42,000; 645 did not contribute any essential information to our determining how many sets to remove initially. The child should be led to focus on that part of the numeral that will help him decide how multiples of thousands, hundreds, tens, or ones can be removed.

Further extensions of this algorithm to include removal of multiples of ten thousands, hundred thousands, millions, and so on, follow the same developmental lines as has the preceding discussion. This algorithm will be discussed

$$16\overline{)42,645}$$

FIGURE 7.14

further in Chapter 11 where we shall be concerned with division in which a decimal notation is used in the algorithm.

7.6. *An Alternate Division Algorithm*

The following presentation probably will be quite familiar to you in that it illustrates the type of division algorithm you undoubtedly were taught. The problem illustrates how the quotient of 32 was obtained using this algorithm:

$$
\begin{array}{r}
32 \\
65\overline{)2080} \\
195 \\
\hline
130 \\
130 \\
\hline
0
\end{array}
$$

The skills needed for the mastery of this algorithm are quite similar to those required for the repeated-subtraction division algorithm. They are multiplication skills, subtraction skills, and inequality relationships such as $65 \times \square = 2000$. However, because it is a more refined algorithm, the inherent meaning behind each step is often masked by the refinement. For example, in the example here, the 195 is in reality 1950, but in simplifying the recording process, the 0 has been omitted.

Let us begin with a one-digit divisor and explore a possible sequence that might be employed in teaching this algorithm.

$3\overline{)963}$ In the example at the left, what is named by the 9? By the 6? By the 3? (900, 60, and 4; or 9 hundreds, 6 tens, and 3 ones.)

This illustration shows us how we might represent the dividend on a place-value chart:

Hundreds	Tens	Ones
▯ ▯ ▯ ▯ ▯ ▯ ▯ ▯ ▯	▯ ▯ ▯ ▯ ▯ ▯	▯ ▯ ▯ → $3\overline{)9}$ hundreds + 6 tens + 3 ones

Beginning at the left, we can partition our hundreds into 3 sets of 3 hundreds. The following illustration and symbolism describes what we did:

Hundreds	Tens	Ones	3 hundreds
▯ ▯ ▯ ▯ ▯ ▯	▯ ▯ ▯ ▯ ▯ ▯	▯ ▯ ▯ → $3\overline{)9}$ hundreds + 6 tens + 3 ones

Likewise, we could partition the tens and ones and indicate by the following illustration and symbolism:

Hundreds	Tens	Ones	3 hundreds + 2 tens + 1 one
□ □ □	□ □ □	□ □ □ →	3)9 hundreds + 6 tens + 3 ones
□ □ □	□ □ □		
□ □ □			

Let us now examine a more complex situation in which regrouping must precede our partitioning. Consider this problem: divide 153 by 3. Let us analyze this situation by the following illustration of a place-value chart:

Hundreds	Tens	Ones
□	□ □ □ □ □	□ □ □

It becomes immediately obvious that the one set of 100 cannot be partitioned into sets of 3. However, if the one set of 100 is regrouped into 10 tens, we can partition the resulting set of 15 tens into 5 sets of 3 tens. This is illustrated by the following picture and symbolism:

Hundreds	Tens	Ones	5 tens + 1 one
	□ □ □	□ □ □ →	3)15 tens + 3 ones
	□ □ □		
	□ □ □		
	□ □ □		
	□ □ □		

Let us now look at an example in which a partial remainder is obtained after regrouping. Consider 420 divided by 3. The following illustration of a place-value chart depicts how 420 would be represented.

Hundreds	Tens	Ones	
□ □ □ □	□ □		→ 3)4 hundreds + 2 tens + 0 ones

After we have partitioned out sets of 3 hundreds, we note we have one set of 100 remaining.

Hundreds	Tens	Ones	1 hundred
□ □ □	□ □		→ 3)4 hundreds + 2 tens + 0 ones
□			3 hundreds
			1 hundred

By regrouping this 1 hundred into 10 tens, we obtain 12 tens that can be partitioned into four sets of 3 tens. This is illustrated and symbolized by the following.

Hundreds	Tens	Ones	
▯ ▯ ▯	▯ ▯ ▯		1 hundred + 4 tens
	▯ ▯ ▯		→ 3)4 hundreds + 2 tens + 0 ones →
	▯ ▯ ▯		3 hundreds
	▯ ▯ ▯		12 tens
	▯ ▯ ▯		12 tens
			0 tens

$$
\begin{array}{r}
140 \\
\to 3\overline{)420} \\
3 \\
\hline
12 \\
12 \\
\hline
0 \\
0 \\
\hline
\end{array}
$$

And finally we find that 0 sets of ones can be partitioned into sets of 3, 0 times. Thus we see that $420 \div 3 = 140$.

By similar investigations you can help the child understand how to cope with situations such as the following:

$$
\begin{array}{r}
1 \text{ hundred} + 0 \text{ tens} \\
3\overline{)3 \text{ hundreds} + 2 \text{ tens} + 1 \text{ one}} \\
3 \text{ hundreds} \\
\hline
2 \text{ tens}
\end{array}
\to
\begin{array}{r}
1 \text{ hundred} + 0 \text{ tens} + 7 \text{ ones} \\
3\overline{)3 \text{ hundreds} + 2 \text{ tens} + 1 \text{ one}} \\
3 \text{ hundreds} \\
\hline
21 \text{ ones} \\
21 \text{ ones} \\
\hline
0
\end{array}
\to
$$

$$
\begin{array}{r}
107 \\
\to 3\overline{)321} \\
3 \\
\hline
21 \\
21 \\
\hline
\end{array}
$$

Notice that there are special cases, such as the 0 tens that was obtained in the quotient 107, that do not have to be taught as special cases with the repeated-subtraction algorithm. For example, notice in the following algorithm how the question of how many sets of 3 in 2 tens does not arise:

$$
\begin{array}{r|l}
3\overline{)321} & \\
300 & 100 \\
\hline
21 & \\
21 & 7 \\
\hline
0 & 107
\end{array}
$$

Gradually, the "types" of divisive cases are extended to two-digit divisors such as the following:

$$20\overline{)640} \qquad 30\overline{)960} \qquad 32\overline{)6496} \qquad 85\overline{)1356}$$

Professional educators have studied the relative efficiency of rounding numbers "up" or "down" in order to arrive at a trial divisor when a problem contains a two-digit divisor. Morton[1] reports that rounding all "two-figure" divisors ending in six, seven, eight, or nine upward, and all "two-figure" divisors ending in one, two, three, four, or five downward results in estimates being correct 73.2 percent of the time.

Although it is statistically impractical for the child to perform an analysis such as the one Morton describes in his article, it is feasible to have a child become aware of the relative "weight" of the ones digit to the tens digit in a two-digit divisor. It is also important that the child be aware of the comparative weight of the various ones. For example, the 2 in 32 can be compared to the 9 in 39 when 32 and 39 are divisors.

There is no new skill involved in teaching children to use divisors greater than two digits. For example, in the analysis required to obtain the trial quotient for 7896 ÷ 372, we would use 40 tens as a trial divisor.

EXERCISES (2)

1. What division facts could be discovered if a child had a deck of 12 cards?
2. Illustrate, using a number line, how you could direct a child to discover that $16 \div 2 = 8$.
3. Explain, using an illustration of a flannel board, together with a dialogue, how you could help a child to discover that $30 \div 6 = 5$.
4. Illustrate four or more possible stages that a child might go through (see Figure 7.10) in using the repeated-subtraction division algorithm to find that $6 \div 2 = 3$.
5. Which of the following problems might be the first problem a child would encounter using the repeated-subtraction division algorithm? Justify your answer.

$$36 \div 4 = \square \qquad 100 \div 10 = \square \qquad 20 \div 2 = \square$$

6. Make up some exercises that would be useful in helping a child develop skill in partitioning multiples of 100 from a number.

[1] R. L. Morton, "Estimating Quotient Figures When Dividing by Two-Place Numbers," Elementary School Journal, XLVIII, 141–148, November, 1947.

7. Make up some exercises that would be useful in helping a child develop skill in partitioning multiples of 10 from a number.
8. Study each of the following problems. Make up a dialogue for each problem that would aid the child in increasing his efficiency.

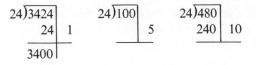

9. Explain the meaning of the 39 in each of the following:

$$\begin{array}{r} 2196 \\ 2)\overline{4392} \end{array} \qquad \begin{array}{r} 40)\overline{7964} \\ 40 \\ \hline 39 \end{array} \qquad \begin{array}{r} 40)\overline{40396} \\ 40 \\ \hline 39 \end{array}$$

7.7. Division "Story" Problems

Just as the teaching of subtraction story problems was complicated by many guises, so is the teaching of division story problems complicated. The three most common guises might be described as the *partitive situation*, the *measurement situation*, and the *missing-factor situation*.

In the partitive situation, the number property of a set is known and the equivalent sets into which the set is to be partitioned are known. It is not known how many will be in each set. The following problem depicts a typical partitive situation.

> John has 12 cards.
> He is to deal out the cards equally to 3 people.
> How many cards will each person get?

This problem translates to the mathematical sentence $12 \div 3 = \square$.

In the measurement situation, the number of the set is known, and the number of each equal set that is removed from the set is known, but the number of sets is not known. The following problem depicts a typical measurement situation:

> John has 12 cards.
> He gives each person 3 cards.
> How many people can get cards?

This problem translates to the mathematical sentence $12 \div 3 = \square$. Notice that both problems translate to the same sentence, even though the physical situations are quite different. In developing the child's attack skills for either of the preceding problems, the teacher should either demonstrate the problem or allow the child to act out the situation. You will want to "compare" partitive situations with measurement situations and discuss how the numerals in the mathematical sentences are derived. For example, given the sentence $35 \div 5 = \square$, if the sentence has been derived from a partitive situation, the 5 tells us how many sets there are; but if the sentence has been derived from a measurement situation, the 5 tells us how many are in each set.

The third type of division story problem, the missing-factor situation, is depicted in the following problem:

Mary gave John some bags of cookies.
Each bag held 5 cookies.
There was a total of 30 cookies in the bags.
How many bags did Mary give John?

Let us use this problem to discuss another technique for developing problem-solving skills. This type of problem provides an excellent opportunity for developing the skill of making a reasonable "guess."

"Would 1 bag be a good guess of how many bags Mary gave John?" (No.)

"Why?" (Because one bag would contain only 5 cookies and not 30 cookies. We wouldn't have enough cookies.)

"If each bag contained 1 cookie, how many bags would we need to get 30 cookies?" (30 bags.) "If Mary had 5 cookies in each bag, would 30 bags be a good guess of how many bags it would take to get 30 cookies?" (No.)

"Why?" (We would have too many cookies with 30 bags.)

"We have found that 1 bag gives us too few cookies and that 30 bags give us too many cookies. If we had to guess another number, where should we guess our number?" (We should guess a number between 1 and 30, because it is between those numbers.)

It is important to explore techniques continually for determining the reasonableness of answers. The preceding technique of finding boundaries that would give us too few and too many is just one technique. Probably the most common technique is rounding off the numbers in our problem, coupled with a "mental" calculation utilizing these rounded-off numbers. For example, consider the problem:

If the total bill for a certain number of items is 136 cents, and if each item costs 17 cents, how many items were purchased?

We can obtain a quick estimate by rounding off 136 cents to 140 cents, and 17 cents to 20 cents; then a quick mental calculation will give us the answer, 7.

Knowing the answer is somewhere close to 7 will make us suspicious of obtaining an answer such as 18, upon dividing 136 by 17. Some children use this "feel" for the relative size of the answer as a clue in deciding which operation is a reasonable one to employ in the solution of a problem. The technique is not unlike that used by the mathematician in searching for a mathematical model to fit a set of data.

EXERCISES (3)

1. Using one or more of the following sources, construct five story problems of a current-events nature involving partitive situations appropriate for a fourth-grade class.
   a. Newspaper   b. *World Almanac*   c. Magazine
2. Using the same sources, construct five story problems of a current-events nature involving measurement situations appropriate for a fourth-grade class.
3. Using the same sources, construct five story problems of a current-events nature involving division and one other operation appropriate for a sixth-grade class.
4. Using the same sources, construct five story problems of a current-events nature involving missing-factor situations appropriate for a sixth-grade class.
5. Make up a word problem for each of the following mathematical sentences:

   a. $394 \div 6 = \square$ d. $(16 + 4) \div 5 = \square$
   b. $\$4.94 \div 6 = \square$ e. $3 \times \square = 900$
   c. $(36 \div 4) + (40 \div 4) = \square$ f. $(80 \div 5) + (60 \div 11) = \square$

REFERENCES

BANKS, J. HOUSTON, *Learning and Teaching Arithmetic*, Boston: Allyn & Bacon, 1964, pp. 244–254, 217–223.

BELL, CLIFFORD, CLELA D. HAMMON, and ROBERT B. HERRERA, *Fundamentals of Arithmetic for Teachers*, New York: John Wiley & Sons, Inc., 1962, pp. 91–104.

CHURCHILL, EILEEN M., *Counting and Measuring*, Great Britain: Routledge & Kegan Paul, 1962, pp. 149–150.

CROUCH, RALPH, GEORGE BALDWIN, and ROBERT J. WISNER, *Preparatory Mathematics for Elementary Teachers*, New York: John Wiley & Sons, Inc., 1965, pp. 104–112.

EDUCATION RESEARCH COUNCIL OF GREATER CLEVELAND, *Key Topics in Mathematics for the Primary Teacher*, Chicago: Science Research Associates, Inc., 1962, pp. 62–66.

FLOURNOY, FRANCES, *Elementary School Mathematics*, Washington, D.C.: The Center for Applied Research in Education, 1964, pp. 10, 36.

MARKS, JOHN L., JAMES R. SMART, and IRENE SAUBLE, *Enlarging Mathematical Ideas*, Boston: Ginn and Company, 1961, pp. 58–59.

NATIONAL COUNCIL OF TEACHERS OF MATHEMATICS, *Enrichment Mathematics for the Grades, Twenty-seventh Yearbook*, Washington, D.C.: The National Council of Teachers of Mathematics, 1963, pp. 227–233.

NATIONAL COUNCIL OF TEACHERS OF MATHEMATICS, *Instruction in Arithmetic, Twenty-fifth Yearbook*, Washington, D.C.: The National Council of Teachers of Mathematics, 1960, pp. 279–281, 345–348.

NATIONAL COUNCIL OF TEACHERS OF MATHEMATICS, *The Growth of Mathematical Ideas, Grades K–12, Twenty-fourth Yearbook*, Washington, D.C.: The National Council of Teachers of Mathematics, 1959, pp. 24–25.

RAPKIN, MINNIE K., and LILLIAN C. HOWITT, *Teaching the Third " R,"* Englewood Cliffs, N.J.: Teachers Practical Press, Inc., 1963, pp. 26–29.

SMITH, SEATON E., JR., *Explorations in Elementary Mathematics*, Englewood Cliffs, N.J.: Prentice-Hall, Inc., 1966, pp. 98–100.

SPENCER, PETER LINCOLN, and MARGUERITE BRYDEGAARD, *Building Mathematical Competence in the Elementary School*, New York: Holt, Rinehart and Winston, Inc., 1966, pp. 136–138, 145–151.

SWAIN, ROBERT L., and EUGENE D. NICHOLS, *Understanding Arithmetic*, New York: Holt, Rinehart and Winston, Inc., 1965, pp. 117–125.

SWENSON, ESTHER J., *Teaching Arithmetic to Children*, New York: The Macmillan Company, 1964, pp. 240–291.

VAN ENGEN, HENRY, MAURICE L. HARTUNG, and JAMES E. STOCHL, *Foundations of Elementary School Arithmetic*, Chicago: Scott, Foresman and Co., 1965, pp. 101–105, 158–164.

WARD, MORGAN, and CLARENCE HARDGROVE, *Modern Elementary Mathematics*, Reading, Mass.: Addison-Wesley, 1964, pp. 149–153.

Programmed materials can be used to motivate a child to learn mathematics.

8

Teaching the Fractional Numbers

8.1. *Introduction*

THE IDEA of a fractional number is a sophisticated concept that requires more maturity and background on the part of the child than the concept of a whole number. Whereas a whole number is the property of a discrete set, a fractional number can be associated with

1. The partitioning of a discrete set
2. The ratio of the number properties of two sets
3. A number associated with the partitioning of a continuous set
4. A number representing the quotient of two whole numbers (the divisor never being zero).

The quotient idea will prove most useful in terms of bridging the concept of whole numbers and the concept of fractional numbers, whereas the partitioning of a continuous set and the idea of subsets of a discrete set will provide a less abstract mathematical model to use with children in giving them an intuitive concept of a fractional number.

In the primary grades, the main emphasis will be on developing an intuitive concept of fractional numbers, and the child will work with such models as polygonal regions, line segments, lines, and discrete sets. A second emphasis will be on developing an intuitive concept of equivalent names for the same fractional number through work with congruent regions and congruent segments.

In the intermediate grades, the main emphasis will be on extending the concept of the fractional number and equivalent fractions and on developing the operations of addition and multiplication along with their respective inverses.

This chapter is concerned with the teaching of fractional numbers and equivalent fractions. In Chapter 12, the concept of fractional numbers will be broadened to include the study of decimal notation and the concepts of ratio and percent.

8.2. *Techniques of Partitioning Continuous Sets*

Before we undertake the presentation techniques of teaching specific fractional numbers, it will be useful to review techniques of partitioning a set.

It is desirable for you to select geometric regions that can be partitioned into the desired "fractional parts" simply by folding the figure over (in order to obtain the partitioning). Notice in Figure 8.1 that if a circle with its interior region is cut out and folded over so that the boundary is superimposed on itself, the crease obtained will partition the region into halves. If we were to repeat this process, utilizing the crease as a boundary, we could partition the circle's region into fourths. Figure 8.1 also depicts how we could obtain fourths and sixths using a hexagonal region, halves using pentagonal and square regions, and fourths using a rhombus. You will want to experiment with these regions to see what other fractional parts can be derived by paper folding.

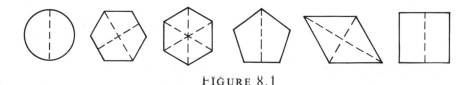

FIGURE 8.1

Figure 8.2 depicts the method of partitioning a line segment into five congruent parts with a compass and a straightedge. This same technique can be used to partition a line segment into any specified number of congruent parts.

STEP 1
Draw a line segment from one endpoint as shown.

STEP 2
Use the compass to measure off
segments of equal length on the new
segment.

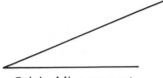

Original line segment

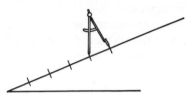

STEP 3
Connect with a line segment the point
where the last arc cuts the line
segment and the other end point on
the first line segment.

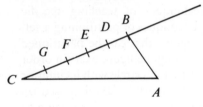

STEP 4
The angle associated with *BA* and
CB is copied, making *D*, *E*, *F*, and
G the vertices of these congruent
angles.

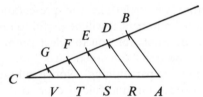

Line segments *CV*, *VT*, *TS*, *SR*, and
RA are congruent.

FIGURE 8.2

8.3. *Definition, Terminology, and Symbolism*

Even though we do not introduce the child to the definition of fractional
numbers in his early intuitive explorations, the basic definition should
always play a role in the teacher's presentation.

A fractional number is defined as the quotient of two whole numbers,
such that the divisor is never zero, or, in other words, a fractional number
is any number that can be named by $\frac{a}{b}$ where a and b are whole numbers
and $b \neq 0$.

A fraction shall be defined as the symbol or name for a fractional
number and shall be of the form $\frac{a}{b}$ where a and b name whole numbers.

Not only is it important to know that a fraction is a name for a fractional number, but it is also important to know when two fractions name the same fractional number.

Two fractions $\frac{a}{b}$ and $\frac{c}{d}$ will name the same fractional number if, and only if, $a \times d = b \times c$.

We say that $\frac{2}{3}$ and $\frac{4}{6}$ name the same fractional number, because $2 \times 6 = 3 \times 4$. This concept will be developed further when the method for teaching equivalent fractions is discussed. When two fractions name the same fractional number, we say that they are equivalent fractions.

In Figure 8.3, we see various numerals and fractions naming fractional numbers. Note that the whole numbers are a subset of the set of fractional numbers. This fact is a consequence of the way a fractional number has been defined. It is important that the child, at an early point in his exploration of fractional numbers, becomes aware of the fact that all whole numbers are also fractional numbers.

Simplest name	Fraction names	Decimal fraction names
3	$\frac{3}{1}, \frac{6}{2}, \frac{9}{3}, \ldots$	$2.99\bar{9}$ or $3.00\bar{0}$ or 3
$\frac{1}{3}$	$\frac{1}{3}, \frac{2}{6}, \frac{3}{9}, \ldots$	$.33\bar{3}$
$\frac{11}{9}*$	$\frac{11}{9}, \frac{22}{18}, \frac{33}{27}, \ldots$	$1.22\bar{2}$

FIGURE 8.3

In this text, we shall use the terms *numerator* and *denominator* in reference to the numbers named by the numerals in the notation $\frac{a}{b}$. The number named by b will be referred to as the denominator and the number named by a will be referred to as the numerator. Because the fractional number named by $\frac{a}{b}$ is defined as the quotient of two whole numbers, it will also be possible to refer to b as a divisor and a as a dividend.

When using the notation $\frac{a}{b}$ to name a fractional number, we read the b with an ordinal designation (with the exceptions of $b = 2$, in which case it is called halves, or $b = 1$, in which case it is called ones) and the a with a cardinal designation. It is for this reason that both the cardinal and the ordinal names should be explored before introducing very many fractional

---

* We can also express this fraction as the sum of a whole number and a fractional number as $1 + \frac{2}{9}$ or the shortened form $1\frac{2}{9}$. This latter notation is often referred to as a mixed numeral.

numbers and their names. Some fractions and the method of reading them are as follows:

$\frac{3}{4}$ three-fourths

$\frac{5}{2}$ five-halves

$\frac{2}{8}$ two-eighths

(Note that the word names for fractional numbers are hyphenated.)

8.4. *Early Experiences with Fractional Numbers*

Children come to school with vague, often misconceived, ideas about fractional numbers. Parents have permitted and encouraged work with imperfect models. To a preschool child, to take one-half of a cookie often means nothing more than not taking all of the cookie. The child's early pre-school experiences do not often involve work with congruent partitioning of sets. It is only when a brother or sister points out the fact that he or she didn't get the same amount that there is concern for "halfness" or "thirdness." The preschool child's method of partitioning a set into equal parts is most often done on a visual basis with only a cursory attempt made to establish real congruence.

One of the first concepts that must be developed by the teacher is this concept of congruence. In other words, we cannot have a model we refer to as halves or thirds or fourths, and so on, until we have satisfied the requirement of congruent measures.

This checking of congruent measures can be accomplished physically by many techniques. The first and most common is that of visually checking something that has been partitioned around points or lines of symmetry, where it is quite clear that the partitioning has formed congruent parts.

Another common technique, and a useful one in conveying the idea that fractional numbers have many equivalent names, is to cut out one of the partitioned regions or partitioned segments and check by overlaying to see if it is congruent with other partitioned regions or segments.

When the mathematical model is a discrete set, such as the one depicted in Figure 8.4, we check the set to see that its number is divisible by the number of the subset.

$$
\begin{array}{cccc}
\bullet & \bullet & \bullet & \bullet \\
0 & 0 & 0 & 0 \quad \dfrac{1}{3} \\
0 & 0 & 0 & 0
\end{array}
$$

FIGURE 8.4

The children should be given opportunities to partition models into congruent parts. The teacher should select models for them that are easy to partition. For example, a circle does not lend itself to easy partitioning by the child, whereas most regular polygons do. Notice in Figure 8.5 that the square and the hexagon lend themselves readily to partitioning.

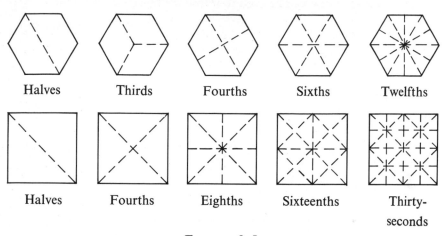

FIGURE 8.5

Partitioning should not be restricted to two-dimensional figures. Experiences such as sawing a board into equal pieces, partitioning a set of cookies into sets equal in number, and cutting up a cake or pie so that everyone gets the same sized piece offer opportunities to extend the concept of fractional numbers through three-dimensional models.

Not only should the child be given experiences with mathematical models that have been partitioned into congruent parts, but he also should have experiences with noncongruent partitioning. In Figure 8.6, two figures are depicted that have been partitioned into noncongruent parts.

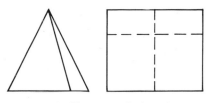

FIGURE 8.6

Some typical questions that might be asked by the teacher, and the responses of the children, are as follows:

"Has the triangle been partitioned into halves?" (No.) "How do you know?" (Because all of the parts are not of equal size.)

After partitioning polygons into halves, thirds, fourths, and so on, and after the children realize the necessity for congruent regions, it is then time to introduce the concept of a subset of the partitioned pieces. It is only through the children's awareness of the relation of the subset to the set that they can gain a complete understanding of fractional numbers. For example, a typical dialogue that can be used to introduce this concept follows:

> (See Figure 8.7.) "Into how many pieces has the square been par-titioned?" (Four.) "Are they congruent to each other?" (Yes.) "What can we say that each piece represents?" (A fourth.) "How many fourths are shaded?" (Two.) "We can tell that two-fourths is shaded by writing $\frac{2}{4}$."

FIGURE 8.7

The child's first experiences with fractional numbers will be with numbers less than or equal to one. When the concept of fractional numbers is extended to include numbers greater than one, the most appropriate teaching aid is the number-line segment. However, a careful effort must be made, when the number-line segment is introduced, to relate the concept of division of whole numbers to the definition of a fractional number as the quotient of two whole numbers (the divisor $\neq 0$). For example, $6 \div 2$ can be interpreted on the number-line segment as two backward jumps of equal length from 6 to 0. (See Figure 8.8.)

Such questions as the following should be asked when bridging the concepts between whole numbers and fractional numbers:

> "What is the length of each of our jumps?" (Three units.) "What is the quotient of 6 and 2?" (Three.) "When we are jumping, where do we find our answer named?" (At the point we start our last jump.)

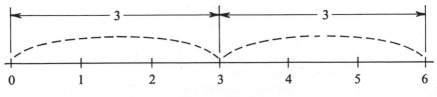

FIGURE 8.8

The children should have many experiences finding the quotient of two whole numbers by manipulations on a number line. These early experiences should involve pairs of numbers where the dividend is divisible by the divisor. The teacher should continually focus the child's attention on the following:

1. The quotient can be associated with the distance of each jump.
2. The point where the last jump is started is always the name of the quotient.

After a child becomes familiar with the technique of finding a whole-number quotient by manipulations on a number-line segment, this technique can be used to introduce the concept of a fractional number as the quotient of any two whole numbers. For example, suppose that we want to find the quotient of 3 and 4. We would start with a number-line segment three units in length. We would then take four jumps of equal length from 3 to 0. The starting point of our last jump is named $\frac{3}{4}$. To check our answer, we count by $\frac{3}{4}$s, starting at zero—$\{0, \frac{3}{4}, \frac{6}{4}, \frac{9}{4}, \frac{12}{4}\}$. Because $\frac{12}{4}$ is another name for 3, we can thus see that we have the correct quotient of 3 and 4. (See Figure 8.9.)

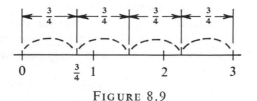

FIGURE 8.9

Such questions as, "Is three-fourths more or less than 1?" and "Is three fourths more or less than one-half?" should be asked at this stage.

The number-line segment is well suited as a model for fractional numbers greater than 1. For example, consider the representation of $9 \div 4$ on a number-line segment as depicted in Figure 8.10.

The child can readily see that $\frac{9}{4}$ is greater than 2 and less than 3. He can also check his work by the process of counting by $\frac{9}{4}$s to discover that $\frac{36}{4}$ is another name for 9.

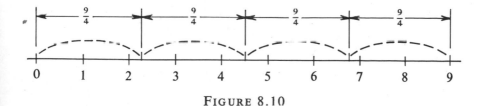

FIGURE 8.10

EXERCISES (1)

1. Draw a line segment three inches long. Use the technique depicted in Figure 8.2 to partition the segment into seven equal parts.
2. What partitionings do each of the following polygons lend themselves to?
   a. Regular pentagon   b. Regular octagon
3. How does a child check to see if a discrete set has been partitioned into sixths?
4. Illustrate each of the following, using a different polygon for each: $\frac{2}{5}, \frac{2}{3}, \frac{5}{8}$.
5. Illustrate $12 \div 4$ on a number-line segment.
6. Illustrate $4 \div 12$ on a number-line segment.
7. Illustrate $1 \div 2$ on a number-line segment.
8. Illustrate $9 \div 7$ on a number-line segment.

8.5. *Equivalent Fractions*

Shortly after introducing the children to the concept of fractional numbers, you should structure situations so they will discover that each fractional number has many names. Questions such as, "Mary has two-fourths of a candy bar and John has one-half of the same candy bar; who has more?" will promote this discovery.

The children should be given many experiences that establish the equivalence of fractional names through subset comparisons before they are introduced to the formal techniques of generating names for fractional numbers. In working with polygons, this experience takes the form either of mentally "seeing" that one partition can be transformed into another partitioning (see Figure 8.11), or of cutting and fitting regions to determine that two methods of partitioning yield the same area.

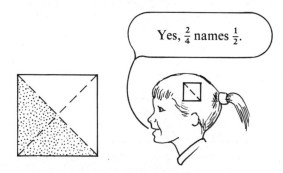

FIGURE 8.11

In checking whether two names are equivalent, using discrete sets, we must use caution that the same discrete set can be partitioned into the subsets named by the two numbers. For example, if we were interested in knowing whether $\frac{2}{7}$ and $\frac{1}{3}$ name the same fractional number, and if not, which one names the larger fractional number, we would need a discrete set that could be partitioned into thirds and sevenths. The most readily constructed set consists of a set with three rows of seven items in each row, or seven rows with three items in each row. It is easy to see in Figure 8.12 that $\frac{1}{3}$ names a larger fractional number than $\frac{2}{7}$, because $\frac{1}{3}$ of this set is seven, and $\frac{2}{7}$ is only six. (Constructing a model of this type is useful to show a child why one can tell whether $\frac{a}{b}$ is equal to, greater than, or less than $\frac{c}{d}$, depending on the relationship of "a times d" to "b times c.")

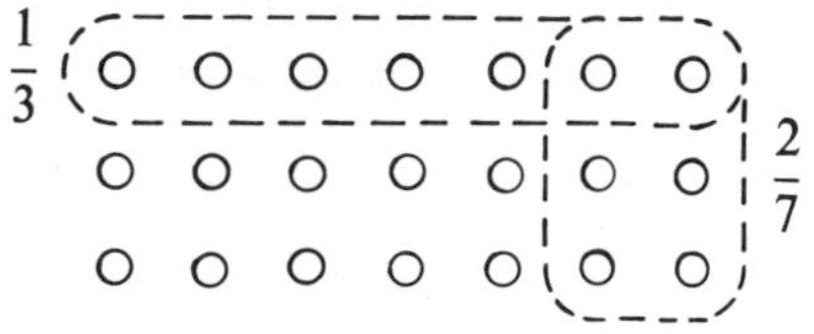

FIGURE 8.12

A rectangular region that has been partitioned into various fractional parts is a very useful aid in getting children to discover equivalent fractions. Figure 8.13 depicts a common form of this aid. The child can easily check for congruence between various partitions. The most common technique for

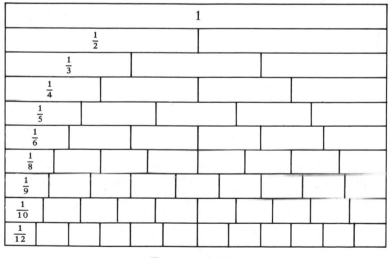

FIGURE 8.13

checking congruence is to move a sheet of paper (with a straightedge running from top to bottom) from left to right across the partitioned region. The child will find which partitioning segments are common to various types of partitioning.

Another useful aid for helping children to discover equivalent fractions is to use many number-line segments that have been partitioned in a manner similar to the partitioning of the rectangular region in Figure 8.13. However, the manner in which the children use this aid is quite different, for they mark off the length of one type of fractional partitioning on the edge of a second sheet of paper and see if other line segments have partitions that correspond to the length. Figure 8.14 depicts a typical model of this teaching aid.

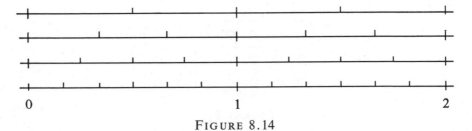

0   1   2

FIGURE 8.14

Using the "multinumber-line segment" pictured in Figure 8.14, the children could discover the following sets of equivalent fractions: $\{\frac{1}{3}, \frac{2}{6}\}$, $\{\frac{1}{2}, \frac{2}{4}, \frac{3}{6}\}$, $\{\frac{2}{2}, \frac{3}{3}, \frac{4}{4}, \frac{6}{6}\}$, $\{\frac{4}{3}, \frac{8}{6}\}$, $\{\frac{3}{2}, \frac{6}{4}, \frac{9}{6}\}$, $\{\frac{5}{3}, \frac{10}{6}\}$, $\{\frac{4}{2}, \frac{6}{3}, \frac{8}{4}, \frac{12}{6}\}$.

When you are developing the concept of quotients of whole numbers via the use of the number-line segments, it is possible to begin developing the idea of equivalent *division expressions*. For example, in Figure 8.15, we see the expressions $12 \div 4$, $9 \div 3$, $6 \div 2$, and $3 \div 1$ represented on different number-line segments.

A dialogue that might accompany this type of exercise and which would introduce the child to equivalent division expressions might be as follows:

> "You can see that 3 has many division names. Can someone tell me some more division names for 3?" (Fifteen-fifths, eighteen-sixths, twenty-one-sevenths, etc.) "If we started with the division name $3 \div 1$, what would we have to do to both the 3 and the 1 to get 6 and 2?" (Multiply both numbers by two.) "How could we get 12 and 4 from 3 and 1? (Multiply the three and the one by four.)
>
> [Write on the board $(3 \times \square) \div (1 \times \square)$.] "Can someone use this pattern to get a division name for 3 that has a 9 for the divisor?" (Twenty-seven divided by nine.) "Can someone use this pattern to get a divisor name for 3 that has a 10 for the divisor?" (Thirty divided by ten.)

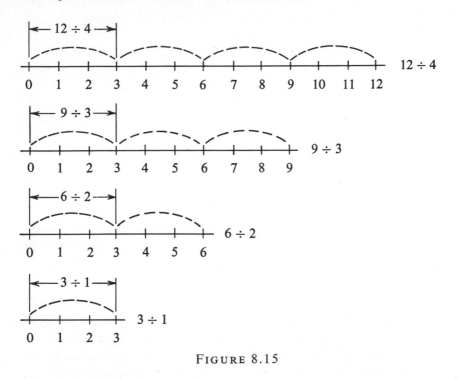

FIGURE 8.15

After the child has used the number-line segment to construct mathematical models of fractional numbers, his concept can be extended with this type of model to include the concept of equivalent fractions. Figure 8.16 depicts how equivalent names for $\frac{5}{4}$ can be discovered using number-line segments.

Sometimes it is advantageous to think of the fraction $\frac{a}{b}$ as $a \times \frac{1}{b}$. For example, in the child's early fractional number experiences, he is asked to determine equivalent fractions by comparing two partitioned polygonal regions. When considering $\frac{a}{b}$ as representing $a \times \frac{1}{b}$, on a number-line segment, it will be important for the child to construct the $\frac{1}{b}$ partition first, and then make a repetition of this type of partition. Figure 8.17 illustrates the steps we must take in showing $\frac{8}{3}$ on a number-line segment when $\frac{8}{3}$ is viewed as $8 \times \frac{1}{3}$.

Although it is true that every equivalent fraction is a suitable name for a fractional number, there are times when one name may be more convenient to use than another. For example, the fraction referred to as being in the simplest form is often the most useful to employ in an operation such as the multiplication of fractions. (A fraction, $\frac{a}{b}$, is said to be in the simplest form of a set of equivalent fractions if the only whole number that both a and b are divisible by is one.)

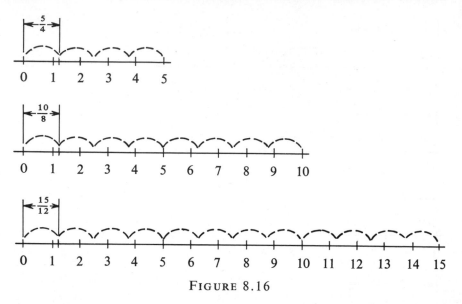

FIGURE 8.16

During the premodern mathematics period, only those fractions "reduced" to lowest terms were deemed acceptable answers to a problem. The teacher should make the child aware that the fraction chosen to express the answer to a problem depends on the problem's context, as well as on the concepts the student is being prepared for. For example, if we are building readiness for decimal notation, $\frac{4}{10}$ may be a much more acceptable form in which to leave the answer than the form $\frac{2}{5}$. Or, if a child is going to have to utilize the idea of $\frac{1}{3}$ with respect to a dozen, the $\frac{4}{12}$ conveys much more meaning when viewed

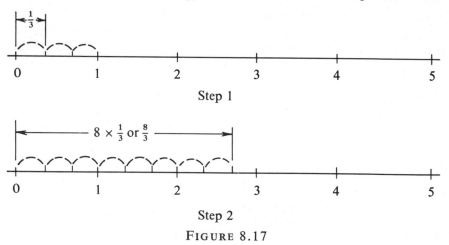

Step 1

Step 2

FIGURE 8.17

as the ratio of 4 to 12. Later when the students study precision of measurements, they will note that $\frac{4}{8}$ tells us that the measurement was made to the nearest $\frac{1}{8}$-inch and that changing the answer to $\frac{1}{2}$-inch would mislead us as to how precise the measurement was.

Even though you should teach your students to find many names for fractional numbers, you should also encourage them to choose the most appropriate name for the situation.

8.6. *Mixed Numerals*

There are many occasions in the everyday affairs of people when a whole-number name is used in conjunction with the name of a fractional number less than one. Such expressions as "$3\frac{1}{4}$ feet of rope," "$4\frac{1}{2}$ million dollars," "$10\frac{2}{5}$ seconds," "$29\frac{8}{10}$ inches of mercury," "$2\frac{3}{8}$ yards of cloth," and "$7\frac{1}{2}$ revolutions per second" are just a few of the mixed numeral expressions that confront us.

There are two important concepts that must be developed when you are teaching the principles of mixed numerals: The first is that a name such as $2\frac{1}{5}$ really is a shortened form for the expression $2 + \frac{1}{5}$; the second is that a name such as $2\frac{1}{5}$ can always be expressed in fraction form, because $2\frac{1}{5} = 2 + \frac{1}{5} = \frac{2}{1} + \frac{1}{5} = \frac{2 \times 5}{1 \times 5} + \frac{1}{5} = \frac{10}{5} + \frac{1}{5} = \frac{11}{5}$.

The first concept can be developed either through the use of a set of discrete polygonal regions or on a number-line segment. Figure 8.18 depicts a representation of $2\frac{3}{4}$ with sets of square regions and on a number-line segment.

The concept of translating mixed numerals to fraction form will be discussed when the concept of addition of fractional numbers is introduced.

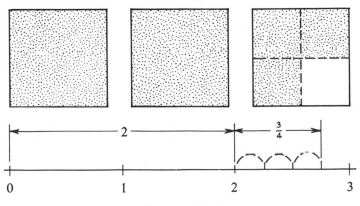

FIGURE 8.18

8.7. *Properties of the Set of Fractional Numbers*

The first property that the children will learn is that zero is the smallest fractional number. The set of fractions for the fractional number zero is the set $\{\frac{0}{1}, \frac{0}{2}, \frac{0}{3}, \ldots\}$. The reader will note that $\frac{0}{0}$ is not a name for zero, because division by zero is undetermined.

One of the most important properties of the set of fractional numbers is that between any two fractional numbers there exists an infinite set of fractional numbers. Suppose you want to demonstrate that we could find as many fractional numbers between $\frac{1}{3}$ and $\frac{1}{2}$ as we desired. Express both fractional numbers as $\frac{2}{6}$ and $\frac{3}{6}$ and ask the students if we are still talking about $\frac{1}{3}$ and $\frac{1}{2}$. Ask them if the quotient will be changed if they multiply the divisor and dividend by the same number. (The answer is "no"; this is merely using the compensation property for division.)

Then suggest multiplying the numerator and denominator of both fractional numbers by one billion. We obtain $\frac{2,000,000,000}{6,000,000,000}$, and $\frac{3,000,000,000}{6,000,000,000}$. It will be easy for the children to see that the set of fractional numbers $\{\frac{2,000,000,001}{6,000,000,000}, \frac{2,000,000,002}{6,000,000,000}, \cdots \frac{2,999,999,999}{6,000,000,000}\}$ are all fractional numbers that are between $\frac{1}{3}$ and $\frac{1}{2}$. By multiplying by one billion, we obtained 999,999,999 numbers between the numbers $\frac{1}{3}$ and $\frac{1}{2}$. If we had multiplied by a larger number, we would have obtained more numbers between $\frac{1}{3}$ and $\frac{1}{2}$. By choosing a number sufficiently large, we could find as many fractional numbers between $\frac{1}{3}$ and $\frac{1}{2}$ as we would choose.

An alternate approach for showing a child that there exists an infinite set of fractional numbers between any two numbers is called the *averaging technique*. This technique involves finding a fractional number between two fractional numbers by averaging. Demonstrate that we could always use this technique to find a new fractional number between the last found fractional number and one of the earlier found fractional numbers or one of the original fractional numbers. For example, take $\frac{1}{2}$ and $\frac{1}{3}$. We average these two fractional numbers by adding $\frac{1}{2}$ and $\frac{1}{3}$ and dividing by two. Thus we obtain the number $\frac{5}{12}$. We demonstrate that this is between $\frac{1}{2}$ and $\frac{1}{3}$ by expressing $\frac{1}{2}$ and $\frac{1}{3}$ in terms of twelfths. We then proceed to find a fractional number either between $\frac{1}{2}$ and $\frac{5}{12}$ or between $\frac{1}{3}$ and $\frac{5}{12}$ by the averaging method. The children will soon see that this averaging method could be used as many times as necessary to find as many fractional numbers between $\frac{1}{2}$ and $\frac{1}{3}$ as desired.

A third property of the set of fractional numbers, which is also a property of the set of whole numbers, is the trichotomy property. Given two fractional numbers, $\frac{a}{b}$ and $\frac{c}{d}$, it is always true that either $\frac{a}{b} < \frac{c}{d}$, or $\frac{a}{b} = \frac{c}{d}$, or $\frac{a}{b} > \frac{c}{d}$.

EXERCISES (2)

1. Demonstrate that $\frac{3}{8}$ and $\frac{6}{16}$ are equivalent fractions by constructing suitable mathematical models of polygons.
2. Demonstrate that $\frac{3}{5}$ and $\frac{6}{10}$ are equivalent fractions by constructing a suitable mathematical model using an array.
3. Make up a partitioned fractional-number bar that could be used to show that $\frac{2}{7}$ and $\frac{4}{14}$ name the same fractional number.
4. Make up a multinumber-line segment to show that $\frac{7}{4}$ and $\frac{21}{12}$ are equivalent fractions.
5. Illustrate each of the following quotients on a number-line segment:

$$\frac{15}{5}, \frac{30}{10} \qquad \frac{3}{4}, \frac{6}{8}, \frac{12}{16} \qquad \frac{4}{3}, \frac{8}{6}, \frac{16}{12}$$

6. Illustrate $\frac{13}{4}$ on a number-line segment where $\frac{13}{4}$ is thought of as $13 \times \frac{1}{4}$.
7. Show that $3\frac{1}{2}$ and $\frac{7}{2}$ are equivalent names by representing both on number-line segments.
8. A child wrote the following:

$$\frac{3}{4} \times \frac{0}{7} = \frac{0}{13}$$

   a. Has the child written the proper product?
   b. Justify your answer.
9. Give a step-by-step explanation to show that there is an infinite set of fractional numbers between $\frac{9}{7}$ and $\frac{9}{8}$, using each of the following techniques:
   a. Compensation property for division
   b. Averaging.

REFERENCES

BANKS, J. HOUSTON, *Learning and Teaching Arithmetic*, Boston: Allyn & Bacon, 1964, pp. 293–299.

BELL, CLIFFORD, CLELA D. HAMMOND, and ROBERT B. HERRERA, *Fundamentals of Arithmetic for Teachers*, New York: John Wiley & Sons, Inc., 1962, pp. 141–150.

BRUMFIEL, CHARLES, ROBERT EICHOLZ, and MERRILL SHANKS, *Fundamental Concepts of Elementary Mathematics*, Reading, Mass.: Addison-Wesley, 1962, pp. 50, 63–68.

CHURCHILL, EILEEN M., *Counting and Measuring*, Great Britain: Routledge & Kegan Paul, 1962, pp. 117–120.

CROUCH, RALPH, GEORGE BALDWIN, and ROBERT J. WISNER, *Preparatory Mathematics for Elementary Teachers*, New York: John Wiley & Sons, Inc., 1965, pp. 299–305, 359–365.

EDUCATION RESEARCH COUNCIL OF GREATER CLEVELAND, *Key Topics in Mathematics for the Primary Teacher*, Chicago: Science Research Associates, Inc., 1962, pp. 67–72.

FLOURNOY, FRANCES, *Elementary School Mathematics*, Washington, D.C.: The Center for Applied Research in Education, 1964, p. 11.

GUNDERSON, AGNES G., and ETHEL GUNDERSON, "Fraction Concepts Held by Young Children," *The Arithmetic Teacher*, vol. 4, pp. 168–173, October, 1957.

HACKER, SIDNEY G., WILFRED E. BARNES, and CALVIN T. LONG, *Fundamental Concepts of Arithmetic*, Englewood Cliffs, N.J.: Prentice-Hall, Inc., 1963, p. 141.

HARTUNG, M. L., "Fractions and Related Symbolism in Elementary School Instruction," *Elementary School Journal*, vol. 58, pp. 377–384, April, 1958.

HEDDENS, JAMES W., *Today's Mathematics, A Guide to Concepts and Methods in Elementary School Mathematics*, Chicago: Science Research Associates, Inc., 1964, pp. 209–219.

MARKS, JOHN L., JAMES R. SMART, and IRENE SAUBLE, *Enlarging Mathematical Ideas*, Boston: Ginn and Company, 1964, pp. 24–25, 35–37.

NATIONAL COUNCIL OF TEACHERS OF MATHEMATICS, *Enrichment Mathematics for the Grades, Twenty-seventh Yearbook*, Washington, D.C.: The National Council of Teachers of Mathematics, 1963, pp. 221–226.

NATIONAL COUNCIL OF TEACHERS OF MATHEMATICS, *Instruction in Arithmetic, Twenty-fifth Yearbook*, Washington, D.C.: The National Council of Teachers of Mathematics, 1960, pp. 55–58, 291–292, 348–349.

NATIONAL COUNCIL OF TEACHERS OF MATHEMATICS, *The Growth of Mathematical Ideas, Grades K–12, Twenty-fourth Yearbook*, Washington, D.C.: The National Council of Teachers of Mathematics, 1959, pp. 29–33.

NATIONAL COUNCIL OF TEACHERS OF MATHEMATICS, *The Learning of Mathematics, Its Theory and Practice, Twenty-sixth Yearbook*, Washington, D.C.: The National Council of Teachers of Mathematics, 1961, pp. 199–201.

OSBORN, ROGER, M. VERE DeVAULT, CLAUDE BOYD, and ROBERT HOUSTON, *Extending Mathematics Understanding*, Columbus, Ohio: Charles E. Merrill Books, Inc., 1961, pp. 34–38, 60–63.

PAGE, DAVID A., *Number Lines, Fractions, and Fundamental Topics*, New York: The Macmillan Company, 1964, pp. 56–75.

PETERSON, JOHN A., and JOSEPH HASHISAKI, *Theory of Arithmetic*, New York: John Wiley & Sons, Inc., 1964, pp. 152–154.

RAPKIN, MINNIE K., and LILLIAN C. HOWITT, *Teaching the Third "R,"* Englewood Cliffs, N.J.: Teachers Practical Press, Inc., 1963, pp. 55–58.

SCHAAF, WILLIAM L., *Basic Concepts of Elementary Mathematics*, New York: John Wiley & Sons, Inc., 1960, pp. 131–132.

SCHOOL MATHEMATICS STUDY GROUP, *Mathematics for the Elementary School*, Stanford, Calif.: Stanford University Press, 1962.

SCHOOL MATHEMATICS STUDY GROUP, *Studies in Mathematics, vol. IX: A Brief Course in Mathematics for Elementary School Teachers*, Stanford, Calif.: Stanford University Press, 1963, pp. 219–228.

SHIPP, DONALD, and SAM ADAMS, *Developing Arithmetic Concepts and Skills*, Englewood Cliffs, N.J.: Prentice-Hall, Inc., 1964, pp. 176–177.

SMITH, SEATON E., JR., *Explorations in Elementary Mathematics*, Englewood Cliffs, N.J.: Prentice-Hall, Inc., 1966, p. 112.

SPENCER, PETER LINCOLN, and MARGUERITE BRYDEGAARD, *Building Mathematical Competence in the Elementary School*, New York: Holt, Rinehart and Winston, Inc., 1966, pp. 214–222.

SWAIN, ROBERT L., and EUGENE D. NICHOLS, *Understanding Arithmetic*, New York: Holt, Rinehart and Winston, Inc., 1965, pp. 135–138.

SWENSON, ESTHER J., *Teaching Arithmetic to Children*, New York: The Macmillan Company, 1964, pp. 302–334.

TRIMBLE, HAROLD C., "Fractions Are Ratios, Too," *Elementary School Journal*, vol. 49, pp. 285–291, January, 1949.

VAN ENGEN, HENRY, MAURICE L. HARTUNG, and JAMES E. STOCHL, *Foundations of Elementary School Arithmetic*, Chicago: Scott, Foresman and Co., 1965, pp. 229–271.

WARD, MORGAN, and CLARENCE HARDGROVE, *Modern Elementary Mathematics*, Reading, Mass.: Addison-Wesley, 1964, pp. 230–233.

WILLIAMS, SAMMIE, GARLAND H. READ, JR., and FRANK L. WILLIAMS, *Modern Mathematics in the Elementary and Junior High Schools*, Syracuse, N.Y.: L. W. Singer, 1961, pp. 37–39.

Active exploration can motivate a child to learn mathematics.

9

Teaching Addition and Subtraction of Fractional Numbers

9.1. *Introduction*

THE INSTRUCTION in addition and subtraction of fractional numbers during the premodern period was essentially a fragmented approach in which the handling of a series of specific cases was learned. In Figure 9.1, we can see all of the various combinations of problems that were taught as distinct learning experiences. One studied how to add proper fractions and proper fractions, proper fractions and improper fractions, proper fractions and mixed numerals. The various other combinations that were treated as special skills requiring specialized instructions can also be traced.

One of the effects of this type of presentation was the students' inability to tie together the general relationships existing for addition and subtraction on the set of whole numbers as well as fractional numbers. A child taught by this technique would view the solution of problems such as $\frac{1}{7} + \frac{3}{7} = \frac{\triangle}{\square}$, and $\frac{14}{7} + \frac{21}{7} = \frac{\triangle}{\square}$, as requiring quite distinct processes in solution. Some reacted

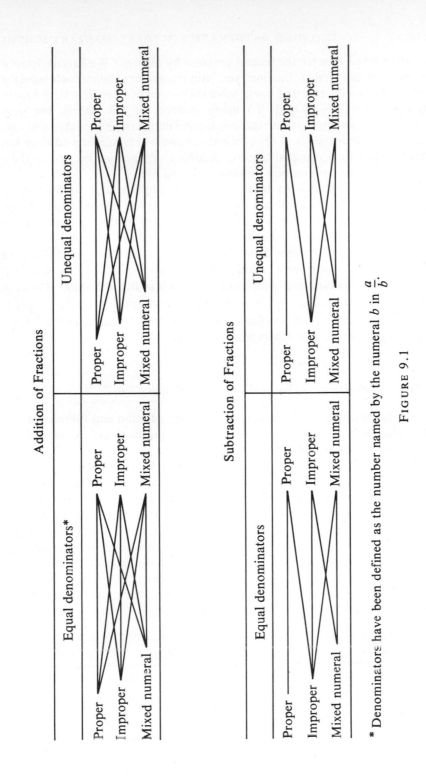

Addition of Fractions

Subtraction of Fractions

Figure 9.1

* Denominators have been defined as the number named by the numeral b in $\frac{a}{b}$.

to being asked to solve the second problem by saying, "We haven't learned how to add that kind of 'fraction' yet." But these same children could solve the first problem with ease and could solve the second problem if it were written as $(14 \div 7) + (21 \div 7) = \square$. To many students of this period, the term fraction was synonymous with those fractional numbers between zero and one, rather than with the set of all quotients of two whole numbers (divisor not zero) greater than or equal to zero. Addition of fractions became to these students addition of numbers between zero and one.

A modern approach to teaching a child addition and subtraction of fractional numbers is to allow those properties he has learned about the set of whole numbers to serve in aiding his mastery of further concepts. As an example of how whole-number concepts can be utilized to teach fractional-number concepts, consider how the exploration of the right distributive property of division over addition in this problem—$(6 \div 2) + (4 \div 2) = (6 + 4) \div 2$—leads naturally into situations such as the following: $(1 \div 2) + (1 \div 2) = (1 + 1) \div 2 = 2 \div 2 = 1$, or, in fraction form, $\frac{1}{2} + \frac{1}{2} = \frac{1+1}{2} = \frac{2}{2} = 1$. In the premodern era, whole-number concepts were set aside while the "new" concepts of fractional numbers were mastered.

9.2. Definition, Terminology, and Symbolism

Before presenting the techniques of teaching addition and subtraction, we shall discuss the basic ideas and symbolism that are employed in our methods of teaching fractional numbers.

Fundamental to all of our discussions will be this question: "What, specifically, do we mean by 'addition' and 'subtraction'?" We defined the concept of sum in terms of the number property associated with the union of two discrete sets. In order to maintain a smooth transition from the addition of whole numbers to the addition of fractional numbers, and to employ a mathematical model that will exhibit properties consistent with the quotient definition of fractional numbers, we shall view the sum of two fractional numbers as the number associated with the union of certain partitioned continuous or discrete sets. A working definition for the sum of two fractional numbers is as follows:

Let $\frac{\triangle}{\square}$ and $\frac{\triangle}{\square}$ be two fractional numbers represented on a number line by segments of measure $\overline{AB}$ and $\overline{CD}$, respectively. The sum of $\frac{\triangle}{\square}$ and $\frac{\triangle}{\square}$ is the number associated with the measure of the union of $\overline{AB}$ and $\overline{CD}$.*

---

* The line segment pictured here can be named by the two endpoints A and B. We use these letters to refer to the line segment as $\overline{AB}$ (read line segment AB).

$$A \text{————————} B$$

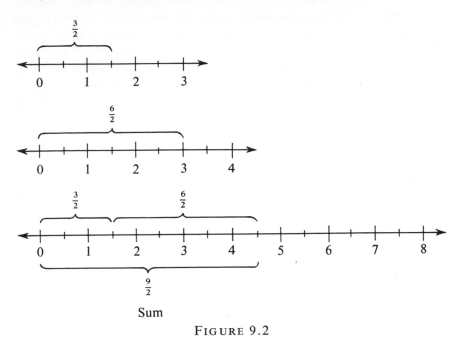

Sum

FIGURE 9.2

Figure 9.2 depicts how this working definition can be used to establish that $\frac{3}{2} + \frac{6}{2} = \frac{9}{2}$.

The utilization of a number line in the definition offers the advantage over most other models we might choose in that it is readily adapted for sums of fractional numbers less than or equal to one, as well as for sums greater than one. (For example, if one finds the sum of $\frac{2}{3}$ and $\frac{2}{3}$ by using regions of a rectangle, the tendency is to view the sum as being $1 + \frac{1}{3}$, rather than as $\frac{4}{3}$.) This idea is illustrated in Figure 9.3.

The reader will note that the working definition requires us to add only those fractional numbers that have the same divisor named in the fraction

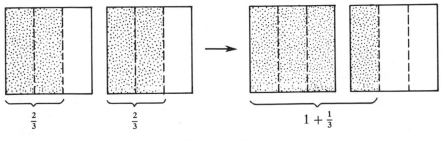

FIGURE 9.3

form. This is an artificial requirement simplifying our determining the number associated with the union of segments $\overline{AB}$ and $\overline{CD}$. Our definition is suitable whether or not the divisors named are the same, provided we have some way of determining the number property of the union of $\overline{AB}$ and $\overline{CD}$. It would be possible to omit this requirement if we were always permitted the luxury of working with a number line. For example, we could measure off $\frac{1}{2}$ and $\frac{1}{4}$ on a number line and determine the number property of the line segment formed by the union by measuring out segments of this length enough times to measure n units. Figure 9.4 illustrates this idea.

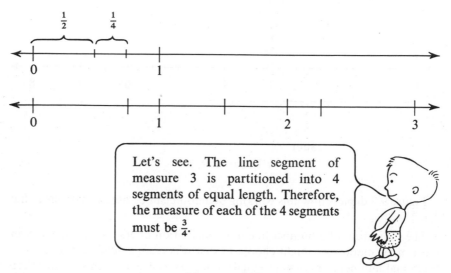

Let's see. The line segment of measure 3 is partitioned into 4 segments of equal length. Therefore, the measure of each of the 4 segments must be $\frac{3}{4}$.

FIGURE 9.4

In the interest of having the child develop the most efficient algorithm for the addition and subtraction of fractional numbers, we shall require that the divisors named in the fractions name the same number. In those cases in which this requirement is not met, we shall teach the child how to select for substitution equivalent names for the same fractional number.

The sum of two fractional numbers $\frac{\triangle}{\square}$ and $\frac{\bigcirc}{\square}$ will be defined as $\frac{\triangle + \bigcirc}{\square}$.

The difference of two fractional numbers $\frac{\triangle}{\square}$ and $\frac{\bigcirc}{\square}$ where $\frac{\triangle}{\square} > \frac{\bigcirc}{\square}$, will be defined as $\frac{\lozenge}{\square}$ if, and only if, $\frac{\triangle}{\square} = \frac{\bigcirc}{\square} + \frac{\lozenge}{\square}$.

Although the difference of two fractional numbers will be defined in this manner, and the child will use this definition to check his work, subtraction will be interpreted concretely in the same manner as it was for the set of whole numbers. This will involve relating subtraction to set separation, set comparison, and excluded subset (missing addend) of a union or joining of sets.

There are several conventional notations for fractional numbers that you will need to teach your students. Figure 9.5 depicts some of the types of notation used in teaching addition and subtraction of fractional numbers.

$$(4 \div 2) + (3 \div 2) = \square \div \triangle$$

$$\frac{4}{2} + \frac{3}{2} = \frac{\square}{\triangle} \rightarrow \quad \frac{4}{2} \rightarrow \quad 2 \rightarrow \quad 2$$
$$\phantom{\frac{4}{2} + \frac{3}{2} = \frac{\square}{\triangle} \rightarrow} \frac{+\frac{3}{2}}{} \quad \frac{+1\frac{1}{2}}{} \quad \frac{+1+\frac{1}{2}}{}$$

$$(4 \div 2) - (3 \div 2) = \square \div \triangle$$

$$\frac{4}{2} - \frac{3}{2} = \frac{\square}{\triangle} \rightarrow \quad \frac{4}{2} \rightarrow \quad 2 \rightarrow \quad 2$$
$$\phantom{\frac{4}{2} - \frac{3}{2} = \frac{\square}{\triangle} \rightarrow} \frac{-\frac{3}{2}}{} \quad \frac{-1\frac{1}{2}}{} \quad \frac{-(1+\frac{1}{2})}{}$$

$$\frac{3}{2} + \frac{\square}{\triangle} = \frac{4}{2} \rightarrow \quad \frac{3}{2} \rightarrow \quad 1\frac{1}{2} \rightarrow \quad 1 + \frac{1}{2}$$
$$\phantom{\frac{3}{2} + \frac{\square}{\triangle} = \frac{4}{2} \rightarrow} \frac{+\frac{\square}{\triangle}}{\frac{4}{2}} \quad \frac{+\frac{\square}{\triangle}}{2} \quad \frac{+\frac{\square}{\triangle}}{2}$$

FIGURE 9.5

The notation "$\frac{3}{4} + \frac{5}{4} = \frac{8}{4}$" can be read in many ways, a few of which follow:

> Three-fourths and five-fourths is eight-fourths.
> Three-fourths and five-fourths equals eight-fourths.
> The sum of three-fourths and five-fourths is eight-fourths.
> The sum of three-fourths and five-fourths equals eight-fourths.
> Five-fourths added to three-fourths is eight-fourths.

Similarly, the notation "$\frac{6}{7} - \frac{2}{7} = \frac{4}{7}$" can be read in many ways, a few of which follow:

> Two-sevenths subtracted from six-sevenths is four-sevenths.
> Two-sevenths subtracted from six-sevenths equals four-sevenths.
> Six-sevenths less two-sevenths is four-sevenths.
> Six-sevenths less two-sevenths equals four-sevenths.
> Six-sevenths subtract two-sevenths is four-sevenths.
> Six-sevenths subtract two-sevenths equals four-sevenths.

The terminology used with fraction addition and subtraction sentences and notations is identical with that used for whole-number addition and subtraction sentences. The terminology used with addition and subtraction notations is depicted in Figure 9.6.

Addend	Addend	Sum		
$\frac{3}{4}$	$+ \quad \frac{6}{4}$	$= \quad \frac{9}{4}$	$\frac{3}{4}$	Addend
			$+\frac{6}{4}$	Addend
			$\frac{9}{4}$	Sum

Minuend	Subtrahend	Difference		
$\frac{5}{4}$	$- \quad \frac{3}{4}$	$= \quad \frac{2}{4}$	Sum $\quad \frac{5}{4}$	Minuend
Sum	Known addend	Missing addend	Known addend $\quad -\frac{3}{4}$	Subtrahend
			Missing addend $\quad \frac{2}{4}$	Difference

Known addend	Unknown addend	Sum
$\frac{3}{4}$	$+ \quad \boxed{\frac{2}{4}}$	$= \quad \frac{5}{4}$

FIGURE 9.6

9.3. *Teaching the Structural Properties of Addition*

Before investigating the methods of teaching the addition and subtraction of fractional numbers, we shall investigate the techniques of presenting the structural properties of addition and subtraction. When these properties are mentioned later, in methods of teaching addition and subtraction to children, it will be understood that they were introduced to the children prior to that point.

One of the first properties that a child discovers is the identity element for addition. In presenting properties for the fractional numbers, you should motivate him to search for those properties that he discovered for the set of whole numbers and that are also properties of the set of fractional numbers. Statements such as the following will serve to motivate him to look for a number: "We have seen that zero is the identity element for the set of whole numbers. Let's see if the fractional numbers have an identity element." Structuring problems to help the child discover the commutative and associative properties of addition for fractional numbers requires certain subtleties not employed for the same whole-number properties. Notice in Figure 9.7 that the paired problems utilize equivalent names, which adds the distraction of equivalence to the search for commutativity and associativity.

(1a) $\frac{2}{4} + \frac{3}{2} = \frac{\triangle}{\square}$ (2a) $(\frac{2}{3} + \frac{1}{6}) + \frac{5}{12} = \frac{\triangle}{\square}$

(1b) $\frac{6}{4} + \frac{2}{4} = \frac{\triangle}{\square}$ (2b) $\frac{4}{6} + (\frac{2}{12} + \frac{5}{12}) = \frac{\triangle}{\square}$

FIGURE 9.7

Whereas the commutative property for the set of whole numbers has a mathematical usage* and a functional usage as well, the commutative and associative properties for the set of fractional numbers have mainly a mathematical usage. For example, knowledge of the commutative property for addition for the set of whole numbers decreases the number of explorations the child needs to make in order to discover the basic addition facts. Because there are no basic fractional facts the child must memorize, the commutative property does not serve to minimize effort when he is mastering addition on the set of fractional numbers.

The techniques for getting the child to discover these mathematical patterns are similar to the ones used for discovering the same patterns for the set of whole numbers. The first stage consists of a structured learning experience where the child is given pairs of problems employing these patterns. After he has discovered the pattern, its reinforcement is established by problems requiring a single solution. In order to focus his mind on the general nature of the pattern that he has discovered, problems requiring multiple solutions are given next. At this stage, a number of the many solutions for each problem should be elicited. The final stage in this learning process consists of giving

	Commutative addition	Associative addition
Problems leading to discovery	(1a) $\frac{3}{4} + \frac{4}{7} = \frac{\triangle}{\square}$ (1b) $\frac{4}{7} + \frac{12}{28} = \frac{\triangle}{\square}$	(1a) $(\frac{1}{2} + \frac{1}{3}) + \frac{2}{5} = \frac{\triangle}{\square}$ (1b) $\frac{2}{4} + (\frac{2}{6} + \frac{4}{10}) = \frac{\triangle}{\square}$
Problems requiring single solutions	$\frac{3}{4} + \frac{4}{5} = \frac{\triangle}{\square} + \frac{21}{28}$	$(\frac{1}{2} + \frac{1}{3}) + \frac{\triangle}{\square} = \frac{1}{2} + (\frac{1}{3} + \frac{2}{9})$
Problems requiring multiple solutions	$\frac{\triangle}{\square} + \frac{3}{8} = \frac{6}{16} + \frac{\triangle}{\square}$	$(\frac{1}{5} + \frac{3}{4}) + \frac{\triangle}{\square} = \frac{2}{10} + (\frac{3}{4} + \frac{\triangle}{\square})$

FIGURE 9.8

* Structural properties have an inherent mathematical usage in providing a means to compare and contrast various number systems.

the child the patterns $\frac{\triangle}{\bigcirc} + \frac{\square}{\bigcirc} = \frac{\square}{\bigcirc} + \frac{\triangle}{\bigcirc}$, and $(\frac{\triangle}{\bigcirc} + \frac{\square}{\bigcirc}) + \frac{\bigcirc}{\triangle} = \frac{\triangle}{\bigcirc} + (\frac{\square}{\bigcirc} + \frac{\bigcirc}{\triangle})$, and asking him to create true mathematical sentences using these patterns.

In Figure 9.8, we have representative problems from the first three stages of teaching the commutative and associative properties for addition of fractional numbers.

EXERCISES (1)

1. Using the working definition for sum, and the number line as a mathematical model, illustrate $\frac{2}{3} + \frac{5}{3} = \frac{7}{3}$.

2. Using a hexagon as a model, illustrate $\frac{1}{6} + \frac{2}{6} = \frac{3}{6}$.

3. Based on the definition of difference, name an addition sentence that would be equivalent to $\frac{7}{3} - \frac{4}{3} = \frac{\triangle}{\square}$.

4. Write four ways that each of the following mathematical sentences can be read:

    a. $\frac{2}{5} + \frac{5}{5} = \frac{7}{5}$ b. $\frac{7}{8} - \frac{3}{8} = \frac{4}{8}$

5. Identify the addends and sum in the following:

    a. $\frac{3}{4} + \frac{5}{4} = \frac{8}{4}$ b. $\begin{array}{r} \frac{3}{4} \\ + \frac{5}{4} \\ \hline \frac{8}{4} \end{array}$

6. Identify the minuend, subtrahend, difference, known addend, missing addend, and sum for each of the following, if applicable:

    a. $\frac{3}{4} + \frac{\boxed{\triangle}}{\boxed{4}} = \frac{4}{4}$ b. $\frac{4}{4} - \frac{1}{4} = \frac{3}{4}$

7. Make up sample problems for each of the first three stages for teaching the commutative property for addition on the set of fractional numbers.

8. Make up sample problems for each of the first three stages for teaching the associative property for addition on the set of fractional numbers.

9.4. *Teaching the Structural Properties of Subtraction*

One of the first structural properties for fractional numbers that a child encounters is the right identity element. Leading him to generalize the concept that $\frac{\triangle}{\square} - \frac{0}{\diamond} = \frac{\triangle}{\square}$ is accomplished in the straightforward manner of presenting him with problems such as $\frac{3}{4} - \frac{0}{5} = \frac{\triangle}{\square}$, and $\frac{6}{7} - \frac{0}{7} = \frac{\triangle}{\square}$. It takes only a few problems of this type for the child to realize the generalization.

The compensation property for subtraction of fractional numbers, although not representing a highly functional property, does represent a mathematically interesting property that you may want to have your students investigate. Problems typically encountered at each stage in the learning process are depicted in Figure 9.9.

Problems
leading to
discovery
$$\begin{cases} \text{(1a) } (\frac{3}{4} + \frac{2}{7}) - (\frac{1}{4} + \frac{2}{7}) = \frac{\triangle}{\square} \\ \text{(1b) } \frac{3}{4} - \frac{1}{4} = \frac{\triangle}{\square} \\ \text{(2a) } (\frac{9}{7} - \frac{2}{5}) - (\frac{6}{7} - \frac{2}{5}) = \frac{\triangle}{\square} \\ \text{(2b) } \frac{9}{7} - \frac{6}{7} = \frac{\triangle}{\square} \end{cases}$$

Problems
requiring
single
solutions
$$\begin{cases} \frac{3}{4} - \frac{1}{2} = (\frac{3}{4} + \frac{\triangle}{\square}) - (\frac{1}{2} + \frac{3}{5}) \\ \frac{16}{7} - \frac{8}{7} = (\frac{16}{7} - \frac{3}{6}) - (\frac{16}{7} - \frac{\triangle}{\square}) \end{cases}$$

Problems
requiring
multiple
solutions
$$\begin{cases} \frac{6}{8} - \frac{3}{8} = (\frac{6}{8} + \frac{\triangle}{\square}) - (\frac{3}{8} + \frac{\triangle}{\square}) \\ \frac{13}{4} - \frac{7}{4} = (\frac{13}{4} - \frac{\triangle}{\square}) - (\frac{7}{4} - \frac{\triangle}{\square}) \end{cases}$$

FIGURE 9.9

The final stage in presenting this concept is to have the student make up mathematical sentences using both of these patterns: $\frac{\triangle}{\square} - \frac{\bigcirc}{\diamond} = (\frac{\triangle}{\square} + \frac{\bigcirc}{\boxtimes}) - (\frac{\bigcirc}{\diamond} + \frac{\bigcirc}{\boxtimes})$, and $\frac{\triangle}{\square} - \frac{\bigcirc}{\diamond} = (\frac{\triangle}{\square} - \frac{\bigcirc}{\boxtimes}) - (\frac{\bigcirc}{\diamond} - \frac{\bigcirc}{\boxtimes})$.

9.5. Teaching the Addition Algorithm

In the early stages of teaching the addition algorithm, the child encounters only situations where the divisors named in the fraction sentence are the same. His first experiences consist of manipulating sets and translating the results of this manipulation into the sum. In Figure 9.10, we can see two types of manipulation that aid the child in finding a sum.

At some stage in the child's early experiences, you should tie together the concepts of the right distributive property of division over addition and the addition of fractional numbers. This should be accomplished after the child has had an opportunity to find sums by manipulating various types of sets.

Find the sum of $\frac{3}{4}$ and $\frac{6}{4}$ by illustrating $\frac{3}{4} + \frac{6}{4}$ on the number line:

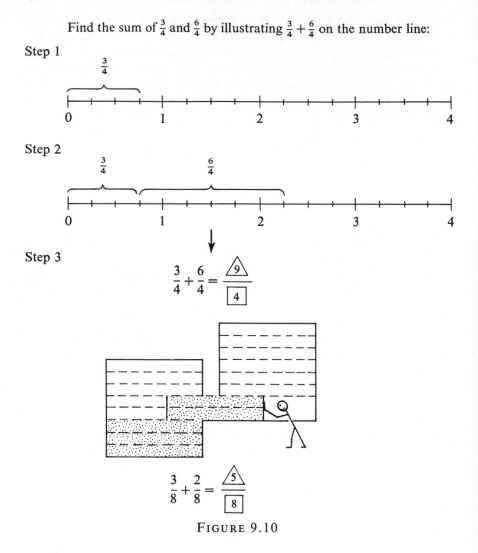

FIGURE 9.10

A typical dialogue that might be used to tie these concepts together is as follows:

"When we were studying division of whole numbers, what other way did we have for finding the answer to $(16 \div 4) + (8 \div 4) = \Box$?" (We could add the sixteen and eight and then divide by the four.) "What are some other notations we could use to show $(16 \div 4) + (8 \div 4) = \Box$?" ($\frac{16}{4} + \frac{8}{4} = \Box$.)

"How could we rewrite $(16 + 8) \div 4 = \Box$ in a fraction form?" ($\frac{16+8}{4} = \Box$.)

"Let's see if we can use this method to find our sum when we are adding fractional numbers. What have we found is the sum of $\frac{2}{4}$ and $\frac{1}{4}$?" (Three-fourths. The assumption is that the students have discovered this sum by working with manipulative devices.) "We can write this as $\frac{2}{4} + \frac{1}{4} = \frac{3}{4}$. How would we write our problem if we were going to solve it by first finding a sum and then dividing?" ($\frac{2+1}{4} = \frac{\triangle}{\square}$.)

"Will we get the same answer?" (Yes.) "Let's work a series of problems by rewriting them and working them by finding the sum first and then dividing. This, you remember, is an alternate way for solving $(a \div c) + (b \div c) = \square$."

STEP 1

The child marks off the length $\frac{1}{2}$ on the edge of a strip of paper, using a halves number-line segment as a guide.

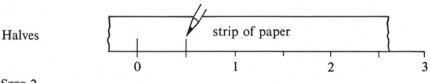

STEP 2

He then places the strip of paper on a thirds number-line segment, placing the mark designating the right end of the $\frac{1}{2}$ length he has just made above the zero mark on the thirds scale. He then marks off a segment $\frac{4}{3}$ in length.

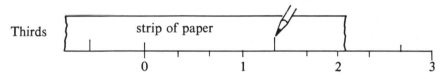

STEP 3

The child now looks for the next number-line segment below halves and thirds that has both halves and thirds marked off on it. He then places the left mark over the zero mark and reads off the number corresponding to the right mark on his strip of paper.

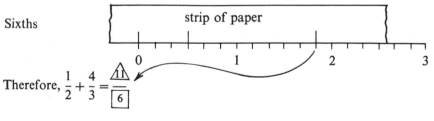

Therefore, $\dfrac{1}{2} + \dfrac{4}{3} = \dfrac{\boxed{11}}{\boxed{6}}$

FIGURE 9.11

After a child has developed competence in adding fractional numbers in which the notation names the same divisor, he is ready to learn how to find the sums of fractional numbers in which the notation names different divisors. But before teaching him to find the least common denominator by mathematical techniques (complete factorization, least common multiple, and so on), you should give him concrete experiences to help him find the suitable equivalent names to permit addition. A multinumber-line-segment chart or a partitioned fractional-number-bar chart are devices that lend themselves to building readiness for finding a least common denominator. Figure 9.11 illustrates how the child can use a multinumber-line-segment chart to find the sum of $\frac{1}{2}$ and $\frac{4}{3}$.

After the child has developed competence in using the multinumber-line segment or a similar device, he should be introduced to the mathematical technique for obtaining the least common denominator. In the following presentation it is assumed that he has been introduced to the completely factored form of the fraction. It will also be assumed that he has competence in obtaining a set of equivalent fractions.

After the children find a series of sums using the multinumber-line segment, have them go back and rewrite their mathematical addend in the form that they use to solve the problem and then in the completely factored form. Figure 9.12 depicts this idea in chart form, where the pattern can be focused on as it develops.

	Form obtained from multinumber line	Completely factored form
$\frac{3}{5}+\frac{2}{3}$	$\frac{9}{15}+\frac{10}{15}$	$\frac{3\times3}{5\times3}+\frac{2\times5}{3\times5}$
$\frac{1}{4}+\frac{3}{2}$	$\frac{1}{4}+\frac{6}{4}$	$\frac{1}{4}+\frac{3\times2}{2\times2}$

FIGURE 9.12

Ask the children to see if they can discover the pattern that shows how to find two fractions with the same divisor. Have them try more examples using this new-found pattern, and have them check their answers using multi-number-line segments.

After a child develops competence in finding the sum of two fractional numbers, it is the teacher's responsibility to help him refine his answers so that the forms he chooses for those answers will suit the use he plans for the answers. Frequently, the simplest form of the fraction is desirable. For example, if the sum $\frac{3}{12}$ is obtained, and if we are interested in using $\frac{3}{12}$ of a pound of butter in a recipe, the $\frac{1}{4}$ form would be more convenient, because butter is packaged in quarter-pound sticks. However, if we are to measure something, and the $\frac{3}{12}$ refers to part of a foot, the $\frac{3}{12}$ form might be the best equivalent name for the answer.

Sometimes a mixed numeral name is preferable to a fraction name. For example, suppose we have found, using addition, that we need $\frac{9}{2}$ yards of material to make a coat. When we get ready to order this, we will specify $4\frac{1}{2}$ yards. However, if we are told that we are going to be paid one dollar for each quarter-bushel of berries we pick, knowing that we picked $\frac{19}{4}$ bushels is more useful to us than knowing that we picked $4\frac{3}{4}$ bushels of berries.

9.6. *Mixed Numerals and Addition*

From the very beginning of a child's work with mixed numerals, he should be made aware of the fact that they name fractional numbers and that a number expressed as a mixed numeral can also be expressed as a fraction. Before he learns to add fractional numbers using only the mixed-numeral form, the teacher should make him aware of the fact that he already knows how to find the sum using the fraction form. For example, he would be able to find the sum of $2\frac{1}{4}$ and $3\frac{1}{7}$ as follows:

$$2\frac{1}{4} + 3\frac{1}{7} = \frac{9}{4} + \frac{22}{7} = \frac{63}{28} + \frac{88}{28} = \frac{151}{28} = 5\frac{11}{28}$$

He can now refine his technique for finding the sum by remembering that $2\frac{1}{4} = 2 + \frac{1}{4}$ and $3\frac{1}{7} = 3 + \frac{1}{7}$. This is illustrated in the following sequence of steps:

$(2 + \frac{1}{4}) + (3 + \frac{1}{7})$

$\downarrow$ repeated use of associative and commutative properties

$(2 + 3) + (\frac{1}{4} + \frac{1}{7})$

$\downarrow$ addition of whole numbers

$5 + (\frac{7}{28} + \frac{4}{28})$

$\downarrow$ addition of fractional numbers

$5 + \frac{11}{28}$

$\downarrow$ definition of mixed numeral

$5\frac{11}{28}$

Similarly, the vertical form for the algorithm can be introduced using this expanded form of the mixed numeral. This sequencing is illustrated in Figure 9.13.

$$
\begin{array}{ccc}
3\frac{1}{4} & 3 + \frac{1}{4} & 3 + \frac{3}{12} \\
+2\frac{1}{3} \rightarrow & +2 + \frac{1}{3} \rightarrow & +2 + \frac{4}{12} \\
\hline
& & 5 + \frac{7}{12} \rightarrow 5\frac{7}{12}
\end{array}
$$

FIGURE 9.13

This work with the expanded form builds readiness for later work with addition using decimal notation.

9.7. *Teaching Subtraction of Fractional Numbers*

Teaching subtraction on the set of fractional numbers is accomplished by techniques identical to those encountered when teaching addition. The child is first taught to find differences of fractional numbers involving fractions

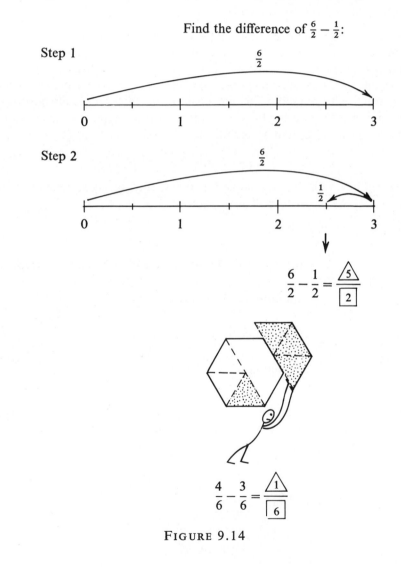

Find the difference of $\frac{6}{2} - \frac{1}{2}$:

$$\frac{6}{2} - \frac{1}{2} = \frac{\boxed{5}}{\boxed{2}}$$

$$\frac{4}{6} - \frac{3}{6} = \frac{\boxed{1}}{\boxed{6}}$$

FIGURE 9.14

with the same divisor named in the minuend and subtrahend. This early exploration is accomplished using manipulative devices similar to those employed for addition of fractional numbers. In Figure 9.14, we see two types of manipulations that aid the child in finding a difference.

The subtraction algorithm for fractional numbers can be introduced via the right distributive property of division over subtraction. The development of this algorithm will be left for the exercises.

Before teaching the child how to utilize the least-common-denominator method to find the difference of two fractional numbers, you should show him how to obtain the difference by working with devices such as the

STEP 1
The child marks off the length $\frac{4}{3}$ on the edge of a strip of paper, using a thirds number line segment as a guide.

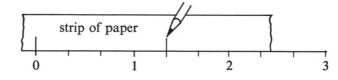

STEP 2
He then places the strip of paper on a halves number-line segment, placing the right end of the $\frac{4}{3}$ length he has just made directly above the $\frac{1}{2}$ mark on the halves scale. He then marks off the length $\frac{1}{2}$, as shown in the illustration.

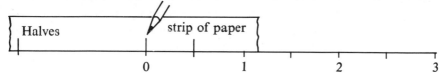

STEP 3
The child now looks for the next number-line segment below halves and thirds that has both halves and thirds marked off on it. He then places the left mark over the zero mark and reads off the number corresponding to the middle mark on his strip of paper.

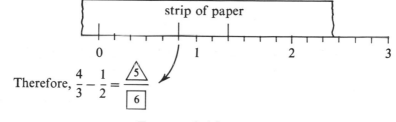

Therefore, $\dfrac{4}{3} - \dfrac{1}{2} = \dfrac{\boxed{5}}{\boxed{6}}$

FIGURE 9.15

multinumber-line segment. Figure 9.15 shows how a child can use a multi-number-line segment to find the difference of $\frac{4}{3}$ and $\frac{1}{2}$.

After the child develops competence in finding the difference of two fractional numbers using the multinumber-line segment, he should be taught the mathematical technique for obtaining the difference by first finding the least common denominator. This is accomplished by having him rewrite the original problem in the form used when he is finding a solution by using the number-line segment. After the subtraction expression is rewritten in a form using the least common denominator obtained from the multinumber-line segments, the expression should be written in the completely factored form. The child will be able to focus on the pattern that unfolds if this activity is conducted on a chart. Figure 9.16 depicts such a chart.

	Form obtained from multinumber line	Completely factored form
$\frac{3}{5} - \frac{1}{3}$	$\frac{9}{15} - \frac{5}{15}$	$\frac{3 \times 3}{5 \times 3} - \frac{1 \times 5}{3 \times 5}$
$\frac{7}{4} - \frac{3}{2}$	$\frac{7}{4} - \frac{6}{4}$	$\frac{7}{4} - \frac{3 \times 2}{2 \times 2}$

FIGURE 9.16

Ask the children to discover the pattern that tells how to find two fractions with the same divisor named. Have them try more examples using their new-found pattern. Have them check their answers by using the multinumber-line segments. They should be taught to refine their answers in the same way that they did when learning addition of fractional numbers.

9.8. *Mixed Numerals and Subtraction*

Teaching subtraction where the numbers involved are expressed as mixed numerals should be viewed as a preparation for teaching the child decimal notation. Expanded notation should be stressed, so that he can see the close relationship between what he has already learned and this new skill.

$$23\tfrac{1}{3} \qquad 20 + 3 + \tfrac{1}{3} \qquad 10 + 12 + \tfrac{4}{3} \qquad 10 + 12 + \tfrac{20}{15}$$
$$- 7\tfrac{4}{5} \to - \quad (7 + \tfrac{4}{5}) \to - \quad (7 + \tfrac{4}{5}) \to - \quad (7 + \tfrac{12}{15})$$
$$\overline{} \qquad \overline{} \qquad \overline{} \qquad \overline{}$$
$$10 + 5 + \tfrac{8}{15}$$
$$\downarrow$$
$$15\tfrac{8}{15}$$

FIGURE 9.17

The vertical notation lends itself to subtraction where the numbers involved are expressed as mixed numerals. The sequencing used in teaching this concept is illustrated in Figure 9.17.

EXERCISES (2)

1. Make up sample problems for each of the first three stages in teaching the compensation property for subtraction.

2. Illustrate each of the following:

    a. $\frac{3}{5} + \frac{6}{5} = \frac{9}{5}$ on a number line   b. $\frac{1}{4} + \frac{2}{4} = \frac{3}{4}$ using square regions

    c. $\frac{6}{7} - \frac{3}{7} = \frac{3}{7}$ using a number line

3. For each of the following, write a corresponding sentence using fraction notation:

    a. $(6 \div 2) + (8 \div 2) = (6 + 8) \div 2$

    b. $(12 \div 5) + (4 \div 5) = (12 + 4) \div 5$

    c. $(4 \div 7) - (2 \div 7) = (4 - 2) \div 7$

    d. $(30 \div 6) - (12 \div 6) = (30 - 12) \div 6$

4. Illustrate how a child could find the sum of $\frac{3}{4}$ and $\frac{2}{3}$ using a multi-number-line segment.

5. Make up a table similar to Figure 9.12 that could be used for discovering how the least common denominator is derived mathematically.

6. Using vertical notation and the expanded form, give step-by-step sequencing showing how to add $3\frac{4}{7}$ and $2\frac{9}{11}$.

7. Illustrate $\frac{6}{5} - \frac{1}{2} = \frac{7}{10}$ using multinumber-line segments.

8. Using vertical notation and the expanded form, give a step-by-step sequencing showing how to subtract $2\frac{9}{11}$ from $3\frac{4}{7}$.

9. Find a circumstance when each of the following sums might be the most desirable form in which to leave an answer:

    a. $\frac{1}{5} + \frac{4}{10} = \frac{6}{10}$ c. $\frac{4}{2} + \frac{6}{2} = \frac{10}{2}$ e. $\frac{3}{4} + \frac{3}{4} - 1\frac{1}{2}$

    b. $\frac{1}{2} + \frac{1}{4} = \frac{75}{100}$ d. $\frac{3}{4} + \frac{3}{4} = \frac{6}{4}$

9.9. *Extending the Child's Problem-Solving Skill*

Children need continuous experience in relating the study of numbers to their environment. The study of numbers in the absence of its relationship to the everyday world is not satisfactory. By the time the child begins to work with problems involving fractional numbers, he has matured to the point where he is ready to learn or discover the more subtle aspects of problem solving. Some of these are

1. How problems arise in his environment
   a. In the experimental setting
   b. In the consumer setting
   c. In the social setting in a more complex type of experience than has been discussed previously
2. How problem solving often involves identifying not only the problem but also those aspects of the data that will lead to a reasonable solution
3. How numerical data are collected, organized, and reported

Let us examine how the first two of these has implications for the teaching of problem solving by relating each to the study of problems involving fractional numbers. The third aspect listed will be studied when we explore the techniques of teaching graphing.

What are some elementary science experiences that will motivate problem solving? Almost any scientific experiment will offer many opportunities for relating problem solving to mathematical models. For example, concepts relative to fractional numbers can be associated with data collected about plant growth, rainfall, temperature, animal growth, and so on. Concepts about operations on fractional numbers can be associated with such experimental areas as the biological, physical, and earth sciences.

For example, Flat A planted with beans receives $\frac{1}{4}$ of an ounce of superphosphate each week for five weeks. Flat B planted in the same way receives $\frac{1}{8}$ of an ounce of superphosphate each week for five weeks. Flat A yields $6\frac{1}{2}$ ounces of beans; Flat B yields $6\frac{1}{3}$ ounces of beans. Problems such as the following could be posted from this situation (although not all could be solved with the given data):

> How much more superphosphate was used in Flat A than Flat B?
> How much more crop was grown in Flat A than Flat B?
> Can we decide whether it would be worthwhile for a farmer with similar soil to decrease his administration of phosphate from the $\frac{1}{4}$ per flat to the $\frac{1}{8}$ per flat rate?

Students should be given many opportunities to collect data, to conjecture problems using these data, and then to solve their problems. In order to nurture their ability to arrive at creative solutions, you should encourage them to search for various ways in which any given problem could be solved. For example, consider the following problem:

> Mary needs 7 strips of paper. Each strip must be $2\frac{1}{2}$ inches in length and $\frac{1}{2}$-inch wide. What would be the minimum length of a rectangular piece of paper from which Mary could cut her strips:

Paper of any width and length

$\frac{1}{2}''$	$\Box \times 2\frac{1}{2} \geq 17\frac{1}{2}$
$1''$	$\Box \times 2\frac{1}{2} + \Box \times 2\frac{1}{2} \geq 17\frac{1}{2}$
$1\frac{1}{2}''$	$\Box \times 2\frac{1}{2} + \Box \times 2\frac{1}{2}\Box \times 2\frac{1}{2} \geq 17\frac{1}{2}$
$2''$	$\Box \times 2\frac{1}{2} + \Box \times 2\frac{1}{2} + \Box \times 2\frac{1}{2} + \Box \times 2\frac{1}{2} + \geq 17\frac{1}{2}$
$2\frac{1}{2}''$	$\Box \times 2\frac{1}{2} + \Box \times 2\frac{1}{2} + \Box \times 2\frac{1}{2} + \Box \times 2\frac{1}{2} + \Box \times 2\frac{1}{2} \geq 17\frac{1}{2}$

Paper $\frac{1}{2}$-inch wide

$$7 \times 2\frac{1}{2} = \Box$$

$$2\frac{1}{2} + 2\frac{1}{2} + 2\frac{1}{2} + 2\frac{1}{2} + 2\frac{1}{2} + 2\frac{1}{2} + 2\frac{1}{2} = \Box$$

$$14 + 7 \times \frac{1}{2} = \Box$$

$$(7 \times 2) + (7 \times \frac{1}{2}) = \Box$$

$$7 \times \frac{7}{2} = \Box$$

$$(8 \times 2\frac{1}{2}) - 2\frac{1}{2} = \Box$$

$$5 + 5 + 5 + 2\frac{1}{2} = \Box$$

Etc.

Or via geometric models

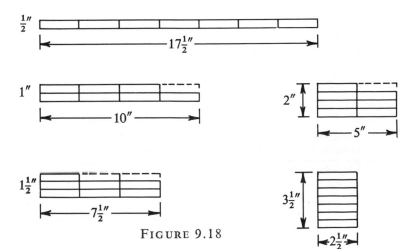

FIGURE 9.18

    1. If the paper she cuts can be of any width or length?
    2. If the paper she uses is $\frac{1}{2}$-inch wide?

Consider the mathematical models in Figure 9.18 that could lead to solutions:

The child should be encouraged to examine his problem solving in terms of answering the questions, "Which way that I solved this problem was the most efficient?" and "Can I describe other types of problems that could be solved in a similar manner?"

While the problems arising from the technical side of our society represent an important area of concern, of equal concern should be the problems arising from consumer experiences. It is important that the child have experiences that will enable him to answer such questions as:

1. Which of two items is the "best buy" in terms of a per item cost?
2. To what extent do we equate durability, quality, and design in determining the best buy?
3. How does volume buying affect the per-unit cost of an item?

You may find one or more of the following activities useful in finding the answers to such questions:

1. Consumer surveys
    a. Item preference
    b. Why the item is preferred
    c. Which preferences have an emotional origin rather than a qualitative or quantitative origin
    (This sort of experience serves as a foundation on which a knowledge of the role of statistics in our society can be built)
2. Quality-control experiments
    a. Durability (wearing, fading, tearing, etc.)
    b. Rate of consumption
    c. Quality comparison
    d. Sampling
    (This will serve as a foundation for learning about the role mathematics plays in the quality of goods that are on the market)
3. Inventory of the hidden costs relative to the purchase of an item
    a. Transportation
    b. Handling
    c. Packaging
    d. Advertising
    e. Production
    (This will help build a foundation for such mathematical topics as linear and nonlinear algebra)

Let us now return to the more common type of problem solving we discussed in a previous chapter—the common problems that arise in everyday living that we must cope with. For example, you might discuss cutting a recipe designed for eight people to one that will be adequate for four people; adjusting an order for lumber that comes in 12-foot lengths when you need a certain number of $3\frac{1}{2}$-foot lengths; creating a budget for your allowance; ordering supplies so that you can arrange a job of cutting lawns in the summer; or planning how to plant a vegetable garden.

Problems arising from most of these situations do not have as many variables as those that occur in experimental settings or in problems of consumer purchase. The number of factors that influences the solution of these everyday problems is limited, as well as being fixed.

You may want to gradually lead the children to solve problems of an increasingly complex nature. The problems may be more complex in that the number of items to be manipulated is increased from two or three to as many as 20 or 30; or in that the student proceeds from problems requiring the use of a single operation for solution to problems requiring several operations and multiple uses of one or more operations; or more complex in that the solution of a problem may require interpreting the data in a more complex way; or in that the child will have to determine which form of the solution will facilitate future problem solving.

You may find one or more of the following activities useful in developing some of these more complex problem-solving skills:

1. Bookkeeping experiences
   a. Records kept of classroom projects, such as a carnival or a play
   b. Records kept on clubs or after-school projects
2. Records of individual projects
   a. Summer or after-school projects
   b. Hobbies

REFERENCES

BANKS, J. HOUSTON, *Learning and Teaching Arithmetic*, Boston: Allyn & Bacon, 1964, pp. 299–306.

BELL, CLIFFORD, CLELA D. HAMMOND, and ROBERT B. HERRERA, *Fundamentals of Arithmetic for Teachers*, New York: John Wiley & Sons, Inc., 1962, pp. 141–162.

BRUMFIEL, CHARLES, ROBERT EICHOLZ, and MERRILL SHANKS, *Fundamental Concepts of Elementary Mathematics*, Reading, Mass.: Addison-Wesley, 1962, pp. 66–67, 101–112.

BRUMFIEL, CHARLES, ROBERT EICHOLZ, MERRILL SHANKS, and P. G. O'DAFFER, *Principles of Arithmetic*, Reading, Mass.: Addison-Wesley, 1963, pp. 150–152, 163–172, 180–182.

CROUCH, RALPH, GEORGE BALDWIN, and ROBERT J. WISNER, *Preparatory Mathematics for Elementary Teachers*, New York: John Wiley & Sons, Inc., 1965, pp. 345–359.

DUTTON, WILBUR, and L. J. ADAMS, *Arithmetic for Teachers*, Englewood Cliffs, N.J.: Prentice-Hall, Inc., 1963, pp. 206–222.

FLOURNOY, FRANCES, *Elementary School Mathematics*, Washington, D.C.: The Center for Applied Research in Education, 1964, pp. 37–38.

HACKER, SIDNEY G., WILFRED E. BARNES, and CALVIN T. LONG, *Fundamental Concepts of Arithmetic*, Englewood Cliffs, N.J.: Prentice-Hall, Inc., 1963, pp. 144, 179.

HANNON, H., "Sets Aid in Adding Fractions," *The Arithmetic Teacher*, vol. 6, pp. 35–38, February, 1959.

HEDDENS, JAMES W., *Today's Mathematics, A Guide to Concepts and Methods in Elementary School Mathematics*, Chicago: Science Research Associates, Inc., 1964, pp. 237–240.

MARKS, JOHN L., JAMES R. SMART, and IRENE SAUBLE, *Enlarging Mathematical Ideas*, Boston: Ginn and Company, 1961, pp. 38–39, 60–62.

MORRIS, DENNIS E., and HENRY D. TOPFER, *Advancing in Mathematics*, Chicago: Science Research Associates, Inc., 1963, pp. 131–142.

OSBORN, ROBERT, M. VERE DeVAULT, CLAUDE BOYD, and ROBERT HOUSTON, *Extending Mathematics Understanding*, Columbus, Ohio: Charles E. Merrill Books, Inc., 1961, pp. 60–67.

PETERSON, JOHN A., and JOSEPH HASHISAKI, *Theory of Arithmetic*, New York: John Wiley & Sons, Inc., 1964, pp. 176–179.

SCHAAF, WILLIAM L., *Basic Concepts of Elementary Mathematics*, New York: John Wiley & Sons, Inc., 1960, pp. 134–136.

SCHOOL MATHEMATICS STUDY GROUP, *Mathematics for the Elementary School* (*Teacher Commentary, Grade 5, Part 2*), Stanford, Calif.: Stanford University Press, 1962, pp. 456–479, 486–492.

SMITH, SEATON E., JR., *Explorations in Elementary Mathematics*, Englewood Cliffs, N.J.: Prentice-Hall, Inc., 1966, pp. 123–133, 140–144.

SPENCER, PETER LINCOLN, and MARGUERITE BRYDEGAARD, *Building Mathematical Competence in the Elementary School*, New York: Holt, Rinehart and Winston, Inc., 1966, pp. 220–222, 228–231.

SWAIN, ROBERT L., and EUGENE D. NICHOLS, *Understanding Arithmetic*, New York: Holt, Rinehart and Winston, Inc., 1965, pp. 139–142.

SWENSON, ESTHER J., *Teaching Arithmetic to Children*, New York: The Macmillan Company, 1964, pp. 335–353.

VAN ENGEN, HENRY, MAURICE L. HARTUNG, and JAMES E. STOCHL, *Foundations of Elementary School Arithmetic*, Chicago: Scott, Foresman and Co., 1965, pp. 238–244, 301–309.

WARD, MORGAN, and CLARENCE HARDGROVE, *Modern Elementary Mathematics*, Reading, Mass.: Addison-Wesley, 1964, pp. 215–218, 226–227.

A mathematics table can help to motivate a child to learn mathematics.

10

Teaching Multiplication and Division of Fractional Numbers

10.1. *Introduction*

HISTORICALLY, multiplication of fractional numbers has not been in its proper sequence in the elementary school curriculum. Traditionally, multiplication is taught after the child learns addition and subtraction, in spite of the fact that he would find it a useful aid in defining equivalent names in terms of multiplication by 1. For example, $\frac{3}{7}$ and $\frac{6}{14}$ name the same number, because $\frac{2}{2}$ is a name for 1, and $\frac{3}{7} = \frac{3}{7} \times \frac{2}{2} = \frac{3 \times 2}{7 \times 2} = \frac{6}{14}$. Instead of using this logical approach to establishing equivalence, we must make use of the compensation property for division, which, although not mathematically incorrect, is considerably more awkward.

The teaching of the multiplication algorithm for whole numbers is dependent on the child's mastery of addition of whole numbers, whereas the teaching of the multiplication algorithm for fractional numbers is not dependent on addition of fractional numbers. Similarly, the successful mastery of the division algorithm for whole numbers is dependent upon one's ability to subtract whole numbers as well as to multiply. There exists no prerequisite of subtraction skills in order to learn the division algorithm for fractional numbers.

10.2. *Definition, Terminology, and Symbolism*

Before presenting the techniques of teaching multiplication and division of fractional numbers, we shall discuss the basic ideas and symbolism to be used in our methods of teaching these concepts.

One of our basic definitions for multiplication on the set of whole numbers is the array definition. In order to provide a smooth transition from multiplication of whole numbers to multiplication of fractional numbers, this definition will be extended to include fractional numbers. Because a mathematical model of a continuous set of finite dimension (that is, capable of being measured) can be associated with fractional number, we shall choose a continuous set as our model, rather than a discrete set.

Abstractly, our definition for the multiplication of fractional numbers is as follows:

The product of $\frac{\triangle}{\square} \times \frac{\bigcirc}{\bigcirc}$ shall be defined as equal to $\frac{\square}{\square}$, where $\square = \triangle \times \bigcirc$, and $\square = \square \times \bigcirc$.

We shall use the following definition involving a mathematical model of a product in our early discussions of product in an attempt to bridge the semiabstract to the abstract:

The product of $\frac{\triangle}{\square}$ and $\frac{\bigcirc}{\bigcirc}$ shall be defined as the number property associated with a $\frac{\triangle}{\square}$ by $\frac{\bigcirc}{\bigcirc}$ rectangular array.

Figure 10.1 depicts how $\frac{5}{4} \times \frac{1}{2}$ can be shown using this array definition:

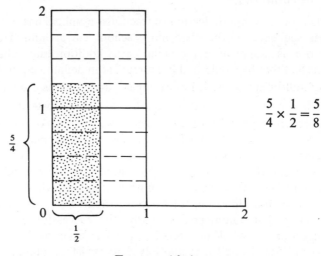

$$\frac{5}{4} \times \frac{1}{2} = \frac{5}{8}$$

FIGURE 10.1

Division is defined as the inverse of multiplication:

The quotient of $\frac{a}{b}$ and $\frac{c}{d}$ will be said to be $\frac{e}{f}$ if, and only if, $\frac{a}{b} = \frac{c}{d} \times \frac{e}{f}$.

For example, the quotient of $\frac{3}{4}$ and $\frac{7}{5}$ is $\frac{15}{28}$, because $\frac{3}{4} = \frac{7}{5} \times \frac{15}{28}$. Although this definition will be used to check the correctness of a quotient, the division algorithm for fractional numbers will be developed from the idea of division by 1, compensation property, and the idea of a number's reciprocal. ($\frac{a}{b}$ will be said to be a reciprocal of $\frac{c}{d}$ if $\frac{a}{b} \times \frac{c}{d} = 1$.)

There are several notations and terminologies you must teach your students. Figure 10.2 depicts some representative types of notations that are used in teaching multiplication and division of fractional numbers. These are expressed in both fraction form and mixed-numeral form.

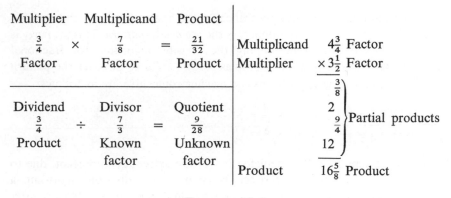

FIGURE 10.2

The sentence "$\frac{3}{2} \times \frac{7}{2} = \frac{21}{4}$" can be read in many ways. A few of them follow:

Three-halves times seven-halves is twenty-one-fourths.
Three halves times seven-halves equals twenty-one-fourths.
The product of three-halves and seven-halves is twenty-one-fourths.
The product of three-halves and seven-halves equals twenty-one-fourths.
Seven-halves multiplied by three-halves is twenty-one-fourths.

Similarly, the sentence "$\frac{2}{3} \div \frac{1}{4} = \frac{8}{3}$" can be read in many ways:

Two-thirds divided by one-fourth equals eight-thirds.
Two-thirds divided by one-fourth is eight-thirds.
The quotient of two-thirds and one-fourth is eight-thirds.
The quotient of two-thirds and one-fourth equals eight-thirds.

10.3. *Teaching the Structural Properties of Multiplication*

Before investigating the methods of teaching multiplication or division on the set of fractional numbers, we shall investigate the properties that will play a central role in the presentation of these operations.

One of the most important properties with which the child needs to become familiar is the identity element for multiplication. It is important that he view the fraction of the form $\frac{\triangle}{\triangle}$ as a name for one and realize its implication as a factor. Several problems of the following type will lead the child toward discovering these relationships:

$$\text{a. } \frac{3}{4} \times \frac{7}{7} = \frac{\triangle}{\square} \qquad \text{c. } \frac{6}{7} \times \frac{\triangle}{\square} = \frac{6}{7}$$

$$\text{b. } \frac{11}{11} \times \frac{6}{7} = \frac{\triangle}{\square} \qquad \text{d. } \frac{\triangle}{\square} \times \frac{9}{5} = \frac{9}{5}$$

A new pattern making its appearance for the first time when a child studies multiplication of fractional numbers is the *reciprocal pattern*. This property is extremely important in developing the division algorithm for fractional numbers. It takes only a few examples for the child to discover the pattern $\frac{a}{b} \times \frac{b}{a} = 1$. Some typical problems the teacher could give are as follows:

$$\text{a. } \frac{3}{4} \times \frac{4}{3} = \frac{\triangle}{\square} \qquad \text{c. } \frac{13}{3} \times \frac{3}{13} = \frac{\triangle}{\square}$$

$$\text{b. } \frac{2}{7} \times \frac{7}{2} = \frac{\triangle}{\square} \qquad \text{d. } \frac{15}{6} \times \frac{\triangle}{\square} = 1$$

Problems similar to that depicted by (d) are extremely important, due to the fact that the child must select, when using the division algorithm, a number that will give a product of one when multiplied by the divisor. After he has discovered the pattern, you should give him the pattern $\frac{\triangle}{\square} \times \frac{\square}{\triangle} = 1$, and ask him to make up true sentences using it.

Teaching the commutative and associative properties for multiplication of fractional numbers requires the same subtleties as was required for the corresponding properties for addition of fractional numbers. Notice in Figure 10.3 that the paired problems utilize equivalent names, adding the distraction of equivalence to the search for commutativity and associativity.

The last stage in teaching these properties consists of having the children make up true sentences using the commutative and associative patterns.

The distributive properties of multiplication over addition and multiplication over subtraction are taught by the same techniques used to teach the corresponding properties for the set of whole numbers. The stages for teaching these distributive properties are shown in Figure 10.4.

The last stage in teaching these properties consists of giving the students the following patterns and asking them to make up true sentences using them:

$$\frac{\triangle}{\heartsuit} \times \left(\frac{\square}{\heartsuit} + \frac{\circ}{\oplus}\right) = \left(\frac{\triangle}{\heartsuit} \times \frac{\square}{\heartsuit}\right) + \left(\frac{\triangle}{\heartsuit} \times \frac{\circ}{\oplus}\right) \text{ and } \frac{\triangle}{\heartsuit} \times \left(\frac{\square}{\heartsuit} - \frac{\circ}{\oplus}\right) = \frac{\triangle}{\heartsuit} \times \left(\frac{\square}{\heartsuit}\right) - \left(\frac{\triangle}{\heartsuit} \times \frac{\circ}{\oplus}\right).$$

	Associative ⟷ multiplication	Commutative multiplication
Problems leading to discovery	$\frac{3}{4} \times \frac{4}{7} = \square$ $\frac{8}{14} \times \frac{3}{4} = \square$	$\frac{3}{5} \times (\frac{4}{7} \times \frac{6}{9}) = \square$ $(\frac{6}{10} \times \frac{4}{7}) \times \frac{18}{27} = \square$
Problems requiring single solutions	$\frac{6}{7} \times \frac{2}{3} = \frac{4}{6} \times \frac{\triangle}{\square}$	$(\frac{3}{4} \times \frac{1}{3}) \times \frac{2}{4} = \frac{3}{4} \times (\frac{2}{6} \times \frac{\triangle}{\square})$
Problems requiring multiple solutions	$\frac{\triangle}{\square} \times \frac{3}{11} = \frac{3}{11} \times \frac{\triangle}{\square}$	$(\frac{3}{4} \times \frac{\triangle}{\square}) \times \frac{1}{6} = \frac{3}{4} \times (\frac{\triangle}{\square} \times \frac{1}{6})$

FIGURE 10.3

	Distributive property multiplication over addition	Distributive property multiplication over subtraction
Problems leading to discovery	$\frac{3}{4} \times (\frac{4}{7} + \frac{3}{5}) = \frac{\square}{\triangle}$ $(\frac{3}{4} \times \frac{4}{7}) + (\frac{3}{4} \times \frac{3}{5}) = \frac{\square}{\triangle}$	$(\frac{1}{3} \times \frac{6}{7}) - (\frac{1}{3} \times \frac{2}{5}) = \frac{\square}{\triangle}$ $\frac{1}{3} \times (\frac{6}{7} - \frac{2}{5}) = \frac{\square}{\triangle}$
Problems requiring single solutions	$\frac{2}{7} \times (\frac{8}{4} + \frac{6}{7})$ $= (\frac{\square}{\triangle} \times \frac{8}{4}) + (\frac{\square}{\triangle} \times \frac{6}{7})$	$\frac{3}{5} \times (\frac{3}{4} - \frac{4}{7})$ $= (\frac{3}{5} \times \frac{\triangle}{\square}) - (\frac{3}{5} \times \frac{4}{7})$
Problems requiring multiple solutions	$\frac{\triangle}{\square} \times (\frac{3}{10} + \frac{4}{5})$ $= (\frac{\triangle}{\square} \times \frac{3}{10}) + (\frac{\triangle}{\square} \times \frac{4}{5})$	$\frac{3}{2} \times (\frac{\triangle}{\square} - \frac{\triangle}{\square})$ $= (\frac{3}{2} \times \frac{\triangle}{\square}) - (\frac{3}{2} \times \frac{\triangle}{\square})$

FIGURE 10.4

EXERCISES (1)

1. Using the definition of multiplication of fractional numbers, and using Figure 10.1, construct an array that depicts "$\frac{3}{4} \times \frac{4}{5}$."

2. Write the corresponding multiplication sentence for each of the following:

   a. $\frac{3}{8} \div \frac{7}{8} = \frac{\triangle}{\square}$ c. $\frac{2}{4} \div \frac{3}{4} = \frac{\triangle}{\square}$

   b. $\frac{9}{2} \div \frac{8}{3} = \frac{\triangle}{\square}$ d. $\frac{3}{4} \div \frac{4}{3} = \frac{\triangle}{\square}$

3. Write four ways that each of the following mathematical sentences can be read:

   a. $\frac{3}{7} \times \frac{9}{8} = \frac{27}{56}$ b. $\frac{3}{7} \div \frac{9}{8} = \frac{24}{63}$

4. Identify the factor, products, and partial products of each of the following, if applicable:

   a. $\frac{3}{5} \times \frac{8}{7} = \frac{24}{35}$ b. $\quad 3\frac{1}{2}$
   $$\begin{array}{r} 3\frac{1}{2} \\ \times 3\frac{1}{2} \\ \hline \frac{1}{4} \\ \frac{3}{2} \\ \frac{3}{2} \\ 9\frac{3}{2} \\ \hline 12\frac{1}{4} \end{array}$$

5. Identify the divisor, dividend, quotient, known factor, unknown factor, and product in the following, if applicable:

   a. $\frac{3}{7} \times \frac{2}{5} = \frac{6}{35}$ b. $\frac{16}{3} \div \frac{5}{2} = \frac{32}{15}$

6. Make up sample problems for each of the first three stages for teaching the commutative property for multiplication on the set of fractional numbers.

7. Make up sample problems for each of the first three stages in teaching the associative property for multiplication on the set of fractional numbers.

8. Make up sample problems for each of the first three stages for teaching the distributive property of multiplication over subtraction on the set of fractional numbers.

9. Make up sample problems for each of the first three stages for teaching the distributive property of multiplication over addition on the set of fractional numbers.

10. Make up five multiplication problems that would aid the child in discovering the reciprocal property.

10.4. *Teaching the Structural Properties of Division*

The structural properties for division of fractional numbers play a crucial role in the development of the division algorithm for fractional numbers. The most important of these properties is the right identity for division. This is the first concept that should be taught when you are beginning division concepts.

The following dialogue illustrates how we might proceed from the concept of division of whole numbers to the concept of dividing a fractional number by one:

"If we have 12 objects and partition them into four sets equal in number, how many will be in each set?" (Three.)

"We could tell this with the sentence $12 \div 3 = 4$." (Write this mathematical sentence on the board.) "If we have 12 objects and distribute them to one set, how many will we have in that one set?" (Twelve.) "What would our mathematical sentence say in order to describe what we did?" ($12 \div 1 = 12$.)

"Suppose we had $\frac{3}{4}$ of something and distributed it to one set. How much would be in that set?" (The $\frac{3}{4}$ of something that we had.) "What would be our mathematical sentence describing what we did?" ($\frac{3}{4} \div 1 = \frac{3}{4}$.)

Create other problems that have a divisor of one, and have the children create the mathematical sentences. Use the definition of division to show that the quotient obtained is correct.

The compensation property for division of fractional numbers makes possible a variety of algorithms that can be developed for division of fractional numbers. In Figure 10.5, two different algorithms are depicted employing the compensation property for division.

$$\frac{8}{4} \div \frac{3}{7} = (\frac{8}{4} \times \frac{7}{3}) \div (\frac{3}{7} \times \frac{7}{3}) = \frac{56}{12} \div 1 = \frac{56}{12}$$

$$\frac{8}{4} \div \frac{3}{7} = (\frac{8}{4} \times \frac{7}{7}) \div (\frac{3}{7} \times \frac{4}{4}) = \frac{56}{28} \div \frac{12}{28} = (56 \times \frac{1}{28}) \div (12 \times \frac{1}{28}) = \frac{56}{12}$$

FIGURE 10.5

The teaching of the compensation property for division is complicated by the fact that we must make use of this property in order to teach the division algorithm. In other words, it is not practical to establish the correctness of this pattern through paired problems, because we want to arrive at a quotient of two fractional numbers using this property. Our establishment of the correctness of this pattern is resolved only through our utilizing the inverse relationship of division. This property is taught as an integral part of teaching the division algorithm. Although the presentation technique for the first stage in teaching this property will be postponed, we shall at this point take a look at later stages in teaching this concept. Figure 10.6 depicts representative problems from these later stages.

	Problems requiring single solutions	Problems requiring multiple solutions
Compensation division	$(\frac{3}{4} \times \frac{4}{7}) \div (\frac{5}{9} \times \frac{4}{7}) = \frac{3}{4} \div \frac{\triangle}{\square}$ $(\frac{11}{13} \div \frac{7}{9}) \div (\frac{5}{2} \div \frac{7}{9}) = \frac{\triangle}{\square} \div \frac{5}{2}$	$(\frac{4}{9} \times \frac{\triangle}{\square}) \div (\frac{6}{5} \times \frac{\triangle}{\square}) = \frac{4}{9} \div \frac{6}{5}$ $(\frac{3}{8} \div \frac{\triangle}{\square}) \div (\frac{2}{5} \div \frac{\triangle}{\square}) = \frac{3}{8} \div \frac{2}{5}$

FIGURE 10.6

The distributive properties for division of fractional numbers are taught with the same stages as were those properties for whole numbers. Figure 10.7 depicts representative problems for these stages.

	Right distributive property Division over addition	Right distributive property Division over subtraction
Problems leading to discovery	$(\frac{3}{7} + \frac{1}{4}) \div \frac{4}{9} = \frac{\triangle}{\square}$ $(\frac{3}{7} \div \frac{4}{9}) + (\frac{1}{4} \div \frac{4}{9}) = \frac{\triangle}{\square}$	$(\frac{3}{5} - \frac{1}{7}) \div \frac{6}{5} = \frac{\triangle}{\square}$ $(\frac{3}{8} \div \frac{6}{5}) - (\frac{1}{7} \div \frac{6}{5}) = \frac{\triangle}{\square}$
Problems requiring single solutions	$(\frac{4}{5} + \frac{3}{8}) \div \frac{\triangle}{\square}$ $= (\frac{4}{5} \div \frac{6}{7}) + (\frac{3}{8} \div \frac{6}{7})$	$(\frac{2}{3} - \frac{1}{5}) \div \frac{1}{7}$ $= (\frac{\triangle}{\square} \div \frac{1}{7}) - (\frac{1}{5} \div \frac{1}{7})$
Problems requiring multiple solutions	$(\frac{3}{5} + \frac{2}{9}) \div \frac{\triangle}{\square}$ $= (\frac{3}{5} \div \frac{\triangle}{\square}) + (\frac{2}{9} \div \frac{\triangle}{\square})$	$(\frac{\triangle}{\square} - \frac{1}{7}) \div \frac{2}{8}$ $= (\frac{\triangle}{\square} \div \frac{2}{8}) - (\frac{1}{7} \div \frac{2}{8})$

FIGURE 10.7

The final stage in teaching the distributive property involves giving the child the following patterns and asking him to use these patterns to create true mathematical sentences: $(\frac{a}{b} + \frac{c}{d}) \div \frac{e}{f} = (\frac{a}{b} \div \frac{e}{f}) + (\frac{c}{d} \div \frac{e}{f})$ and $(\frac{a}{b} - \frac{c}{d}) \div \frac{e}{f} = (\frac{a}{b} \div \frac{e}{f}) - (\frac{c}{d} \div \frac{e}{f})$.

10.5. *Teaching the Multiplication Algorithm*

A skill that is one of the easiest to teach children is the multiplication algorithm for fractional numbers. The ease of teaching is due not only to the naturalness of multiplying the numerators and the denominators, but also to the availability of a concrete approach to develop the meaning of this algorithm. This concrete approach closely parallels the approach used in teaching multiplication of whole numbers.

In the early stages of teaching this algorithm, it may be useful, although not necessary, to restrict your first examples to factors less than one. For example, the product of $\frac{3}{5}$ and $\frac{2}{3}$ might be developed as follows:

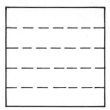

The unit square at the left has been partitioned into five rectangular regions of equal area. If we consider these rectangular regions as rows in an array, we have five rows.

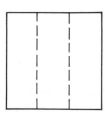

Let's consider just three of the five rows. Let's let the fraction $\frac{3}{5}$ mean that we are thinking of just three of the five rows. Let's dot three of the five rows to show which of the rows we are thinking of.

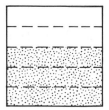

Let's look at a second unit square that has been partitioned into three rectangular regions of equal area. If we consider the rectangular regions as columns in an array, then we have three columns.

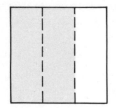

Let's consider just two of the three columns. Let's let the fraction $\frac{2}{3}$ mean we are thinking of just two of the three columns. Let's shade two of the columns to show which of the columns we are thinking of.

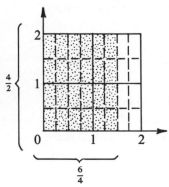

At the left is an array that depicts a unit square that simultaneously considers $\frac{3}{5}$ and $\frac{2}{3}$. (This is equivalent to our simultaneously thinking of an array of three rows and two columns and saying the product is six.) Notice that our unit is now partitioned into a 5-by-3 array, of which we are considering only three rows and two columns, or a 3-by-2 array. (Notice this corresponds to the intersection of the two sets.) Thus, we see that when we think of a $\frac{3}{5}$-by-$\frac{2}{3}$ array, we are also thinking of an array of six together with a unit-square array of 15. Thus, $\frac{3}{5} \times \frac{2}{3} = \frac{6}{15}$. Let's see how this idea can be extended to fractional numbers greater than one.

The only modification (this is not really a modification but a highlight of the way we referred to our partitioning) is that the divisor will always refer to the manner in which the unit squares are partitioned, and the dividend will denote the array under consideration.

Thus, $\frac{4}{2} \times \frac{6}{4}$ is interpreted by considering sufficient unit squares on unit squares partitioned into two rows by four columns such that we can observe an array of three rows by six columns. The intersection of the shaded area and the dotted area in the square gives a mathematical model for the product of $\frac{4}{2}$ and $\frac{6}{4}$.

10.6. *Teaching the Division Algorithm*

The tendency in a traditional curriculum was to tell the child that in order to divide fractional numbers, we simply "inverted" the divisor and then multiplied. Giving him the rule without any justification often led to his forgetting the exact rule but remembering that something was to be inverted. Thus, to be doubly safe, he inverted both the divisor and the dividend. Some students, remembering that something was to be inverted, inverted the dividend rather than the divisor. In order to establish a bridge of reason over which the child can return to reconstruct his rule, we help him understand "why."

The following dialogue is typical of one that might be used to establish the why of the division algorithm. The problem presented is $\frac{3}{4} \div \frac{4}{5} = \frac{\triangle}{\square}$.

"Instead of a divisor of $\frac{4}{5}$, what would be the ideal divisor for this problem?" (One.) "Why?" (Because we have seen that division by one yields a quotient equal to the dividend.)

"What pattern have we learned that could help us get a name for 1?" (The reciprocal pattern, or $\frac{\triangle}{\square} \times \frac{\square}{\triangle} = 1$.)

"What does the reciprocal pattern tell us we have to multiply $\frac{4}{5}$ by in order to get a product of 1?" (Five-fourths.)

"When we had a quotient of two whole numbers and multiplied the divisor by a nonzero number, what did we have to do to the dividend so that our quotient did not change?" (We multiplied the dividend times the same number.) "Let's see if this same pattern works when the quotient is a fractional number. How will we be able to check to see if the quotient that we have found is correct?" (Multiply the divisor times the quotient and see if we get the dividend.)

Now place the following problem on the board: $(\frac{3}{4} \times \frac{5}{4}) \div (\frac{4}{5} \times \frac{5}{4}) = \frac{15}{16} \div 1$ $= \frac{\triangle}{\square}$.

"We have seen that if the dividend is a fractional number and the divisor is one, we will get what for a quotient?" (The quotient will be equal to the dividend.)

"Therefore, what is our quotient?" (Fifteen-sixteenths.)

"Let's check our quotient to see if it is the correct answer: $\frac{15}{16} \times \frac{4}{5} = \frac{60}{80} = \frac{3}{4}$. As we can see, $\frac{15}{16}$ is the correct answer."

Figure 10.8 depicts a possible step-by-step presentation of this algorithm.

$$\frac{5}{7} \div \frac{3}{4}$$

$\downarrow$ – – – – – compensation property

$(\frac{5}{7} \times \frac{4}{3}) \div (\frac{3}{4} \times \frac{4}{3})$ The $\frac{4}{3}$ was selected because we want to use the reciprocal property

$\downarrow$ – – – – reciprocal property

$(\frac{5}{7} \times \frac{4}{3}) \div 1$

$\downarrow$ – – – – – multiplication algorithm

$\frac{5 \times 4}{7 \times 3} \div 1$

$\downarrow$ – – – – – multiplication

$\frac{20}{21} \div 1$

$\downarrow$ – – – – – division by 1

$\frac{20}{21}$

FIGURE 10.8

10.7. *Multiplication Involving Mixed Numeral Algorithms*

Multiplication involving mixed numerals has limited social application, because it is more convenient to represent the mixed numerals either as fractions or decimals; however, we shall see that work with the vertical form of the mixed-numeral algorithm will serve to highlight the general nature of the multiplication algorithm. Having the students study this algorithm will also provide readiness for the decimal algorithm.

In Figure 10.9, we see a mathematical model depicting $2\frac{1}{2} \times 1\frac{1}{4}$.

Notice that these labeled fractions correspond to the similarly labeled areas in Figure 10.9:

a. $\frac{1}{8}$ c. $\frac{2}{4}$
b. $\frac{1}{2}$ d. 2

Notice further that numbers corresponding to the area regions are represented as partial products when we use the distributive property to multiply $(2 + \frac{1}{2})$ and $(1 + \frac{1}{4})$:

In the expanded form we have

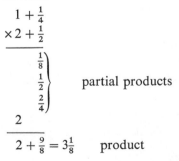

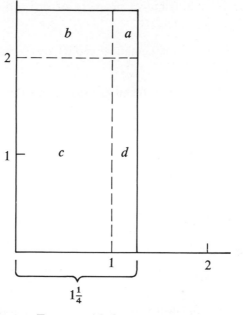

FIGURE 10.9

In the standard form we have

$$
\begin{array}{r}
1\frac{1}{4} \\
\times 2\frac{1}{2} \\
\hline
\frac{1}{8} \\
\frac{1}{2} \\
\frac{2}{4} \\
2 \\
\hline
2\frac{9}{8} = 3\frac{1}{8}
\end{array}
$$

EXERCISES (2)

1. Make up sample problems for the stage requiring single solutions and the stage requiring multiple solutions for teaching the compensation property for division of fractional numbers.
2. Make up sample problems for the first three stages for teaching the right distributive property of division over addition of fractional numbers.

3. Make up sample problems for the first three stages for teaching the right distributive property of division over subtraction of fractional numbers.

4. Construct a mathematical model that could be used to show "$\frac{3}{2} \times \frac{1}{5} = \frac{3}{10}$."

5. Identify each step taken in the following presentation:

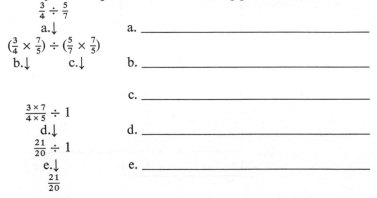

a. _____

b. _____

c. _____

d. _____

e. _____

6. Some elementary series present a common-denominator method of division. Identify each step in this algorithm:

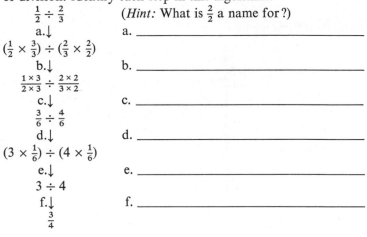

(*Hint:* What is $\frac{2}{2}$ a name for?)

a. _____

b. _____

c. _____

d. _____

e. _____

f. _____

7. Construct a mathematical model for teaching $2\frac{2}{3} \times 3\frac{1}{4}$.

8. Find the product of $2\frac{2}{3}$ and $3\frac{1}{4}$ using the vertical algorithm and the expanded form. Identify each partial product in terms of a region of your mathematical model in Exercise 7.

REFERENCES

BANKS, J. HOUSTON, *Learning and Teaching Arithmetic*, Boston: Allyn & Bacon, 1964, pp. 306–314.

BELL, CLIFFORD, CLELA HAMMOND, and ROBERT HERRERA, *Fundamentals of Arithmetic for Teachers*, New York: John Wiley & Sons, Inc., 1962, pp. 163–176.

BRUMFIEL, CHARLES, ROBERT EICHOLZ, MERRILL SHANKS, and P. G. O'DAFFER, *Principles of Arithmetic*, Reading, Mass.: Addison-Wesley, pp. 163–170, 180–184.

CHRISTOFFERSON, H. C., "Division by a Fraction Made Meaningful," *Mathematics Teacher*, vol. 41, pp. 32–35, January, 1948.

CROUCH, RALPH, GEORGE BALDWIN, and ROBERT J. WISNER, *Preparatory Mathematics for Elementary Teachers*, New York: John Wiley & Sons, Inc., 1965, pp. 326–345.

DUTTON, WILBUR, and L. J. ADAMS, *Arithmetic for Teachers*, Englewood Cliffs, N.J.: Prentice-Hall, Inc., 1963, pp. 225–238.

FLOURNOY, FRANCES, *Elementary School Mathematics*, Washington, D.C.: The Center for Applied Research in Education, 1964, pp. 38–42.

HACKER, SIDNEY G., WILFORD E. BARNES, and CALVIN T. LONG, *Fundamental Concepts of Arithmetic*, Englewood Cliffs, N.J.: Prentice-Hall, Inc., 1963, pp. 146, 159.

HEDDENS, JAMES W., *Today's Mathematics, A Guide to Concepts and Methods in Elementary School Mathematics*, Chicago: Science Research Associates, Inc., 1964, pp. 263–269.

KOLESNIK, T. S., "Illustrating Multiplication and Division of Common Fractions," *Arithmetic Teacher*, vol. 10, pp. 268–271, May, 1963.

MARKS, JOHN L., C. RICHARD PURDY, and LUCIEN B. KINNEY, *Teaching Arithmetic for Understanding*, McGraw-Hill Book Company, Inc., 1958, pp. 207–218.

MARKS, JOHN L., JAMES R. SMART, and IRENE SAUBLE, *Enlarging Mathematical Ideas*, Boston: Ginn and Company, 1961, pp. 69–77.

MORRIS, DENNIS E., and HENRY D. TOPFER, *Advancing in Mathematics*, Chicago: Science Research Associates, Inc., 1963, pp. 142–152.

OSBORN, ROGER, VERE DeVAULT, CLAUDE BOYD, and ROBERT HOUSTON, *Extending Mathematics Understanding*, Columbus, Ohio: Charles E. Merrill Books, Inc., 1961, pp. 67–72.

SCHAAF, WILLIAM L., *Basic Concepts of Elementary Mathematics*, New York: John Wiley & Sons, Inc., 1960, pp. 133–136.

SCHOOL MATHEMATICS STUDY GROUP, *Studies in Mathematics, Vol. IX: A Brief Course in Mathematics for Elementary School Teachers*, Stanford, Calif.: Stanford University Press, pp. 257–273, 275–291.

SHIPP, DONALD, and SAM ADAMS, *Developing Arithmetic Concepts and Skills*, Englewood Cliffs, N.J.: Prentice-Hall, Inc., 1964, pp. 286–287.

SMITH, SEATON E., JR., *Explorations in Elementary Mathematics*, Englewood Cliffs, N.J.: Prentice-Hall, Inc., 1966, pp. 117–119, 134–138.

SPENCER, PETER LINCOLN, and MARGUERITE BRYDEGAARD, *Building Mathematical Competence in the Elementary School*, New York: Holt, Rinehart and Winston, Inc., 1966, pp. 222–228, 240–252.

SWAIN, ROBERT L., and EUGENE D. NICHOLS, *Understanding Arithmetic*, New York: Holt, Rinehart and Winston, Inc., 1965, pp. 74–77, 81–83, 107–125.

SWENSON, ESTHER J., *Teaching Arithmetic to Children*, New York: The Macmillan Company, 1964, pp. 353–383.

THORPE, CLEATA B., *Teaching Elementary Arithmetic*, New York: Harper & Row, Publishers, Inc., 1962, pp. 177–183.

VAN ENGEN, HENRY, MAURICE L. HARTUNG, and JAMES E. STOCHL, *Foundations of Elementary School Arithmetic*, Chicago: Scott, Foresman and Co., 1965, pp. 245–252, 259–265, 306–309.

WARD, MORGAN, and CLARENCE HARDGROVE, *Modern Elementary Mathematics*, Reading, Mass.: Addison-Wesley, 1964, pp. 219–226.

Charts can be used to motivate a child to learn mathematics.

11

Teaching Numeration Systems

11.1. *Introduction*

IN THIS chapter we shall study both ancient numeration systems and "modern" nondecimal systems. We shall study how to teach ancient numeration systems in order to provide the child with a better understanding of his own system. Although the comparative aspect of this system will be stressed, you will also want to study each system with respect to its stage of evolution and to the role it played in its culture.

We shall want to look at certain properties of nondecimal systems that are characteristic of the system of numeration, rather than look at properties of number systems per se. It is through this experience with nondecimal numeration systems that a child is able to isolate those properties relating to the numeration system. You will also want to examine with your students the role of these nondecimal systems in our modern society. The comparative aspect of the nondecimal systems will also be discussed, with the goal of giving the child a better understanding of his own system.

11.2. *Numeration Systems of Early Civilizations*

We can only speculate about man's first numeration system. Certainly the cave man's picture of deer being killed in a hunt was one of the first attempts to convey to others the number property of a set. It appears that notches cut in sticks found in the graves of these early men corresponded in number to the number of possessions (such as bone bracelets and pottery) placed in the grave with the body. If this interpretation is correct, we might say that it represented an early attempt by man to set up a one-to-one correspondence between a set of objects and a set of notches.

We can observe this type of matching among shepherds of the early Christian era who maintained a sack of pebbles whose number corresponded to the number of sheep in the flock. As the sheep were brought in each day, the shepherd matched his pebbles one-to-one with the sheep. If pebbles matched one-to-one, the shepherd knew that all the sheep were accounted for.

11.3. *An Egyptian Numeration System*

The first numeration system we shall look at in great detail is that of the Egyptians. Five thousand years ago, Egypt was a prosperous country in which well-developed numeration systems made possible complex trade transactions. The Egyptian numeration systems predate the Christian era. They used three numeration systems identified as the *hieratic*, *demotic*, and *hieroglyphic*. We shall be especially interested in the characteristics of the hieroglyphics, which were chiseled into stone and used to record historical data. If we were to travel to Egypt and visit the pyramids, we could see the accomplishments of the Pharaohs recorded on the walls of the pyramids. These recordings include such things as the number of prisoners taken, the number of bushels of wheat harvested, the number of cattle raised, and so on. What makes the hieroglyphic system of special interest to the student of mathematics is the similarities and dissimilarities that exist between the Egyptian numeration system and our own. Let us look at their system and compare.

Figure 11.1 shows how the Egyptian stone mason depicted the numerals 1 through 9. Notice that the numeral 6 is created by six repetitions of the symbol for one. (When a symbol is used again to create a name for a number and names the same number each time it is used, we say that this system displays the characteristic of repetition.) Thus we see that the Egyptian system possessed the characteristic of repetition.

Notice that the Egyptian numerals for numbers one through nine are not unlike our tally system, which is occasionally used to denote the number of something being counted.

The Egyptians introduced a new symbol for 10, rather than employ a symbol using 10 ones. The symbol ∩ for 10 is often referred to as the heel-bone symbol. This radical change in symbolism upon reaching 10 helps us to identify what we call the base of the system. In our own base-ten system; the

Egyptian numerals	I	II	III	I III	II III	III III	I III III	II III III	III III III
Our numerals	1	2	3	4	5	6	7	8	9

FIGURE 11.1

base is not signaled by the introduction of a new symbol, but rather by the process of going from the use of one digit to denote a number to the use of two digits to denote a number. Figure 11.2 shows how the Egyptians could designate the tens—from 10 to 90. Notice that repetition is again employed.

With the set of numerals for ones and the set for tens, the Egyptians were able to name any number from one to 99. For example, 75 would be represented by ∩∩∩∩ II III, and 92 by ∩∩∩ ∩∩∩ II.

Note that if 92 were denoted ∩∩∩∩∩ ∩∩II∩∩, it would still be possible to decipher the number to which the symbols refer. When the repositioning of the symbols does not change the meaning that we associate with each symbol, we say the system does not have place value. This is in contrast to our system, in which the repositioning does affect the value that we associate with each symbol. For example, consider 34 and 43. In the first case, the 3 represents 3 tens and the 4 represents 4 ones; in the second case, the 3 represents 3 ones and the 4 represents 4 tens. Notice that we are saying that the value associated with an *individual symbol* is changed in order for place value to be represented. (We are not saying that just because a new value for the numeral is obtained by shifting the individual symbols that place value is necessarily present. For example, in the Roman numerals IX and XI, the I symbol means one, whether it is positioned on the left or the right, but the *value* represented by the whole numeral is changed by this repositioning. Therefore, we say that the Roman system does not have place value.)

The Egyptians changed symbols at 100, 1000, 10,000, 100,000, and 1,000,000. Figure 11.3 shows how multiples of each of these are depicted.

With these symbols, the Egyptian could name any number from one to

Egyptian numerals	∩	∩∩	∩∩∩	∩ ∩∩∩	∩∩ ∩∩∩	∩∩∩ ∩∩∩	∩ ∩∩∩ ∩∩∩	∩∩ ∩∩∩ ∩∩∩	∩∩∩ ∩∩∩ ∩∩∩
Our numerals	10	20	30	40	50	60	70	80	90

FIGURE 11.2

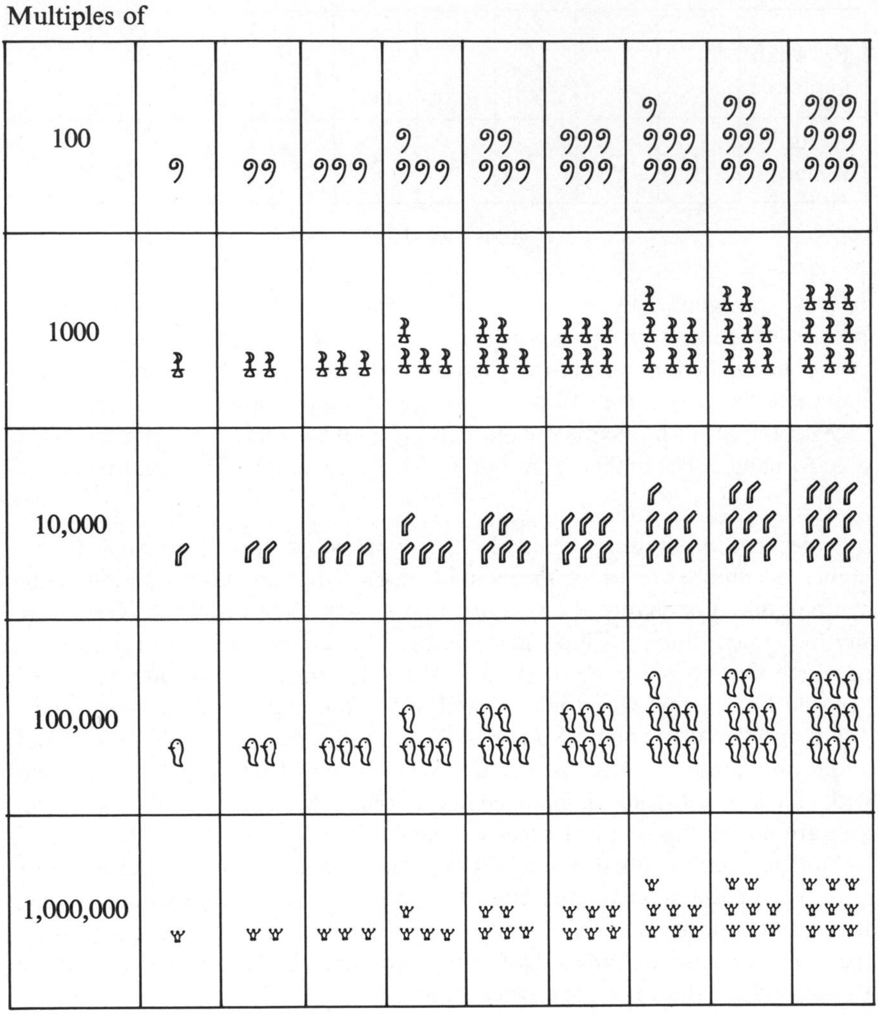

Multiples of

100	9	99	999	9 over 999	99 over 999	999 over 999	9 over 999 over 999	99 over 999 over 999	999 over 999 over 999
1000	⌇	⌇⌇	⌇⌇⌇	⌇ over ⌇⌇⌇	⌇⌇ over ⌇⌇⌇	⌇⌇⌇ over ⌇⌇⌇	⌇ over ⌇⌇⌇ over ⌇⌇⌇	⌇⌇ over ⌇⌇⌇ over ⌇⌇⌇	⌇⌇⌇ over ⌇⌇⌇ over ⌇⌇⌇
10,000	⌐	⌐⌐	⌐⌐⌐	⌐ over ⌐⌐⌐	⌐⌐ over ⌐⌐⌐	⌐⌐⌐ over ⌐⌐⌐	⌐ over ⌐⌐⌐ over ⌐⌐⌐	⌐⌐ over ⌐⌐⌐ over ⌐⌐⌐	⌐⌐⌐ over ⌐⌐⌐ over ⌐⌐⌐
100,000	ৡ	ৡৡ	ৡৡৡ	ৡ over ৡৡৡ	ৡৡ over ৡৡৡ	ৡৡৡ over ৡৡৡ	ৡ over ৡৡৡ over ৡৡৡ	ৡৡ over ৡৡৡ over ৡৡৡ	ৡৡৡ over ৡৡৡ over ৡৡৡ
1,000,000	Ⴟ	Ⴟ Ⴟ	Ⴟ Ⴟ Ⴟ	Ⴟ over Ⴟ Ⴟ Ⴟ	Ⴟ Ⴟ over Ⴟ Ⴟ Ⴟ	Ⴟ Ⴟ Ⴟ over Ⴟ Ⴟ Ⴟ	Ⴟ over Ⴟ Ⴟ Ⴟ over Ⴟ Ⴟ Ⴟ	Ⴟ Ⴟ over Ⴟ Ⴟ Ⴟ over Ⴟ Ⴟ Ⴟ	Ⴟ Ⴟ Ⴟ over Ⴟ Ⴟ Ⴟ over Ⴟ Ⴟ Ⴟ

FIGURE 11.3

9,999,999. For example, 2,000,035 could be represented by ⚷ ⚷ ⌒⌒ ||. Notice that we do not need a zero symbol to represent the absence of a particular type of group. Because the Egyptians did not employ a zero symbol, we say that this characteristic was not present in their system. This is in contrast to our system, in which we need to indicate the absence of a particular type of group. For example, in 305 the 0 denotes zero groups of 10.

To determine the value of an Egyptian numeral, we simply add the numbers named by each symbol. For example, the value of ⚷ ⚷ ⚷ ∩∩ is determined

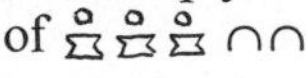

as follows: $1000 + 1000 + 1000 + 10 + 10 = 3020$. Because of the technique of adding numbers to determine the number named, we say that the
Egyptian system is an *additive system*. This characteristic is also possessed
by our system, although the word names of the system mask this characteristic. For example, the value of 317 is obtained by adding 3 hundreds to 1 ten
to 7 ones and obtaining three hundred seventeen.

We have seen that the Egyptian numeration system is repetitive, has base
ten, has no place value, has no zero, and is an additive system. In contrast,
we see that our system is not repetitive, has a zero, and has place value.
Like the Egyptian system it is additive and a base ten system.

11.4. *The Mayan Numeration System*

Let us look at still another numeration system that has several interesting
characteristics. From about the beginning of the Christian era, the Mayan
Indians on the Yucatan Peninsula in Central America had a highly efficient
numeration system. What made this system especially remarkable was that it
utilized a symbol for zero, a characteristic that was not present in the European
version of our numeration system until the thirteenth century. With their
system, the Mayans were able to develop a fairly complex society. They had a
well-developed calendar consisting of a 360-day official year and a solar year
of 365+ days.

Figure 11.4 depicts how the Mayans made their numerals for one to 20.

The first characteristic we note is that repetition is very much in evidence
in this system. Notice that one dot is used repetitively to denote 2, 3, and 4,
and one bar is used repetitively to denote 10 and 15.

In detecting major changes in notation, we observe that a new symbol is
introduced at both 5 and 20. We might say that there are two bases operable
in this system except for the fact that the change of symbolism at the 5 does not
represent a recurring pattern consistent with other changes that take place at
25, 125, 625, and so on. Because this change in symbolism is restricted to one
instance, in contrast to the Egyptian system where at each power of ten (10,

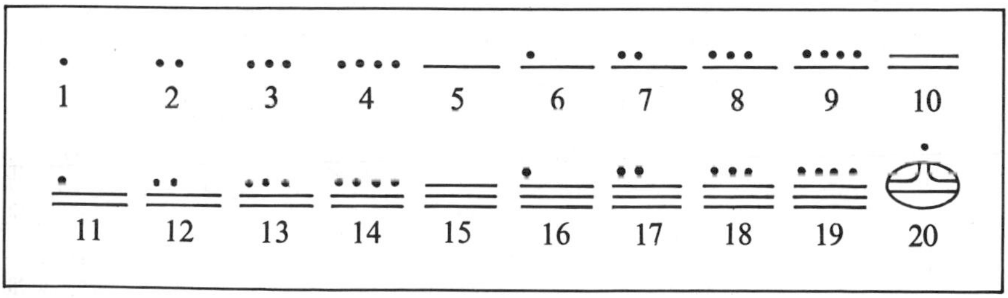

FIGURE 11.4

100, 1000, 10,000) a new symbol was introduced, we shall not say that this is a base-five system. We shall say that this system is a base-twenty system, even though there will be exceptions to the scheme of having a new place value designated at every power of 20.

Let us see how other numbers were designated. Note that in Figure 11.5 digits occupying the second level in the numeral name sets of twenties. Because the positioning of the numeral changes the value of the individual symbol, we say that this system has place value. Note that the Mayan place-value system names ones on the bottom, twenties at the second level, and three hundred and sixties at the third level.

• Second level	Twenties	• • • ⟶ 20 + 20 + 20 = 60
• • • Bottom level	Ones	• ⟶ 1
23		61

| • • Third level ⟶ 360 |
| ⊖ Second level ⟶ 0 |
| ▭ Bottom level ⟶ 5 + 5 |
| 370 |

FIGURE 11.5

The Mayan system, like our own system, was additive. Once the value of each level is determined, we simply add these numbers together to determine the number named by the numeral.

11.5. *The Roman Numeration System*

Not only shall we examine the characteristics of the Roman system,* but we shall also discuss techniques of teaching this system, because it is the most frequently taught ancient numeration system. This is not to say that it has more intrinsic merits than either of the two previously discussed systems. As a matter of fact, it was an awkward system that probably inhibited the Romans from making any significant contribution in the area of number

* Actually, the system we shall discuss, and the one usually identified as the Roman system, represents a modification of the Roman system. This modification was made, to a large extent, during the Middle Ages.

theory. However, its continued maintenance probably stems from the continuing impact of the Roman culture and philosophy on our Western civilization. The Roman numerals served a "scholarly" purpose long after they were supplemented for practical applications by our more efficient Hindu-Arabic system.

Let us examine how we might utilize patterns to teach the Roman numerals. Notice in Figure 11.6 that we have partitioned the Roman numerals into three sets. First the child would learn to associate the numbers from one to 10 with their corresponding Roman numerals. Then he would be asked to find the pattern that exists between the first column and the second and third columns. Notice that there is a very consistent pattern that is identical for ones, tens, and hundreds.

ONES	TENS	HUNDREDS
I	X	C
II	XX	CC
III	XXX	CCC
IV	XL	CD
V	L	D
VI	LX	DC
VII	LXX	DCC
VIII	LXXX	DCCC
IX	XC	CM

FIGURE 11.6

After the child has discovered the pattern that exists for ones, tens, and hundreds, we can give him experience in translating from our system to the Roman and from the Roman to our system. For example, we can write 247 by selecting the name for 200 from the hundreds column, the name for 40 from the tens column, and the name for seven from the ones column. We thus see that CCXLVII is a name for 247. We can also translate DCCXLIV to our system by recognizing that DCC comes from the seventh position in the hundreds column, XL from the fourth position in the tens column, and IV from the fourth position in the ones column. Therefore, DCCXLIV names 744.

After many similar translating activities, if you want to have the children reach a skill level for which a table is not needed, you will have them memorize the pattern for one through nine, and the names for 10, 50, 100, and 500. With this information and their previous experience with the development of the pattern, the children can easily recreate the table mentally and translate freely in either direction.

To further develop the children's competence, you will want to examine with them the characteristics of this system. In III and XXX we see evidence of the characteristic of repetition. As the Egyptian system, it does not have a zero numeral. Notice that there is a consistent change in numerals at 5, 50, and 500, and also at 10, 100, and 1000. Might we say that the Roman system has utilized aspects of both a base-five and a base-ten system?

Certainly the additive property is one of the characteristics, as evidenced by LXVII being equal to $50 + 10 + 5 + 1 + 1 = 67$. But the system also has a subtractive characteristic, as can be evidenced by IX being equal to $10 - 1 = 9$, or XL being equal to $50 - 10 = 40$.

We might be tempted to say that the Roman system has place value, because it makes a difference whether we place a I to the left or the right of an X. However, remember that the value of this symbol must change as a prerequisite for the designation of place value. And because the value of I in IX and in XI remains a name for one regardless of its location, it does not show place value.

EXERCISES (1)

1. What are the characteristics?

Symbols	a	aa	aaa	b	ba	baa	baaa	bb
Corresponding number of dots	•	• •	• • •	• • • •	• • • • •	• • • • • •	• • • • • • •	• • • • • • • •

2. What are the characteristics?

Symbols	a	b	c	aa	ab	ac	ba	bb	bc	ca
Corresponding number of dots	•	• •	• • •	• • • •	• • • • •	• • • • • •	• • • • • • •	• • • • • • • •	• • • • • • • • •	• • • • • • • • • •

3. What are the characteristics?

Symbols	a	b	c	ak	aa	ab	ac	bk
Corresponding number of dots	•	• •	• • •	• • • •	• • • • •	• • • • • •	• • • • • • •	• • • • •

4. What are the characteristics?

Symbols	a	b	c	ak	k	ka	kb	kc	kak
Corresponding number of dots	•	• •	• • •	• • • •	• • • • •	• • • • • • •	• • • • • • • •	• • • • • • • • •	• • • • • • • • •

5. What are the characteristics?

Symbols	a	b	c	bb	d	bc	e	bbb	cc	bd
Corresponding number of dots	•	• •	• • •	• • • •	• • • • •	• • • • • •	• • • • • • •	• • • • • • • •	• • • • • • • • •	• • • • • •

6. What are the characteristics?

Symbols	a	aa	baa	aa aa	b	ba	a ba	a baa	baa aa	bb
Corresponding number of dots	•	• •	• • •	• • • •	• • • • •	• • • • • •	• • • • • • •	• • • • • • • •	• • • • • • • • •	• • • • • •

11.6. *Grouping*

In order to demonstrate how stories can be utilized to develop concepts, we shall develop the concepts of this unit allegorically: Pretend you work in a factory that makes and packages paper cups. Each day the shipping room of this factory receives many orders specifying various types of packaging for the cups. The packaging foreman has discovered that, by classifying these orders into the basic type of grouping that each order represents and by organizing his workers into teams that are responsible for handling a specific type of grouping, he can efficiently fill the orders with a minimum chance of error.

For example, suppose he reads an order and notices that the purchaser of the cups wants the cups packaged into various groups of 3, 9, 27, 81, and so on. Noticing that each of the groupings the purchaser has requested factors as follows—1 × 3, 3 × 3, 3 × 3 × 3, 3 × 3 × 3 × 3—he sends this

Paper-cup-
making
machine

FIGURE 11.7

order over to his "three-grouping" table. Each person sitting at the table has been given these directions: "Wait until you have three groups in front of you, then stack these groups of cups into one stack of cups and pass them to the person on your right."

These cups drop out of a paper-cup-making machine one at a time. When the first person in the line gets three cups in front of him, he groups them into a stack of three and passes them on to the next person. This person waits until three stacks of three cups are in front of him and he then groups these into one stack of three threes and passes these on to the next person, and so on. The packaging foreman, by noting the progress of cups on the line at any given moment, is able to tell how many cups have been packaged. Let us see how he does this.

Let us assume that you have had children acting out the various roles in our story, as in Figure 11.7. The foreman's reasoning to determine the number of cups on the table might go something like this: The cups in front of the girl near the machine are in groups of ones, because if she had grouped them she would have passed them on. The stack in front of the boy is in a group of three and he is waiting for two more such stacks so that he can make a group of three threes and pass it on. Each stack in front of the second girl from the machine is in a group of three threes, because she received each of these stacks from the boy on her left. She is waiting for one more stack of three threes so that she can make a stack of three three threes.

The foreman finds that there are 23 cups on the table by reasoning: Two cups in front of the first girl and one set of three—or three cups—in front of the boy, and two sets of three threes—or two sets of nine, or 18 cups—in front of the second girl; thus, $18 + 3 + 2 = 23$.

The foreman decides that if he labels each person in such a way as to tell how many times the sets have been grouped at that position, it will be easier for him to compute how many cups are on the table. Figure 11.8 shows how the people looked after he attached the labels.

FIGURE 11.8

The 0 told him that the cups in front of this person had been grouped zero times—in other words, they were still in groups of ones just as they had come from the machine. The 1 tells him that the objects in front of the boy had been grouped one time by the girl to his left. The 2 tells him that the objects in front of the girl have been grouped twice—once by the girl near the machine and a second time by the boy.

Because the foreman had a great many tables to keep track of, he devised a system to keep track of what type of grouping was taking place at each table. He did it in such a way that he could look at any person at any table and tell what sort of grouping was taking place at that table. Figure 11.9 depicts how he placed the numeral 3 to the left and below the numeral that indicates the number of times the cups have been grouped.

Now when he looked at a table and noticed a 4^2, he knew that people were grouping by fours at this table, and that stacks in front of this person had been grouped two times before coming to that point. In other words, he knew that 4^2 meant that four ones had been grouped and then four sets of this four had been grouped to form a set of four fours, or 16 cups.

FIGURE 11.9

One day, the foreman was showing a visitor through his packaging plant. The visitor said that he understood what the numerals on the front of the workers meant, but he did not understand why there were not more stacks in front of each worker. The foreman explained that at a table grouping by three, no person could ever have more than two stacks left in front of him, because as soon as he got three of something, he would group them and pass them on.

The visitor said, "Oh, I see. That would mean that at a table grouping by fives, four stacks would be the largest number that could ever be left in front of a worker, because as soon as he got five stacks, he would group them and pass the new stack on. Why, that means that if you are grouping by tens, the most you could ever have left would be nine stacks."

The visitor suggested that he should place another numeral on the front of the workers to show how many of a given group the worker had left in front of him. Figure 11.10 shows how the workers looked after he added the numerals to name the number of groups in front of each worker. From left to right, we can read 2×3^2 as two sets of three threes; 1×3^1 as one set of three; and 2×3^0 as two sets of ones.

In constructing a story for use in presenting mathematical concepts, it is not necessary that each concept be developed fully. By carefully phrased questions during and following the story, you can extend the concepts outlined in your story and develop other related concepts. For example:

"What is the smallest number of cups that could be left in front of a worker when the production is stopped?" (Zero.)

"Can any number of cups be grouped by threes if we have enough people?" (Yes.)

"How many people would we need to group 1025 cups if we grouped by twos?" (Eleven. Let the children arrive at this number by considering the sequence, 1, 2, 4, 8, 16, 32, 64, 128, 256, 512, 1024.)

FIGURE 11.10

Special vocabulary is probably taught best in a situation where these words can be focused on best. For example, the numeral that identifies the type of grouping being done is called the *base*. In 3^5, the 3 is identified as the base. The number that indicates the number of times that grouping has taken place by the base number is called the *exponent*. In 3^5, the 5 is identified as the exponent.

11.7. *Nondecimal Place Value*

If we were to denote numbers in the manner of the last stage of development used by the foreman, there would be little trouble deciphering the number named. For example, let us consider how $4 \times 5^2 + 0 \times 5^1 + 2 \times 5^0$ immediately tells us that we are grouping by fives and that we have four groups of five fives, zero groups of five, and two ones. In other words, we are referring to 102 of something.

In our attempt to simplify the effort required to write the name of this number, we "strip" "$\times 5^2 + \times 5^1 + \times 5^0$" from our notation, leaving only 402. We place the 4 and 0 and 2 close together and affix the word *five* to let everyone know that we are grouping by fives (402_{five}). We leave to the reader the task of identifying the 2 as two ones, the 0 as zero fives, and the 4 as four five fives.

It is the teacher's responsibility to help the child reconstruct the inherent meaning in the nondecimal numeral by translation experience. Figure 11.11 depicts sample translations. Note that these translations are made in both directions.

$$3201_{\text{four}} \xrightarrow{\text{translates to}} 3 \times 4^3 + 2 \times 4^2 + 0 \times 4^1 + 1 \times 4^0$$

$$2650_{\text{seven}} \xrightarrow{\text{translates to}} 2 \times 7^3 + 6 \times 7^2 + 5 \times 7^1 + 0 \times 7^0$$

$$3 \times 9^2 + 8 \times 9^1 + 0 \times 9^0 \xrightarrow{\text{translates to}} 380_{\text{nine}}$$

$$9 \times 10^2 + 3 \times 10^1 + 7 \times 10^0 \xrightarrow{\text{translates to}} 937_{\text{ten}}$$

FIGURE 11.11

We can explore the meaning of this symbolism at this abstract level if we proceed from the type of explanation represented by the paper cup factory. We can also develop nondecimal numeration systems via a sequence of activities quite similar to those we used to develop the concepts relating to our place-value systems. Figure 11.12 depicts such a sequence of activities that could be used to develop the concepts relating to nondecimal notation.

The study of nondecimal systems can be motivated by making a study of how these systems are utilized in our culture. Such activities as relating

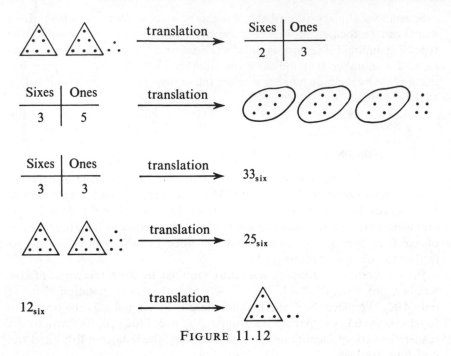

FIGURE 11.12

dozen and gross to base twelve, or nickels and quarters to base five, or computer calculations to base two, will serve to motivate the study of these particular bases.

11.8. *Scientific Notation*

The idea of the arbitrariness of grouping coupled with the idea of base and exponent can be utilized to develop the concept of scientific notation. You will want to tell your children that they are going to study a new system of notation used by scientists to simplify numerals that would normally require many digits to write. For example, 2,000,000 can be written as 2×10^6, which greatly reduces the number of symbols needed to name the number.

By convention, scientific notation always uses a base of 10. Also by convention, the numeral that names the number of the particular grouping of 10 to which you are referring is either one or a number between one and 10. For example, 3,500,000 is expressed as 3.5×10^6 in scientific notation, because 3.5 is between one and 10, and 10^6 indicates that a base of 10 has been used for grouping.

In the elementary school, almost all of the child's experiences with this notation involve translating large numbers to scientific notation. Figure 11.13 depicts some typical translations:

$$3,000 \xrightarrow{\text{translates to}} 3 \times 10^3$$
$$30,000 \xrightarrow{\text{translates to}} 3 \times 10^4$$
$$36,000 \xrightarrow{\text{translates to}} 3.6 \times 10^4$$
$$36,400 \xrightarrow{\text{translates to}} 3.64 \times 10^4$$
$$1,000 \xrightarrow{\text{translates to}} 1 \times 10^3$$

FIGURE 11.13

EXERCISES (2)

1. For each of the following illustrations, describe the base, the number of cups in piles (a), (b), and (c), and the total number of cups pictured.

(a)

(b)

Paper-cup-making machine

(a)   (b)   (c)

(c)

2. Construct a set of translation activities similar to Figure 11.11 that could be used to develop place value for a base-eight system.
3. Construct a sequence of activities similar to those depicted by Figure 11.12 that could be used to develop a base-two (binary) system.
4. Construct an ordered sequence of translation activities that would aid the child in learning to convert from a standard numeral to scientific notation.

REFERENCES

BANKS, J. HOUSTON, *Learning and Teaching Arithmetic*, Boston: Allyn & Bacon, 1964, pp. 20–24.

BELL, CLIFFORD, CLELA HAMMOND, and ROBERT HERRERA, *Fundamentals of Arithmetic for Teachers*, New York: John Wiley & Sons, Inc., 1962, pp. 20–35.

BRUMFIEL, CHARLES, ROBERT EICHOLZ, and MERRILL SHANKS, *Fundamental Concepts of Elementary Mathematics*, Reading, Mass.: Addison-Wesley, 1962, pp. 14–49.

CHURCHILL, EILEEN M., *Counting and Measuring*, Great Britain: Routledge & Kegan Paul, 1962, pp. 11–44.

EDUCATION RESEARCH COUNCIL OF GREATER CLEVELAND, *Key Topics in Mathematics for the Primary Teacher*, Chicago: Science Research Associates, 1962, pp. 23–30.

EVENSON, A. B., *Modern Mathematics: Introductory Concepts and Their Implications*, Chicago: Scott, Foresman and Co., 1962, pp. 25–32.

FLOURNOY, FRANCES, *Elementary School Mathematics*, Washington, D.C.: The Center for Applied Research in Education, 1964, pp. 9–10, 20–24.

HAMILTON, E. W., "Number Systems, Fad or Foundation," *The Arithmetic Teacher*, vol. 8, pp. 242–245, May, 1961.

HEDDENS, JAMES W., *Today's Mathematics, A Guide to Concepts and Methods in Elementary School Mathematics*, Chicago: Science Research Associates, Inc., 1964, pp. 73–80, 91–92.

HOLLIS, LOYE Y., "Why Teach Numeration?" *The Arithmetic Teacher*, vol. 11, pp. 94–95, February, 1964.

JOHNSON, DONOVAN A., and WILLIAM H. GLENN, *Understanding Numeration Systems*, St. Louis, Mo.: Webster, 1960, pp. 2–10.

NATIONAL COUNCIL OF TEACHERS OF MATHEMATICS, *Enrichment Mathematics for the Grades, Twenty-seventh Yearbook*, Washington, D.C.: The National Council of Teachers of Mathematics, 1963, pp. 234–244.

NATIONAL COUNCIL OF TEACHERS OF MATHEMATICS, *Instruction in Arithmetic, Twenty-fifth Yearbook*, Washington, D.C.: The National Council of Teachers of Mathematics, 1960, pp. 12–15, 277–278.

NATIONAL COUNCIL OF TEACHERS OF MATHEMATICS, *The Growth of Mathematical Ideas, Grades K–12, Twenty-fourth Yearbook*, Washington, D.C.: The National Council of Teachers of Mathematics, 1959, pp. 17–19.

PETERSON, JOHN A., and JOSEPH HASHISAKI, *Theory of Arithmetic*, New York: John Wiley & Sons, Inc., 1964, pp. 1–13.

SHIPP, DONALD, and SAM ADAMS, *Developing Arithmetic Concepts and Skills*, Englewood Cliffs, N.J.: Prentice-Hall, Inc., 1964, pp. 47–52.

SMITH, D. E., *History of Mathematics, Vol. II*, New York: Dover Publications, Inc., 1958, pp. 36–77.

SMITH, SEATON E., JR., *Explorations in Elementary Mathematics*, Englewood Cliffs, N.J.: Prentice-Hall, Inc., 1966, pp. 31–46, 175–185.

SPENCER, PETER LINCOLN, and MARGUERITE BRYDEGAARD, *Building Mathematical Competence in the Elementary School*, New York: Holt, Rinehart and Winston, Inc., 1966, pp. 61–67, 71–74.

SWAIN, ROBERT L., and EUGENE D. NICHOLS, *Understanding Arithmetic*, New York: Holt, Rinehart and Winston, Inc., 1965, pp. 1–27.

SWENSON, ESTHER J., *Teaching Arithmetic to Children*, New York: The Macmillan Company, 1964, pp. 4–55.

VANDERWAERDEN, B. L., *Science Awakening: Egyptian, Babylonian, Greek Mathematics*, New York: Oxford University Press, 1961.

VAN ENGEN, HENRY, MAURICE L. HARTUNG, and JAMES E. STOCHL, *Foundations of Elementary School Arithmetic*, Chicago: Scott, Foresman and Co., 1965, pp. 120–144.

WARD, MORGAN, and CLARENCE HARDGROVE, *Modern Elementary Mathematics*, Reading, Mass.: Addison-Wesley, 1964, pp. 66–69.

WILLIAMS, SAMMIE, GARLAND H. READ, JR., and FRANK L. WILLIAMS, *Modern Mathematics in the Elementary and Junior High Schools*, Syracuse, N.Y.: L. W. Singer, 1961, pp. 1–10.

Small-group instruction motivates a child to learn mathematics.

12

Teaching Decimal Notation, Ratio, and Percentage

12.1. *Introduction*

ALTHOUGH there is evidence that decimal notation was used earlier, it "came of age" in the sixteenth century. Standardization of notation, however, was not immediate. As a matter of fact, the symbolism remains incompletely standardized to this date.[1] For example, in the United States we represent $2\frac{3}{10}$ as 2.3; in England, $2\frac{3}{10}$ is represented as 2·3. During the early use of decimal notation, a numeral that names a number less than one was distinguished from the part of the numeral that names a number one or greater than one in one of the following ways:

$$2.3 = 2_3 = 2\overline{3} = 2\cdot3 = 2\ 3\ 1$$

As can be easily seen, the dot that we refer to as the decimal point plays only a minor role in the decimal system, because the system of decimal notation can exist independent of this symbol.

---

[1] David Eugene Smith, *History of Mathematics*, Boston: Ginn and Company, 1953, vol. II, p. 246.

Decimal notation represents an extension of our place-value notation, which makes possible the representation of all fractional numbers in terms of place-value notation.

12.2. *Definition, Terminology, and Symbolism*

These decimals, which we use for naming fractional numbers, also will be useful at the junior high level for extending the concepts of rational numbers (of which the fractional numbers constitute a subset) and irrational numbers. At the elementary level, we shall be especially interested in the types of decimal notation called *terminating decimals* and *periodic (or repeating) decimals*.

A terminating decimal is a decimal that contains a finite number of digits. All terminating decimals can be expressed in the form $\frac{c}{2^a \cdot 5^b}$, such that a, b, and c are elements of the set of whole numbers.

Definition: A periodic decimal is a decimal consisting of a finite series of digits that repeat infinitely. ($.33\overline{3}$, $3.2474\overline{747}$ are examples of periodic decimals. The bar over the digits indicates that this series of digits repeats infinitely. Every terminating decimal can be expressed as a periodic decimal simply by affixing three zeros with a bar over the last zero on the right. For example, $.5$ can be expressed as a periodic decimal as follows: $.500\overline{0}$.)

Figure 12.1 depicts an analysis of a numeral in terms of the standard numeral form, the expanded form, and the fractional form. It also depicts the meaning of the place value.

12.3. *Teaching Decimal Notation*

The child's first encounter with decimal notation (other than its use with various types of measure) is its use as an alternate way of naming a fractional number. The teacher should establish certain relationships between concepts the child has mastered using fractions and the new decimal notation. Along with this establishment of parallel concepts, the teacher should help the child to see that decimal notation greatly simplifies the computational skills involving fractional numbers.

When money is not used as a vehicle to introduce decimal notation, it is common practice to begin a child's introduction to decimal notation with tenths, just as it is common technique to begin the study of enumerating the

FIGURE 12.1

Ways of reading

- five hundred   sixty -   four   and one thousand seven hundred   eighty - nine ten thousandths   nine
- five,   six,   four point.   one,   seven,   eight,   nine

Notations

5	6	4	.	1	7	8	9	← Standard numeral

$$500 + 60 + 4 + \frac{1}{10} + \frac{7}{100} + \frac{8}{1000} + \frac{9}{10,000}$$ ← Expanded form

$$5 \times 100 + 6 \times 10 + 4 \times \frac{10}{10} + 1 \times \frac{1}{10} + 7 \times \frac{1}{100} + 8 \times \frac{1}{1000} + 9 \times \frac{1}{10,000}$$

$$5 \times 10^2 + 6 \times 10^1 + 4 \times 10^0 + 1 \times 10^{-1} + 7 \times 10^{-2} + 8 \times 10^{-3} + 9 \times 10^{-4}$$ Junior high level

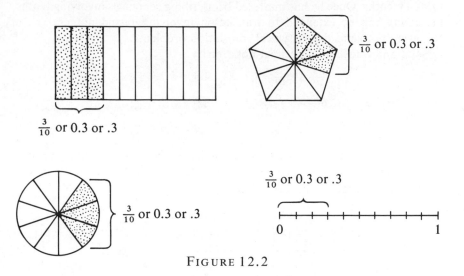

FIGURE 12.2

set of whole numbers with the ones. It is desirable at the beginning to employ mathematical models to which the child can make reference. Partitioned rectangular regions, pentagonal regions, circular regions, and unit line segments serve as useful models. Figure 12.2 depicts how each of these aids would be used to illustrate $\frac{3}{10}$ or 0.3 (or .3).

The teacher can make the child's practice in renaming a fractional number expressed as a fraction more meaningful by using complete mathematical sentences instead of simply having the child rewrite fractions in decimal form. The following examples illustrate how using complete sentences helps the child see the parallel between computations involving fraction notation and computations involving decimal notation:

the child's translation of the sentence:

$$\frac{3}{10} + \frac{4}{10} = \frac{7}{10} \longrightarrow \qquad .3 + .4 = .7$$

$$\frac{8}{10} - \frac{3}{10} = \frac{5}{10} \longrightarrow \qquad .8 - .3 = .5$$

At this early stage in mastering decimal notation, we should help the child see that 1.0 names both ten-tenths and one. Translation of sentences in fraction form offers a convenient vehicle for conveying these concepts:

the child's translation of the fraction sentence:

$$\frac{3}{10} + \frac{7}{10} = \frac{10}{10} = 1 + \frac{0}{10} \longrightarrow \qquad .3 + .7 = 1 = 1.0$$

It is important to have the child master the many ways of interpreting the decimals. For example, 4.3 can be interpreted as 4 ones and three-tenths, or as 43 tenths. Once he has mastered transcribing sentences involving tenths, his ability can be extended to translation involving mixed numerals. The following problems depict typical translation problems.

Solve and translate to decimal notation:

$$4\tfrac{3}{10} + 5\tfrac{2}{10} = \square \quad \rightarrow \quad 4.3 + 5.2 = \square$$

$$6\tfrac{9}{10} + 8\tfrac{7}{10} = \square \quad \rightarrow \quad 6.9 + 8.7 = \square$$

$$4\tfrac{7}{10} - 2\tfrac{4}{10} = \square \quad \rightarrow \quad 4.7 - 2.4 = \square$$

The concept of decimal notation for hundredths is introduced and developed in a manner similar to that employed for tenths. Figure 12.3 depicts a mathematical model that can be used to show $\tfrac{13}{100}$ or 0.13.

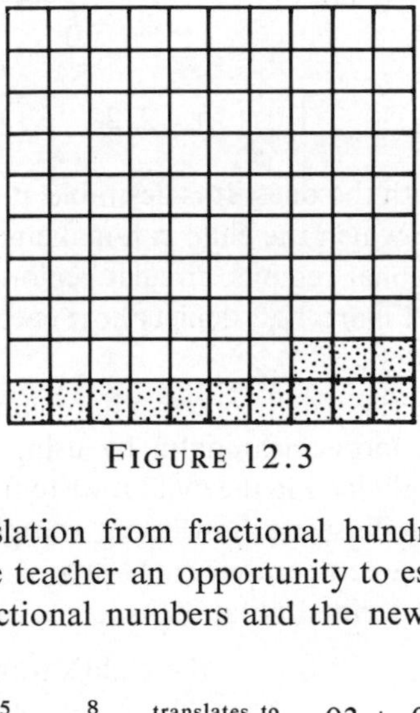

FIGURE 12.3

The process of translation from fractional hundredths to decimal hundredths again offers the teacher an opportunity to establish the relationship of the concepts for fractional numbers and the new decimal notation. For example:

$$\tfrac{3}{100} + \tfrac{5}{100} = \tfrac{8}{100} \xrightarrow{\text{translates to}} .03 + .05 = .08$$

$$\tfrac{14}{100} + \tfrac{9}{100} = \tfrac{23}{100} \xrightarrow{\text{translates to}} .14 + .09 = .23$$

$$\tfrac{35}{100} - \tfrac{17}{100} = \tfrac{18}{100} \xrightarrow{\text{translates to}} .35 - .17 = .18$$

This process of translation should include examples involving tenths and hundredths. For example:

$$\tfrac{3}{10} + \tfrac{4}{100} = \tfrac{30}{100} + \tfrac{4}{100} = \square$$

$$.3 + .04 = .30 + .04 = \square$$

$$\tfrac{63}{100} - \tfrac{4}{10} = \tfrac{63}{100} - \tfrac{40}{100} = \square$$

$$.63 - .4 = .63 - .40 = \square$$

These translations should progress to the vertical notation, because one of the advantages of our decimal notation is that it provides a smooth transition from the algorithms developed for whole numbers to the algorithms developed for fractional numbers. Some typical translations are shown as follows:

$$\begin{array}{ccccc}
\dfrac{3}{10} & \dfrac{30}{100} & & .3 & .30 \\[6pt]
+\dfrac{9}{100} \rightarrow & +\dfrac{9}{100} & \xrightarrow{\text{translates to}} & +.09 \rightarrow & +.09 \\[4pt]
\hline \\[-8pt]
\dfrac{63}{100} & \dfrac{63}{100} & & .63 & .63 \\[6pt]
-\dfrac{4}{10} \rightarrow & -\dfrac{40}{100} & \xrightarrow{\text{translates to}} & -.4 \rightarrow & -.40 \\[4pt]
\hline
\end{array}$$

Figure 12.4 shows how the translation technique can be used to give meaning to the development of the decimal subtraction algorithm.

$$
\begin{array}{c|c}
\begin{array}{r} 12.1 \\ -4.76 \\ \hline \end{array} &
\begin{array}{r} 12\frac{1}{10} \\ -4\frac{76}{100} \\ \hline \end{array} \rightarrow
\end{array}
\quad -\left(4 + \frac{7}{10} + \frac{6}{100}\right)
$$

$$12 + \frac{1}{10} + \frac{0}{100}$$

$$\downarrow \qquad\qquad\qquad \downarrow$$

$$
\begin{array}{r} 12.00 \\ -4.76 \\ \hline \end{array}
\qquad
\begin{array}{r} 12 + \frac{0}{10} + \frac{10}{100} \\ -\left(4 + \frac{7}{10} + \frac{6}{100}\right) \\ \hline \frac{4}{100} \end{array}
$$

$$
\begin{array}{r} 11.10 \\ -4.76 \\ \hline 4 \end{array}
$$

$$
\begin{array}{r}
11 + \frac{10}{10} + \frac{10}{100} \\
-\left(4 + \frac{7}{10} + \frac{6}{100}\right) \\
\hline
7 + \frac{3}{10} + \frac{4}{100}
\end{array}
$$

$$
\begin{array}{r} 12.10 \\ -4.76 \\ \hline 7.34 \end{array}
$$

FIGURE 12.4

Extension of concepts involving thousandths, ten-thousandths, hundred-thousandths, and so on, parallel in the development of the concepts for tenths and hundredths.

12.4. Common Terminating Decimals

The teacher should establish decimal names for halves, fourths, fifths, and twentieths at an early stage in presenting the decimal notation. At this early stage, the children will not have the advantage of the decimal division algorithm to derive the correct translation from fraction to decimal. Even though the child does not have the decimal division algorithm, he has other skills that can provide him with sufficient understanding to make this translation meaningful. For example, the compensation property of division provides a means of justifying such relationships as $\frac{1}{4} = .25$, $\frac{1}{5} = .20$, and $\frac{1}{2} = .50$. For example, a series of questions and statements such as the following might be used to establish that .75 and $\frac{3}{4}$ are equivalent names:

"Let's see if we can find a decimal name for a fraction that is not expressed in tenths or hundredths or thousandths. Let's try to find a decimal name for $\frac{3}{4}$."

"What property have we studied that helps us find other equivalent fractions?" (Compensation property for division.)

"Is there a whole number we can multiply times the divisor and the dividend in 3 divided by 4 such that we can get a divisor of 100?" (Twenty-five.)

$$\frac{3}{4} = \frac{3 \times 25}{4 \times 25} = \frac{75}{100}; \text{ therefore, } \frac{3}{4} = .75$$

With the introduction of the decimal division algorithm, we can reestablish that $\frac{1}{2} = .5$, $\frac{1}{5} = .2$, $\frac{1}{4} = .25$, and so on. For example:

$$2\overline{)1.0}$$
$$\underline{1.0} \quad .5; \text{ because } .5 \times 2 = 1.0$$
$$0$$

12.5. *Periodic Decimals*

The repeating or periodic decimals are developed concurrently with the development of the decimal division algorithm. For example, consider the following algorithm depicting $1 \div 3$.

$$3\overline{)1.000}$$
$$\underline{.900} \quad .3$$
$$.100$$
$$\underline{.090} \quad .03$$
$$.010$$
$$\underline{.009} \quad .003$$
$$.001$$

If we look at the quotients and remainders, it becomes evident why the quotient of 1 and 3 is named by a repeating decimal.

First division: $1 \div 3 = \frac{3}{10} + \frac{1}{30} = \frac{3}{10} + (\frac{1}{3} \times \frac{1}{10})$

Second division: $1 \div 3 = \frac{3}{10} + \frac{3}{100} + \frac{1}{300} = \frac{3}{10} + \frac{3}{100} + (\frac{1}{3} \times \frac{1}{100})$

Third division: $1 \div 3 = \frac{3}{10} + \frac{3}{100} + \frac{3}{1000} + \frac{1}{3000} = \frac{3}{10} + \frac{3}{100} + \frac{3}{1000} +$

$$(\frac{1}{3} \times \frac{1}{1000})$$

The following types of questions will be useful for developing the concept of a repeating decimal:

"What will we obtain if we divide a fourth time?" $(1 \div 3 = \frac{3}{10} + \frac{3}{100} +$ $\frac{3}{1000} + \frac{3}{10,000} + \frac{1}{300,000})$

"Our first remainder was $\frac{1}{3 \times 10}$, our second was $\frac{1}{3 \times 10 \times 10}$, our third was $\frac{1}{3 \times 10 \times 10 \times 10}$; what will our ninth remainder be?" $(\frac{1}{3 \times 10 \times 10 \times 10 \times 10 \times 10 \times 10 \times 10 \times 10 \times 10})$

"Will we always get a remainder?" (Yes.) "Can we know what our remainder will be after we have divided 4,328,265 times?" (Yes.)

It is suggested that concepts such as the following be developed intuitively with many examples: If a number is divided by n, then the number of digits in the repeating series of digits cannot exceed n; if a divisor n is of the form $2^x \cdot 5^y$ (x and y being whole numbers), then the resulting decimal will be terminating; a recurrent digit signals a repeating series of digits when the recurrence has taken place after a series of zeros and there are no nonzero digits from that point on in the dividend.

The child should be asked to focus on these concepts by such well-designed questions as the following:

"John, the pattern of digits keeps repeating. Can you see anything that might tell you this would continue on and on?"

"Mary, your pattern of digits keeps repeating on and on. Can you notice anything about the remainders that might have told you that this would happen? When could you have first known this would happen?"

EXERCISES (1)

1. We can show that $\frac{7}{2 \times 2 \times 2 \times 5}$ can be named by a terminating decimal as follows: $\frac{7}{2 \times 2 \times 2 \times 5} \times \frac{5 \times 5}{5 \times 5} = \frac{7 \times 5 \times 5}{(2 \times 5) \times (2 \times 5) \times (2 \times 5)} = \frac{175}{1000} = .175.$ Show that each of the following can be named by a terminating decimal by a similar technique:

a. $\frac{375}{2}$ b. $\frac{41}{5 \times 5}$ c. $\frac{3714}{2 \times 5 \times 5}$

2. Solve and then translate each of the following sentences into decimal notation:

a. $\frac{3}{10} + \frac{6}{10} = \frac{\triangle}{\square}$ c. $\frac{3}{10} - \frac{1}{10} = \frac{\triangle}{\square}$

b. $\frac{4}{10} + \frac{7}{100} = \frac{\triangle}{\square}$ d. $\frac{8}{10} - \frac{9}{100} = \frac{\triangle}{\square}$

3. Make up problems using fraction notation (to be translated to decimal notation) that could be used to illustrate the following:

a. $a + b = b + a$

b. $(a + b) + c = a + (b + c)$

c. $a - b = (a - d) - (b - d)$

d. $a - b = (a + d) - (b + d)$

e. $a + b = (a - c) + (b + c)$

f. $a + 0 = 0 + a = a$

4. If you were to divide by each of the following numbers, indicate the number of possible remainders you could obtain:

a. 17   b. 259   c. 371   d. 179,387,241

5. Derive decimal names for each of the following. (*Hint:* Give this problem some thought before working it.)

a. $\frac{1}{9}$ d. $\frac{4}{9}$ g. $\frac{1}{11}$ j. $\frac{100}{11}$

b. $\frac{2}{9}$ e. $\frac{5}{9}$ h. $\frac{2}{11}$ k. $\frac{10}{11}$

c. $\frac{1}{3}$ f. $\frac{2}{3}$ i. $\frac{3}{11}$ l. $\frac{121}{11}$

12.6. *Decimal Notation for Multiplication and Division*

The development of decimal notation for multiplication and division closely parallels our development of this notation for addition and subtraction.

Problem	Solution	Translation
$\frac{3}{10} \times \frac{4}{10} = \frac{\triangle}{\square}$	$\frac{12}{100}$	$.3 \times .4 = .12$
$\frac{2}{10} \times \frac{4}{10} = \frac{\triangle}{\square}$	$\frac{8}{100}$	$.2 \times .4 = .08$
$\frac{3}{10} \times \frac{8}{100} = \frac{\triangle}{\square}$	$\frac{24}{1000}$	$.3 \times .08 = .024$
$\frac{45}{10} \times \frac{2}{10} = \frac{\triangle}{\square}$	$\frac{90}{100}$	$4.5 \times .2 = .90$

FIGURE 12.5

Early experiences involve the child in translating from fraction to decimal notation. Figure 12.5 depicts typical translations of multiplication.

In making the type of translation depicted in Figure 12.5, it is hoped the child will begin to discover a rule for placing the decimal point in the name for the product. Translations of this type will provide the child with readiness for extending the standard multiplication algorithm to the decimal-multiplication algorithm. Notice in Figure 12.6 how the multiplication algorithm is developed by relating the decimal partial products to those obtained using fraction names.

$$3.67$$
$$.014$$

$.00028$	$\leftarrow$	$\frac{4}{1000} \times \frac{7}{100} = \frac{28}{100,000}$	$\frac{28}{100,000}$
$.0024$	$\leftarrow$	$\frac{4}{1000} \times \frac{6}{10} = \frac{24}{10,000}$	$\frac{240}{100,000}$
$.012$	$\leftarrow$	$\frac{4}{1000} \times \frac{3}{1} = \frac{12}{1000}$	$\frac{1200}{100,000}$
$.0007$	$\leftarrow$	$\frac{1}{100} \times \frac{7}{100} = \frac{7}{10,000}$	$\frac{70}{100,000}$
$.006$	$\leftarrow$	$\frac{1}{100} \times \frac{6}{10} = \frac{6}{1000}$	$\frac{600}{100,000}$
$.03$	$\leftarrow$	$\frac{1}{100} \times \frac{3}{1} = \frac{3}{100}$	$+\frac{3000}{100,000}$
$.05138$			$\frac{5138}{100,000}$

FIGURE 12.6

The technique for refining this complete partial-products algorithm to the standard multiplication algorithm is the same as the one we used for relating the whole-number-multiplication algorithms.

In Figure 12.7, we see the stages of the transition from the complete partial-products algorithm to the standard decimal-multiplication algorithm.

3.2	3.2	3.2
$\times 2.4$	2.4	2.4
.08	1.28	128
1.2	6.4	64
.4	7.68	7.68
6.		because tenths $\times$ tenths $=$ hundredths
7.68		

FIGURE 12.7

The development of the division algorithm is closely related to the development of the multiplication algorithm. Although there exist many versions of the decimal-division algorithm, in this section, we will take a careful look at what we shall call the decimal-variable-subtraction-division algorithm.* The ease with which this algorithm is developed will be directly proportional to the depth of understanding the children have of the multiplication algorithm. Let us use the technique of tracing through a dialogue that might be associated with the development of this algorithm:

$3 \times \Box = 12$	In the sentence at the left, what are we asking? (We are asking, "3 times what number equals 12?") What is that number? (Four.) What algorithm could we use to find our answer? (The division algorithm.)
$6 \times \Box = 3$	In the sentence at the left, what are we asking? (We are asking, "6 times what number equals 3?")
	Let us see if our division algorithm can be remodeled to help us find the quotient.
$6\overline{)3}$	If we had a set of 3 objects, would it be possible to take away 1 set of 6 objects, or 6 sets of 1 object? (No.) Suppose we took one set of 3 objects and partitioned each object into tenths. How many tenths would we get? (Thirty.)
$6\overline{)3.0}$	At the left, we have indicated these 30-tenths by writing 3.0. If we take our set of 30-tenths and partition these into 6 equivalent sets, what would be in each set? (Five-tenths.) If we remove 6 of these sets of five-tenths, how many tenths would we have left? (Zero.)
$6\overline{)3.0}$ $\underline{3.0}$ | .5 0 | .5	At the left, we have shown mathematically what we did.
$6 \times .5 = 3.0$	At the left, we see as we check our answer that .5 is the quotient of 3 and 6. Let us look at a more complex problem.
$.014\overline{)3.1244}$	Whenever our divisor is not a whole number, we can make use of the compensation property to restructure the problem in a manner that creates a divisor that is a whole number. For example, if we multiply the divisor and dividend in the problem at

---

* The author has selected this less refined algorithm for development because he feels it will be an easier transition to the more complex algorithm for the teacher than if a more refined algorithm were used and then the transition to the simpler algorithm were attempted.

the left by 1000, we derive a new problem that will have the same quotient as our original problem.

$$.014 \times 1000\overline{)3.1244 \times 1000}$$
$$14\overline{)3124.4}$$

The notation at the left depicts this process of using the compensation property.

(As you will see, all division problems can, by the use of the compensation property, be resolved to a division problem with a whole-number divisor. Thus, if the child is taught to master the use of an algorithm involving a whole-number divisor, he will be able to derive the quotient of any two fractional numbers.)

Let us specify that we are searching for a quotient to the nearest tenth. This will mean that we will compute our answer to hundredths and "round" the answer back to tenths. We will place a numeral zero in the hundredths position to indicate that we are eventually going to be grouping sets of hundredths. Can we get 14 sets of 100 from 3124.40? (Or can we get 100 sets of 14 from 3124.40?) (Yes.) Can we get 14 sets of 200 from 3124.40? (Or 200 sets of 14?) (Yes.) If we take 14 sets of 200, or 2800, from 3124.40, how do we determine how much we will have left? (We subtract 2800 from 3124.40.) Can we get 14 sets of 10 from 324.40? (Or 10 sets of 14?) (Yes.) Can we get 14 sets of 20 from 324.40? (Or 20 sets or 14?) (Yes.) How much do we have left after we have taken 14 sets of 200 and 14 sets of 20 from 3124.40? (44.40.)

$$
\begin{array}{r|l}
14\overline{)3124.40} & \\
 & 200 \\
\end{array}
$$

$$
\begin{array}{r|l}
14\overline{)3124.40} & \\
2800.00 & 200. \\
\hline
324.40 & \\
280.00 & 20. \\
\hline
44.40 & \\
\end{array}
$$

$$
\begin{array}{r|l}
14\overline{)3124.40} & \\
2800.00 & 200. \\
\hline
324.40 & \\
280.00 & 20. \\
\hline
44.40 & \\
42.00 & 3. \\
\hline
2.40 & \\
\end{array}
$$

Are there 14 sets of one in 44.40? (Yes.)
14 sets of 2? (Yes.)
14 sets of 3? (Yes.)
14 sets of 4? (No.)

```
14)3124.40
   2800.00 | 200.
   -------
    324.40
    280.00 | 20.
    -------
     44.40
     42.00 | 3.
     -------
      2.40
      1.40 | .1
     -------
      1.00
       .98 | .07
      -------
       .02
```

Are there 14 sets of one-tenth in 2.40? (Yes.)

Are there 14 sets of two-tenths in 2.40? (No.)

Are there 14 sets of one-hundredth in 1.00? (Yes.)

Are there 14 sets of seven-hundredths? (Yes.)

Renaming $(200 + 20 + 3 + .1 + .07)$, we obtain 223.17 as the quotient of 3.1244 and .014.

Even though this example depicts a problem a student will encounter in the later stages of mastering this algorithm, it contains all of the essential techniques he must master if he is to develop efficiency in using this algorithm.

12.7. *Teaching Rate Pairs (Ratio)*

There are many occasions in our society when we are interested in a many-to-many correspondence. For example, if apples are selling at three apples for ten cents, then the following sets of ordered pairs represent this relationship: $\{(3, 10), (6, 20), (9, 30), \ldots\}$. Commonly, we express these ordered pairs using fractional notation. When we use a pair of numbers under conditions of many-to-many in a social application we shall refer to this pair of numbers as a *rate pair*. We shall define two rate pairs $\frac{a}{b}$ and $\frac{c}{d}$ as being equivalent, if, and only if, $a \times d = b \times c$. For example, $\frac{3}{4} = \frac{6}{8}$ because $3 \times 8 = 4 \times 6$.

At the elementary level, a student's main concern with rate pairs is that of finding a suitable equivalent name from a set of equivalent names or, possibly, of constructing equivalent names. For example, if three apples cost ten cents, how many apples can be bought for sixty cents? This problem involves teaching the child how to proceed to obtain the equivalent name knowing $\frac{\triangle}{60}$ and $\frac{3}{10}$. Our definition of equivalent pairs helps us find the proper rate pair. We know that $\triangle \times 10 = 3 \times 60$, or $\triangle \times 10 = 180$ if $\frac{\triangle}{60}$ is to be a member of the same set of equivalent rate pairs to which $\frac{3}{10}$ belongs. Therefore, we see that $\triangle = 18$ and that we could buy 18 apples for sixty cents if apples are being sold three for ten cents.

The child's first experience with rate pairs should involve constructing many-to-many correspondence. Figure 12.8 represents a child's construction of sets matched three to four.

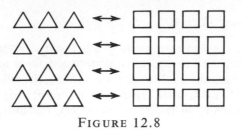

FIGURE 12.8

Questions such as the following, referring to Figure 12.8, will aid in developing the idea of rate pair.

"How many squares are matched with six triangles?" (Eight.) "When we have a 5 by 3 array of triangles, what array would we have for squares?" (Five by four.) "How many triangles are matched with 16 squares?" (Twelve.)

As children become competent in the construction of sets of equivalent rate pairs, the teacher should involve them in rate-pair applications. Some of the more common types of rate-pair situations from which the teacher can construct problems are as follows:

Length to time: miles per hour
Length to length: feet per mile
Area to area: square feet per acre
Volume to volume: pints per quart
Items to money: n cans per m cents
Money to weight: cents per pound
Money to money: dimes per dollar

Sometimes we are interested in comparing two rate pairs when the possibility exists that they are not from the same class. For example, in a supermarket, we notice that cans of beans are priced at three cans for eleven cents and two cans for eight cents. We are interested in buying the brand that represents the greatest saving. We accomplish our comparison by finding equivalent rate pairs with the same cents named. We find that $\frac{3}{11} = \frac{24}{88}$ and $\frac{2}{8} = \frac{22}{88}$. Thus, we can see that the beans selling at three cans for eleven cents represent the best buy.

There are many times when we are interested in making relative comparisons of rate pairs. This relative comparison is accomplished by selecting rate pairs that have the same denominator named. When we select a denominator of 100 in order to make the comparison of rate pairs, we give this type of rate pair a special name. We refer to each of the numerators as so many percent. For example, in $\frac{30}{100}$, the 30 can be referred to as 30 percent.

12.8. *Teaching Percent*

Percent notation is used extensively in our society. Because it is useful for reducing statistical data to an easily understood form and for conveying relationships in business applications of number, it will be important to develop not only the mathematical meaning of percent (that percent is another notation used to represent fractional numbers), but also its function as a "comparator."

Percent is not studied extensively at the elementary level. Only the foundation for working with percent notation is presented. In this section, we shall discuss only those aspects of percent that are applicable to the elementary school curriculum.

The first concept taught is that the "cent" in percent refers to a set of 100 and that when we talk about percent we are referring to so many items per hundred. For example, 23 percent means that we are comparing 23 elements of a set to the 100-element set. We introduce the symbol, %, which is read "percent," and which conveys the idea of "per hundred."

The child's early experiences should consist of direct translation experiences involving subsets of 100. This type of activity is illustrated by the table in Figure 12.9.

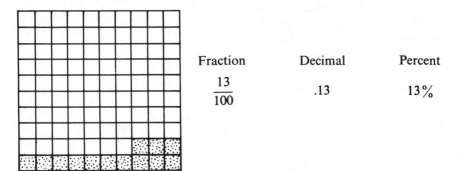

Fraction	Decimal	Percent
$\dfrac{13}{100}$	.13	13%

FIGURE 12.9

Because the concept of rate pair has preceded the development of percent, and because percent is being taught as a special case of the rate pair, it is important that once the concept of n per hundred is developed, sets of equivalent rate pairs are developed for percents. For example, not only should the students recognize that 50% is the rate pair $\frac{50}{100}$, but they also should know that there exists the infinite set of rate pairs $\{\frac{1}{2}, \frac{2}{4}, \frac{3}{6}, \ldots\}$, each element of which is equivalent to 50%.

Finding the percent form when given a rate pair is accomplished with ease via our definition of equivalent rate pairs. For example, $\frac{3}{4}$ is equivalent to $\frac{\triangle}{100}$, if, and only if, $3 \times 100 = 4 \times \triangle$. Therefore, $\triangle = 75$, and therefore, $\frac{3}{4}$ is equivalent to 75%. Further concepts relating to percent will be developed in the exercises.

EXERCISES (2)

1. Solve and then translate each of the following to decimal notation:

   a. $\frac{3}{10} \times \frac{17}{100} = \frac{\triangle}{\square}$ b. $\frac{4}{100} \times \frac{5}{100} = \frac{\triangle}{\square}$ c. $\frac{42}{10} \times \frac{35}{100} = \frac{\triangle}{\square}$

2. Solve each of the following problems using the decimal-variable-subtraction-division algorithm.

   a. $471 \div 64$ (to the nearest tenth)
   b. $47.1 \div 64$ (to the nearest tenth)
   c. $47.1 \div 6.4$ (to the nearest hundredth)
   d. $471 \div .064$ (to the nearest tenth)
   e. $47.1 \div .64$ (to the nearest tenth)

3. Using the definition $\frac{a}{b} = \frac{c}{d}$, if, and only if, $a \times d = b \times c$, find the missing information:

   a. $\frac{30}{1} = \frac{\triangle}{4}$ *Situation:* If John travels 30 miles per hour, how many miles can he travel in four hours?

   b. $\frac{12}{1} = \frac{144}{\triangle}$ *Situation:* If there are 12 inches in one foot, how many feet are there in 144 inches?

   c. $\frac{3}{4} = \frac{\triangle}{36}$ *Situation:* If three pieces of candy cost four cents, how many pieces can be bought for thirty-six cents?

4. Find five "rate pairs" equivalent to $\frac{3}{7}$.

5. Find equivalent rate pairs that would enable you to compare the following:

$$\frac{4}{7} \text{ to } \frac{9}{16}$$

6. % can be interpreted as $\times \frac{1}{100}$ (read "times one hundredth"). Using this interpretation, find the fraction names for each of the following:

   a. 3%   b. 130%

7. % can be interpreted as $\times .01$ (read "times one hundredth"). Using this interpretation, find the decimal names for each of the following:

   a. 22%   b. 4%   c. .1%

8. Make up a story problem for each of the following:

$$\text{a. } \frac{3}{5} = \frac{n}{100} \qquad \text{c. } \frac{14}{10} = \frac{n}{100}$$

$$\text{b. } \frac{4}{1} = \frac{n}{100} \qquad \text{d. } \frac{n}{8} = \frac{25}{100}$$

$$\text{e. } 25\% \text{ of } 456 = n$$

REFERENCES

AMSTUTZ, M. G., "Let's 'Place' the Decimal Point, Not Move It," *Arithmetic Teacher*, vol. 10, pp. 205–207, April, 1963.

BANKS, J. HOUSTON, *Learning and Teaching Arithmetic*, Boston: Allyn & Bacon, 1964, pp. 64–69.

BELL, CLIFFORD, CLELA HAMMOND, and ROBERT HERRERA, *Fundamentals of Arithmetic for Teachers*, New York: John Wiley & Sons, Inc., 1962, pp. 179–196.

BRUMFIEL, CHARLES, ROBERT EICHOLZ, and MERRILL SHANKS, *Fundamental Concepts of Elementary Mathematics*, Reading, Mass.: Addison-Wesley, 1962, pp. 141–148.

BRUMFIEL, CHARLES, ROBERT EICHOLZ, MERRILL SHANKS, and P. G. O'DAFFER, *Principles of Arithmetic*, Reading, Mass.: Addison-Wesley, 1963, pp. 211–251.

CROUCH, RALPH, GEORGE BALDWIN, and ROBERT J. WISNER, *Preparatory Mathematics for Elementary Teachers*, New York: John Wiley & Sons, Inc., 1965, pp. 372–375.

DAVIS, PHILIP J., *The Lore of Large Numbers*, New Haven, Conn.: Yale University Press, 1961, pp. 5–46, 115–143.

DUTTON, WILBUR, and L. J. ADAMS, *Arithmetic for Teachers*, Englewood Cliffs, N.J.: Prentice-Hall, Inc., 1963, pp. 254–275.

FLOURNOY, FRANCES, *Elementary School Mathematics*, Washington, D.C.: The Center for Applied Research in Education, 1964, pp. 20–23.

HACKER, SIDNEY G., WILFORD E. BARNES, and CALVIN T. LONG, *Fundamental Concepts of Arithmetic*, Englewood Cliffs, N.J.: Prentice-Hall, Inc., 1963, p. 231.

HEDDENS, JAMES W., *Today's Mathematics, A Guide to Concepts and Methods in Elementary School Mathematics*, Chicago: Science Research Associates, Inc., 1964, pp. 209–219, 306–307.

HONER, WENDALL W., "Jimmy's Equivalents for the Sevenths," *The Arithmetic Teacher*, vol. 10, pp. 197–198, April, 1963.

MORRIS, DENNIS E., and HENRY D. TOPFER, *Advancing in Mathematics*, Chicago: Science Research Associates, Inc., 1963, pp. 227–249, 251–271.

OSBORN, ROGER, VERE DeVAULT, CLAUDE BOYD, and ROBERT HOUSTON, *Extending Mathematics Understanding*, Columbus, Ohio: Charles E. Merrill Books, Inc., 1961, pp. 72–86.

PETERSON, JOHN A., and JOSEPH HASHISAKI, *Theory of Arithmetic*, New York: John Wiley & Sons, Inc., 1964, pp. 200–209.

RAPPAPORT, D., "Percentage—Noun or Adjective," *The Arithmetic Teacher*, vol. 8, pp. 25–26, January, 1961.

SCHOOL MATHEMATICS STUDY GROUP, *Studies in Mathematics, Vol. IX: A Brief Course in Mathematics for Elementary School Teachers*, Stanford, Calif.: Stanford University Press, 1963, pp. 293–325.

SMITH, SEATON E., JR., *Explorations in Elementary Mathematics*, Englewood Cliffs, N.J.: Prentice-Hall, Inc., 1966, pp. 31–33, 152–154.

SPENCER, PETER LINCOLN, and MARGUERITE BRYDEGAARD, *Building Mathematical Competence in the Elementary School*, New York: Holt, Rinehart and Winston, Inc., 1966, pp. 61–63, 208–211.

SWAIN, ROBERT L., and EUGENE D. NICHOLS, *Understanding Arithmetic*, New York: Holt, Rinehart and Winston, Inc., 1965, pp. 150–163, 186, 237–238, 240–245.

SWENSON, ESTHER J., *Teaching Arithmetic to Children*, New York: The Macmillan Company, 1964, pp. 390–392.

VAN ENGEN, HENRY, MAURICE L. HARTUNG, and JAMES E. STOCHL, *Foundations of Elementary School Arithmetic*, Chicago: Scott, Foresman and Co., 1965, pp. 184–190, 278–295, 312–324.

VAN ENGEN, HENRY, "Rate, Pairs, Fractions and Rational Numbers," *The Arithmetic Teacher*, vol. 7, pp. 389–399, December, 1960.

WARD, MORGAN, and CLARENCE HARDGROVE, *Modern Elementary Mathematics*, Reading, Mass.: Addison-Wesley, 1964, pp. 69–71, 295–312.

WENDT, A., "Per Cent without Cases," *The Arithmetic Teacher*, vol. 6, pp. 209–214, October, 1959.

WILLIAMS, SAMMIE, GARLAND H. READ, JR., and FRANK L. WILLIAMS, *Modern Mathematics in the Elementary and Junior High Schools*, Syracuse, N.Y.: L. W. Singer, 1961, pp. 56–57.

Books can be used to motivate a child to learn mathematics.

13

Teaching Elementary Number Theory

13.1. *Introduction*

THERE are some who believe that elementary number-theory experiences offer the teacher a real opportunity to convey to the child the real essence of mathematics. Number-theory experiences can provide the child with the thrill of pursuit and discovery when he tries to unlock the secret of a number pattern and then follows up his speculation or conjecture by testing the conjecture.

The area of number theory offers one of the frontiers in mathematics in which a persistent novice has a chance of making a new mathematical discovery. The basic tools required for discovery are neither elaborate nor highly abstract. Each discovery that the child makes (even those discoveries new only to that child) unlocks doors to rooms filled with other patterns and relationships beckoning to be discovered.

A very useful by-product of stimulating a child's interest in number theory is that the path to discovery requires him to make many calculations. He is thus stimulated to practice calculating in a meaningful way—the calculations are directed toward the satisfaction of a goal, rather than used simply for the sake of practice.

A second useful by-product of the study of number theory is that it develops the child's "number sense" and provides information that enhances the child's computational skills, such as how to find a least common multiple that has direct application in finding the least common denominator for adding fractional numbers.

13.2. *Primes, Composites, and Unit*

In this chapter, we are concerned with the set of counting numbers. The following designate the set of counting numbers: 1, 2, 3, 4, 5, ... Another way of describing the set of counting numbers is to say that it is the set of all whole numbers except zero.

We are interested in partitioning this subset of the whole numbers into three disjoint subsets. We shall perform our partition on the basis of some of the factor names of these counting numbers. Consider the following factor names for the first six counting numbers. (See Figure 13.1.)

1	$1 \times 1, 1 \times 1 \times 1, 1 \times 1 \times 1 \times 1$
2	$1 \times 2, 2 \times 1, 1 \times 1 \times 2$
3	$1 \times 3, 3 \times 1, 1 \times 1 \times 3$
4	$1 \times 4, 4 \times 1, 2 \times 2, 1 \times 1 \times 4$
5	$1 \times 5, 5 \times 1, 1 \times 1 \times 5$
6	$1 \times 6, 6 \times 1, 2 \times 3, 3 \times 2, 1 \times 1 \times 6$

FIGURE 13.1

As you can see, a person could use 1 as a factor as many times as he desired and get as many factor names as he wanted. In order to restrict the number of names that we get, we shall say that 1 cannot be used as a factor more than once. And, in order to restrict further the number of factor names we obtain, we shall say that if two names use exactly the same factors but in different order, those two names are the same. With the new restrictions, our original lists of factor names are reduced to the arrangement shown in Figure 13.2.

1	No factor names
2	1×2
3	1×3
4	$1 \times 4, 2 \times 2$
5	1×5
6	$1 \times 6, 2 \times 3$

FIGURE 13.2

When a number has no factor names, it will be called a *unit;* when it has only one factor name, it will be called a *prime number;* and when it has two or more factor names, it will be called a *composite number.* Thus, we see that 1 is the only number that can be classified as a unit, because by using 1 and any other counting number we can always obtain one factor name for any number but 1.

Now that we have defined how we shall partition the set of counting numbers, we shall explore different techniques that could be used with children to decide systematically when a number has only one factor name. To do this, let us review the meaning of such factor names as 1×4 and 2×2 based on the array definition:

1×4 means 1 row of 4 or $\cdot\ \cdot\ \cdot\ \cdot$

2×2 means 2 rows of 2 or $\vdots\vdots$

One way we could discover if a number is a prime or composite is to start with a set of objects of that number and see if an array other than an array with one row or one column can be constructed. For example, the child could discover that 12 is not a prime number, because any one of the following arrays could be constructed, besides the 1×12 array and the 12×1 array:

4×3 2×6 3×4 6×2

2	4	6	8	10	12	14	16
1 × 2	2 × 2	3 × 2	4 × 2	5 × 2	6 × 2	7 × 2	8 × 2

FIGURE 13.3

Similarly, the child could discover that 11 is a prime, because he will be unable to construct any arrays other than the 11 × 1 and the 1 × 11. The set definition also could be used to explore for prime and composite numbers.

As the child matures, more sophisticated procedures can be developed. The first of these involves noting the relationships that exist between primes and various sequences. In Figure 13.3, we note that the factor names of every number are multiples of 2. And notice that every number larger than 2 in this sequence has at least one other name than the name using the 1 as a factor. From this we can conclude that no number greater than 2 in our list can be a prime.

3	6	9	12	15	18	21
1 × 3	2 × 3	3 × 3	4 × 3	5 × 3	6 × 3	7 × 3

FIGURE 13.4

The same logic can be applied to starting a sequence with a 3 and considering every third number. In Figure 13.4, we see that every number larger than 3 in this type of sequence has at least one other name than the name using the 1 as a factor. Therefore, no number greater than 3 in our list in Figure 13.4 can be a prime.

We could set up similar sequences for 5, 7, 11, and so on, and study the resulting tables to determine which of our counting numbers can be established as composites. We can, however, help the children devise a more efficient technique for discovering the primes, now that we have established the

1	2	3	4	5	6	7	8	9	10
11	12	13	14	15	16	17	18	19	20
21	22	23	24	25	26	27	28	29	30

FIGURE 13.5

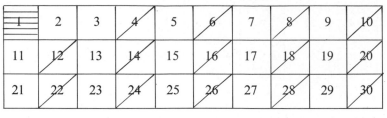

FIGURE 13.6

logical reason why every second counting number after 2 is a composite, why every third counting number after 3 is a composite, and so forth.

Consider the table depicted in Figure 13.5. We have shaded in the 1 box, because the 1 has been identified as a unit.

Now, if we mark every second number from 2, we shall have eliminated all the multiples of 2 that are composites. We have done this in Figure 13.6.

We notice that 3 is the next number after the 2 that is not marked. Because it obviously cannot be a multiple of 2, and it could not be a multiple of a number larger than itself, it must be a prime. We can now eliminate all the multiples of this number that are composite by marking out every third number larger than 3. We have done this in Figure 13.7.

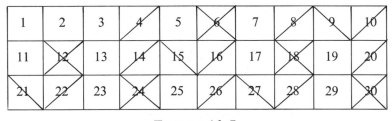

FIGURE 13.7

By a similar development, we can discover larger and larger primes. This process is called *sieving*. At this stage, the student is ready for more refined ways of sieving out the primes. This involves having the child discover the fact that any counting number can be expressed as $6 \times \square + \triangle$, where the replacements for $\square$ and $\triangle$ come from the set $\{0, 1, 2, 3, 4, \ldots\}$. Consider the following pattern:

a. $6 \times 0 + 1 = 1$ $6 \times 1 + 1 = 7$ $6 \times 2 + 1 = 13$
b. $6 \times 0 + 2 = 2$ $6 \times 1 + 2 = 8$ $6 \times 2 + 2 = 14$
c. $6 \times 0 + 3 = 3$ $6 \times 1 + 3 = 9$ $6 \times 2 + 3 = 15$
d. $6 \times 0 + 4 = 4$ $6 \times 1 + 4 = 10$ $6 \times 2 + 4 = 16$
e. $6 \times 0 + 5 = 5$ $6 \times 1 + 5 = 11$ $6 \times 2 + 5 = 17$
f. $6 \times 0 + 6 = 6$ $6 \times 1 + 6 = 12$ $6 \times 2 + 6 = 18$

By having the child extend this pattern, you will help him to recognize that any counting number can be expressed by it.

Notice that the numbers named by (b), (d), and (f) are all even numbers and have multiples of 2. Notice that row (c) names multiples of 3. This means that, other than the primes 2 and 3, we shall find all other primes in rows (a) and (e). Figure 13.8 depicts a table that can utilize this information.

1	7	13	19	25	31	37
2	8	14	20	26	32	38
3	9	15	21	27	33	39
4	10	16	22	28	34	40
5	11	17	23	29	35	41
6	12	18	24	30	36	42

FIGURE 13.8

Even though this technique provides a convenient method of eliminating the multiples of 2 and 3 from consideration, it is still necessary to sieve out the multiples of 5, 7, 11, and so on. The technique of sieving is a useful technique for isolating the smaller primes, but it is not an efficient technique to use in deciding whether or not 4809 is a prime.

13.3. *Divisibility Rules*

In order to proceed further with our study of primes and their applications, it will be necessary to develop some rules of divisibility. We shall find it useful to define the divisibility of two counting numbers in terms of a quotient and a remainder.

> *Definition:* $\triangle$ will be said to be divisible by $\square$ if the quotient of $\triangle$ and $\square$ is equal to a counting number and the remainder is zero.

For example, 8 will be said to be divisible by 2, because the quotient of 8 and 2 is 4, and the remainder is equal to zero.

It is important that we have the children discover the following relationship existing between the resulting remainders when they use the right distributive property of division over addition. Study the pattern in Figure 13.9 and see if you can generalize the relationships that exist between the remainders and quotients.

	Quotients	Remainders
$(35 + 23) \div 11$	5	3
$(35 \div 11) + (23 \div 11)$	3, 2	2, 1
$(24 + 25) \div 9$	5	4
$(24 \div 9) + (25 \div 9)$	2, 2	6, 7
$(45 + 39) \div 4$	21	0
$(45 \div 4) + (39 \div 4)$	11, 9	1, 3

FIGURE 13.9

If we express the quotients as mixed numerals, the relationship is easily seen:

$$(35 + 23) \div 11 = 5\frac{3}{11}$$
$$(35 \div 11) + (23 \div 11) = 3\frac{2}{11} + 2\frac{1}{11} = 5\frac{2+1}{11} = 5\frac{3}{11}$$

also

$$(24 + 25) \div 9 = 5\frac{4}{9}$$
$$(24 \div 9) + (25 \div 9) = 2\frac{6}{9} + 2\frac{7}{9} = 4\frac{6+7}{9} = 4\frac{13}{9} = 5\frac{4}{9}$$

also

$$(45 + 39) \div 4 = 21\frac{0}{4}$$
$$(45 \div 4) + (39 \div 4) = 11\frac{1}{4} + 9\frac{3}{4} = 20\frac{1+3}{4} = 20\frac{4}{4} = 21$$

As can easily be seen, it is possible to determine a remainder on division by considering the sequence of remainders obtained on division when the dividend is expressed as a sequence of addends.

This basic property will aid us in helping children develop rules of divisibility. Let us see how it will aid us in developing rules of divisibility for 2, 3, 5, and 9.

We have seen that the sum of the partial remainders can be used to identify what the remainder will be when the number is divided. Let us express our numerals in expanded notation and observe the partial remainders when the number is divided by 2. Figure 13.10 shows several numbers that have been divided by 2 and the remainders obtained.

By working a series of problems of this type, the child will be ready to speculate that he needs only observe the remainder from the ones in order

$$\frac{300 + 35 + 1}{2)\overline{600 + 70 + 3}}$$
$$\frac{600 \quad 70 \quad 1}{0 \quad\ \ 0 \quad\ \ 1}$$

$$\frac{3500 + \ \ 50 + 1}{2)\overline{7000 + 100 + 2}}$$
$$\frac{7000 \quad 100 \quad 2}{0 \quad\ \ 0 \quad\ \ 0}$$

$$\frac{1500 + 100 + 3}{2)\overline{3000 + 200 + 7}}$$
$$\frac{3000 \quad 200 \quad 6}{0 \quad\ \ 0 \quad\ \ 1}$$

$0 + 0 + 1 = 1$;
therefore,
$673 \div 2$ gives us a
remainder of 1

$0 + 0 + 0 = 0$;
therefore,
$7102 \div 2$ gives us a
remainder of 0

$0 + 0 + 1 = 1$;
therefore,
$3207 \div 2$ gives us a
remainder of 1

FIGURE 13.10

to tell whether a number is divisible by 2. As a teacher, you will want to explore with your students why hundreds, thousands, ten thousands, and so on, will always be divisible by 2. By structuring a similar set of problems, we can get a child to discover the rules for divisibility by 3. Figure 13.11 depicts such a structured set of problems.

Enter the remainder for each of the following:

Remainder		Remainder		Remainder		Remainder	
$1 \div 3$		$10 \div 3$		$100 \div 3$		$1000 \div 3$	
$2 \div 3$		$20 \div 3$		$200 \div 3$		$2000 \div 3$	
$3 \div 3$		$30 \div 3$		$300 \div 3$		$3000 \div 3$	
$4 \div 3$		$40 \div 3$		$400 \div 3$		$4000 \div 3$	
$5 \div 3$		$50 \div 3$		$500 \div 3$		$5000 \div 3$	
$6 \div 3$		$60 \div 3$		$600 \div 3$		$6000 \div 3$	
$7 \div 3$		$70 \div 3$		$700 \div 3$		$7000 \div 3$	
$8 \div 3$		$80 \div 3$		$800 \div 3$		$8000 \div 3$	
$9 \div 3$		$90 \div 3$		$900 \div 3$		$9000 \div 3$	

FIGURE 13.11

By completing such a table, the child will discover the relationship between the number being divided by 3 and its remainder. This discovery will facilitate the next step in his formation of the rule. He should now be able to compute mentally the remainder of a number such as 6532 on division by 3. (His mental process will be something similar to the following: 6000 leaves a remainder of 0, 500 a remainder of 2, 30 a remainder of 0, and 2 a remainder of 2. Therefore, when 6532 is divided by 3, a remainder of 1 will be obtained.)

Similarly, he can be led to generalize a rule for divisibility by 5, as the direct attack we used for developing the rule for divisibility by 2 can be utilized. Figure 13.12 illustrates some of the problems that might be constructed to lead the child to see that the ones digit, in a base-ten numeral, will identify whether a number is divisible by 5.

$$
\begin{array}{r}
120 + 8 + 0 \\
\hline
5\overline{)600 + 40 + 3} \\
600 \quad 40 \quad 0 \\
\hline
0 \quad 0 \quad 3
\end{array}
\qquad
\begin{array}{r}
800 + 18 + 1 \\
\hline
5\overline{)4000 + 90 + 6} \\
4000 \quad 90 \quad 5 \\
\hline
0 \quad 0 \quad 1
\end{array}
\qquad
\begin{array}{r}
1800 + 120 + 1 \\
\hline
5\overline{)9000 + 600 + 5} \\
9000 \quad 600 \quad 5 \\
\hline
0 \quad 0 \quad 0
\end{array}
$$

$0 + 0 + 3 = 3$; therefore, $643 \div 5$ gives us a remainder of 3

$0 + 0 + 1 = 1$; therefore, $4096 \div 5$ gives us a remainder of 1

$0 + 0 + 0 = 0$; therefore, $9605 \div 5$ gives us a remainder of 0

FIGURE 13.12

By structuring a set of problems similar to those constructed for developing the rules of three, we can have the child discover a rule of divisibility by nine. Figure 13.13 depicts such a table.

Enter the remainder for each of the following:

	Remainder		Remainder		Remainder		Remainder
$1 \div 9$		$10 \div 9$		$100 \div 9$		$1000 \div 9$	
$2 \div 9$		$20 \div 9$		$200 \div 9$		$2000 \div 9$	
$3 \div 9$		$30 \div 9$		$300 \div 9$		$3000 \div 9$	
$4 \div 9$		$40 \div 9$		$400 \div 9$		$4000 \div 9$	
$5 \div 9$		$50 \div 9$		$500 \div 9$		$5000 \div 9$	
$6 \div 9$		$60 \div 9$		$600 \div 9$		$6000 \div 9$	
$7 \div 9$		$70 \div 9$		$700 \div 9$		$7000 \div 9$	
$8 \div 9$		$80 \div 9$		$800 \div 9$		$8000 \div 9$	
$9 \div 9$		$90 \div 9$		$900 \div 9$		$9000 \div 9$	

FIGURE 13.13

From this table, the child can discover quickly that n tens divided by 9 gives a remainder of n, and that x hundreds divided by 9 gives a remainder of x, and so on. He should now be able, after a brief mental calculation, to give the remainder when any four-digit number is divided by 9.

EXERCISES (1)

1. Illustrate, using a picture of an array, why 33 is not a prime number.
2. Construct a six-row sieve from 1 to 100. Systematically cross out all numerals that do not name primes.
3. Devise a test for divisibility by four. (*Hint:* Write several numerals in expanded notation and make use of the right distributive property of division over addition. Observe which numbers are always divisible by four.)
4. Working with expanded notation, see if you can construct a rule for divisibility by 15. (*Hint:* Is 15 a prime number?)
5. Find the remainders for each pair of problems and then see if you can construct a rule for divisibility by 11:

   a. $11\overline{)(7000 + 20) + (300 + 4)}$ $11\overline{)7324}$

   b. $11\overline{)(7000 + 50) + (500 + 7)}$ $11\overline{)7557}$

   c. $11\overline{)90 + (600 + 3)}$ $11\overline{)693}$

   d. $11\overline{)(3000 + 80) + 0}$ $11\overline{)3080}$

   e. $11\overline{)(9000 + 90) + (300 + 4)}$ $11\overline{)9394}$

6. Make up a rule for divisibility by six.
7. Find the answer to the following questions by using one or more of the references at the end of this chapter:
   a. How many prime numbers are there?
   b. What are twin primes?
   c. What are prime triplets?
   d. What is Goldbach's Conjecture?
   e. What is Wilson's Theorem?

13.4. *Perfect Numbers*

Undertaking the task of classifying various subsets of the set of counting numbers will necessitate our first studying the technique of deriving the set of divisors of a given number.

In constructing the set of divisors, we find that 1 and the number itself are always members of this set. Our rules for divisibility will facilitate finding other divisors. For example, let us find the set of divisors of the number 276. Figure 13.14 illustrates how our analysis might proceed.

Number	Divisors	Reason
276	1 and 276	Every number is divisible by itself and the number 1
	2	Satisfies rule for divisibility by 2
	138	Because $276 \div 2 = 138$ implies $276 \div 138 = 2$
	3	Satisfies rule for divisibility by 3
	92	Because $276 \div 3 = 92$ implies $276 \div 92 = 3$
	4	Because 276 is divisible by 4
	69	Because $276 \div 4 = 69$ implies $276 \div 69 = 4$
	6	Because divisible by both 2 and 3
	46	Because $276 \div 6 = 46$ implies $276 \div 46 = 6$
	12	Because divisible by both 3 and 4
	23	Because $276 \div 12 = 23$ implies $276 \div 23 = 12$

FIGURE 13.14

Thus, we have discovered the set of divisors of 276 is {1, 2, 3, 4, 6, 12, 23, 46, 69, 138, 276}. Sometimes we can eliminate a divisor on the basis of a divisibility rule, such as in the case of eliminating 5 as a divisor of 276, because the ones place contains neither 5 nor 0. Other times, such as in the case of 7 and 13, where a simple rule of divisibility is absent, we must perform the division. When we reach a point—in this case, 23—where we have tested all numbers up to one of the divisors in our descending sequence of divisors, we no longer have to test any larger numbers.

We refer to the set of all divisors of a number, except the number itself, as a set of *proper divisors*. This set of proper divisors will be very important in our effort to repartition the set of counting numbers. Figure 13.15 depicts several sets of proper divisors.

If a number is equal to the sum of its proper divisors, we call it a *perfect number*. If a number is less than the sum of its proper divisors, it is called an *abundant number*. And if a number is neither an abundant nor a perfect

Set of proper divisors

1	∅
2	{1}
3	{1}
30	{1, 2, 3, 5, 6, 10, 15}
36	{1, 2, 3, 4, 6, 9, 12, 18}

FIGURE 13.15

number, we say it is a *deficient number.* For example, 12 is an abundant number, because $12 < 1 + 2 + 3 + 4 + 6$. 6 is a perfect number, because $6 = 1 + 2 + 3$. And 10 is a deficient number, because $10 > 1 + 2 + 5$.

13.5. *Constructing Factor Trees*

Our technique of using either divisibility tests or actually testing a trial divisor by division is an inefficient technique for obtaining the set of proper divisors. In this section, we shall explore more refined techniques of determining the proper divisors of a number.

As we have seen, each number can have an infinite set of factor names if we allow 1 to be used as a factor. In order to restrict the number of factors a number can have, we shall restrict the use of ones to those numbers that would have no factor names if 1 were excluded. For example, $1 = 1 \times 1$, and $13 = 1 \times 13$. We shall further restrict the number that can serve as a factor by specifying that each factor must be either a prime or the number 1.

The following factor names satisfy our present restrictions: $3 \times 1, 1 \times 3$, $2 \times 3 \times 5, 7 \times 7 \times 2 \times 5, 2 \times 5 \times 7 \times 7, 2 \times 7 \times 5 \times 7, 7 \times 2 \times 7 \times 5$. Upon obtaining the product using these factor names, you would recognize that names with the same factors, regardless of order, name the same product. Because changing the order of the factors does not give us a new number, we shall by convention order our factor names from the smallest factor named on the left, and proceeding in a left-to-right manner, list the larger factor named always to the right of the smaller factors. For example, $2 \times 2 \times 3 \times 7 \times 13 \times 29$ follows this technique of ordering factors.

Let us examine how we can obtain systematically a factor name in this form. Consider the number 60: we find that 2 is a factor giving us 2×30;

2 is a factor of 30 giving us $2 \times 2 \times 15$; 3 is a factor of 15, giving us $2 \times 2 \times 3 \times 5$; and because 5 is a prime, we are finished. Figure 13.16 denotes this analysis using a factor tree. Note that our factors are located at the ends of the branches.

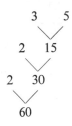

FIGURE 13.16

Figure 13.17 depicts several factor trees that have been derived by such analysis. (Note that when the original number is a prime, the branches consist of 1 and the prime.)

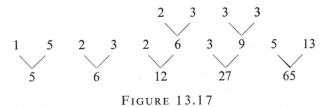

FIGURE 13.17

Because we shall have a need later to distinguish between the fact that 2 is a factor of a given number and 2 twos are factors of a given number, we shall identify our factors by subscripts. For example, 2_1 will indicate that this is the first 2, and 2_2 will indicate that this is the second 2. By using subscripts we can talk about the complete set of prime factors for a given number. For example, $\{2_1, 2_2, 3_1, 3_2\}$ is the complete set of prime factors of 36.

13.6. *Least Common Multiple*

By obtaining the union of two complete sets of prime factors for two numbers, it is possible to find the least common multiple of these two numbers. Figure 13.18 depicts the derivation of several least common multiples via the union of complete sets of prime factors.

We use the least common multiple to obtain a common divisor when adding fractional numbers. For example, knowing that 8 is the least common multiple of 4 and 8, shows us how to modify $\frac{3}{4} + \frac{1}{8}$ to $\frac{3 \times 2}{4 \times 2} + \frac{1}{8} = \frac{6}{8} + \frac{1}{8}$ so that the right distributive property of division over addition can be used.

Set of numbers	Union of complete sets of factors	Least common multiple
35 and 25	$\{5_1, 7_1\} \cup \{5_1, 5_2\} = \{5_1, 5_2, 7_1\}$	$5 \times 5 \times 7 = 175$
6 and 8	$\{2_1, 3_1\} \cup \{2_1, 2_2, 2_3\} =$ $\{2_1, 2_2, 2_3, 3_1\}$	$2 \times 2 \times 2 \times 3 = 24$
3 and 10	$\{1_1{}^*, 3_1\} \cup \{2_1, 5_1\} = \{1_1, 2_1, 3_1, 5_1\}$	$1 \times 2 \times 3 \times 5 = 30$
4 and 8	$\{2_1, 2_2\} \cup \{2_1, 2_2, 2_3\} = \{2_1, 2_2, 2_3\}$	$2 \times 2 \times 2 = 8$

* 1 is not a prime, but it is needed in order to make it possible to list 3 as a factor.

FIGURE 13.18

13.7. *Greatest Common Divisor*

By obtaining the intersection of two complete sets of prime factors for two numbers, it is possible to find the greatest common divisor of these two numbers. Figure 13.19 depicts the derivation of several greatest common divisors via the intersection of complete sets of prime factors.

We use the greatest common divisor to find the simplest form for a set of equivalent fractions. For example, given $\frac{18}{24}$, the intersection of the complete set of factors of 18 and 24 is $\{2_1, 3_1, 3_2\} \cap \{2_1, 2_2, 2_3, 3_1\} = \{2_1, 3_1\}$; therefore, 6 is the greatest common divisor. Using the compensation property $\frac{18 \div 6}{24 \div 6}$, we obtain $\frac{3}{4}$, which is the simplest form in the set of equivalent fractions.

Set of numbers	Intersection of complete sets of factors	Greatest common divisor
35 and 25	$\{5_1, 7_1\} \cap \{5_1, 5_2\} = \{5_1\}$	5
12 and 8	$\{2_1, 2_2, 3_1\} \cap \{2_1, 2_2, 2_3\} = \{2_1, 2_2\}$	$2 \times 2 = 4$
3 and 10	$\{1_1, 3_1\} \cap \{2_1, 5_1\} = \{\quad\}$	1*
4 and 8	$\{2_1, 2_2\} \cap \{2_1, 2_2, 2_3\} = \{2_1, 2_2\}$	$2 \times 2 = 4$

* Because no common prime factor was obtained and because 1 is a factor of every number, the greatest common divisor must be 1.

FIGURE 13.19

13.8. *Figurate "Numbers"*

Figurate "numbers" get their name from the fact that the mathematical model of dots used to represent a set with a stated number property can be structured to depict triangles, squares, pentagons, and so forth. For example, 4 is said to be a square number because it can be depicted as " :: "

Of special importance in studying figurate numbers is not the model, but the series that relates to this model. For example, consider the following representations of triangular numbers as shown in Figure 13.20. Notice that the series 1, 1 + 2, 1 + 2 + 3, 1 + 2 + 3 + 4, and so forth, is suggested by these models.

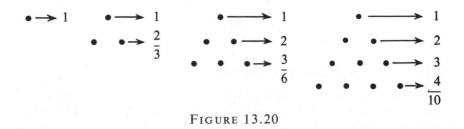

FIGURE 13.20

Of even greater interest is the series generated for square numbers. Notice in Figure 13.21 the remarkable relationship that exists between the sum of n consecutive odd numbers and n^2.

Such unusual relationships, which are found through exploration with number patterns, provide the child with a sense of discovery and achievement. The child who recognizes that any series of calculations may reveal a remarkable pattern views such calculations not as a task, but as a vehicle to discovery. It is the teacher's responsibility to "unlock the door to the hallway of number theory," because through this hall many children gain their first

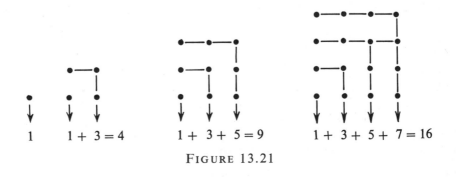

1   1 + 3 = 4   1 + 3 + 5 = 9   1 + 3 + 5 + 7 = 16

FIGURE 13.21

glimpses and appreciation of the real beauty of mathematics. Number theory truly offers the child his first opportunity to explore mathematics on his own.

EXERCISES (2)

1. Which of the following are perfect numbers?
   a. 284   b. 220   c. 284   d. 496
2. Construct factor trees for the following numbers:
   a. 990   b. 611   c. 492   d. 512
3. Find the least common multiple for each pair of numbers:
   a. 234, 126   b. 108, 125   c. 221, 26   d. 184, 123
4. The following dot patterns serve as models for pentagonal numbers. What is the accompanying series?

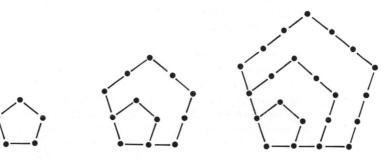

5. Find the answers to the following questions by using one or more of the references at the end of this chapter:
   a. What are the Mersenne numbers?
   b. What do we know about the number of perfect numbers?
   c. What do we know of odd perfect numbers?
   d. What are amicable numbers?
   e. What are magic squares?

REFERENCES

BANKS, J. HOUSTON, *Learning and Teaching Arithmetic*, Boston: Allyn & Bacon, 1964, pp. 204, 356–362.

BELL, CLIFFORD, CLELA D. HAMMOND, and ROBERT HERRERA, *Fundamentals of Arithmetic for Teachers*, New York: John Wiley & Sons, Inc., 1962, pp. 59–77, 117–130.

BRUMFIEL, CHARLES, ROBERT EICHOLZ, and MERRILL SHANKS, *Fundamental Concepts of Elementary Mathematics*, Reading, Mass.: Addison-Wesley, 1962, pp. 69–79, 112–115.

BRUMFIEL, CHARLES, ROBERT EICHOLZ, MERRILL SHANKS, and P. G. O'DAFFER, *Principles of Arithmetic*, Reading, Mass.: Addison-Wesley, 1963, pp. 75–93.

CROUCH, RALPH, GEORGE BALDWIN, and ROBERT J. WISNER, *Preparatory Mathematics for Elementary Teachers*, New York: John Wiley & Sons, Inc., 1965, pp. 122–125, 224, 229–234.

DUTTON, WILBUR, and L. J. ADAMS, *Arithmetic for Teachers*, Englewood Cliffs, N.J.: Prentice-Hall, Inc., 1963.

EDUCATIONAL RESEARCH COUNCIL OF GREATER CLEVELAND, *Key Topics in Mathematics for the Primary Teacher*, Chicago: Science Research Associates, Inc., 1962, pp. 48–66.

EVENSON, A. B., *Modern Mathematics: Introductory Concepts and Their Implications*, Chicago: Scott, Foresman and Co., 1962, pp. 37–40.

FLOURNOY, FRANCES, *Elementary School Mathematics*, Washington, D.C.: The Center for Applied Research in Education, 1964, pp. 29–32.

HACKER, SIDNEY G., WILFORD E. BARNES, and CALVIN T. LONG, *Fundamental Concepts of Arithmetic*, Englewood Cliffs, N.J.: Prentice-Hall, Inc., pp. 14, 201, 207, 217, 224.

HEDDENS, JAMES W., *Today's Mathematics, A Guide to Concepts and Methods in Elementary School Mathematics*, Chicago: Science Research Associates, Inc., 1964, pp. 169–170, 193–200.

MARKS, JOHN L., JAMES R. SMART, and IRENE SAUBLE, *Enlarging Mathematical Ideas*, Boston: Ginn and Company, 1961, pp. 13–17.

NATIONAL COUNCIL OF TEACHERS OF MATHEMATICS, *Enrichment Mathematics for the Grades, Twenty-seventh Yearbook*, Washington, D.C.: The National Council of Teachers of Mathematics, 1963, pp. 266–268.

NATIONAL COUNCIL OF TEACHERS OF MATHEMATICS, *Instruction in Arithmetic, Twenty-fifth Yearbook*, Washington, D.C.: The National Council of Teachers of Mathematics, 1960, pp. 81–83.

NATIONAL COUNCIL OF TEACHERS OF MATHEMATICS, *The Growth of Mathematical Ideas, Grades K–12, Twenty-fourth Yearbook*, Washington, D.C.: The National Council of Teachers of Mathematics, 1959, pp. 61, 134.

OSBORN, ROGER, VERE DEVAULT, CLAUDE BOYD, and ROBERT HOUSTON, *Extending Mathematics Understanding*, Columbus, Ohio: Charles E. Merrill Books, Inc., 1961, pp. 41–49, 52–58.

SCHOOL MATHEMATICS STUDY GROUP, *Studies in Mathematics, Vol. IX: A Brief Course in Mathematics for Elementary School Teachers*, Stanford, Calif.: Stanford University Press, 1963, pp. 77–91, 93–105, 107–126.

SMITH, SEATON E., JR., *Explorations in Elementary Mathematics*, Englewood Cliffs, N.J.: Prentice-Hall, Inc., 1966, pp. 91–99.

STEWART, B. M., *Theory of Numbers*, 2nd ed., New York: The Macmillan Company, 1964, pp. 33–34, 50, 54.

SWAIN, ROBERT L., and EUGENE D. NICHOLS, *Understanding Arithmetic*, New York: Holt, Rinehart and Winston, Inc., 1965, pp. 207–209.

SWENSON, ESTHER J., *Teaching Arithmetic to Children*, New York: The Macmillan Company, 1964, pp. 294–333.

THORPE, CLEATA B., *Teaching Elementary Arithmetic*, New York: Harper & Row, Publishers, Inc., 1962, pp. 132–142, 144–156.

VAN ENGEN, HENRY, MAURICE L. HARTUNG, and JAMES E. STOCHL, *Foundations of Elementary School Arithmetic*, Chicago: Scott, Foresman and Co., 1965, pp. 216–223, 227.

WARD, MORGAN, and CLARENCE HARDGROVE, *Modern Elementary Mathematics*, Reading, Mass.: Addison-Wesley, 1964, pp. 85–91.

WILLIAMS, SAMMIE, GARLAND H. READ, JR., and FRANK L. WILLIAMS, *Modern Mathematics in the Elementary and Junior High Schools*, Syracuse, N.Y.: L. W. Singer, 1961, pp. 48–50.

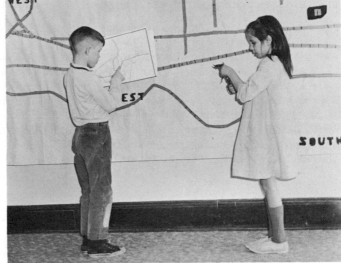

Maps can be used to motivate a child to learn mathematics.

14

Teaching the Integers

14.1. *Introduction*

L ONG BEFORE the child formally studies the set of directed numbers we call *integers*, he has been exposed to many instances of their application. For example, listening to reports of weather around the country he hears the announcer say that it is 20 degrees below zero in Bismarck, North Dakota. Listening to his father discuss his business affairs, he hears that the company went a thousand dollars into the "red" that year. Watching a rocket being launched on television, he sees . . . , $-9, -8, -7, -6, -5, -4, -3, -2,$ $-1, 0, 1, 2, 3, . . .$ flashed on the screen, one numeral at a time. Playing a game, he notes that he has gone five in the "hole" by landing on a disk that says to take 10 points from your score. He hears the teacher refer to "three hours ago," or the football announcer say that the team made a "minus 34-yard gain in the first half."

Whereas a rigorous introduction of integers is postponed until the junior high, the basic properties of integers and operations on the set of integers are developed intuitively at the elementary level. Although there exists an isomorphic relationship between the non-negative directed numbers and the set of whole numbers that the child has studied, these sets are quite distinct. For example, let a, b, c, and d be whole numbers and let a^1, b^1, c^1, and d^1 be the integers we associate with a, b, c, and d. We then say that there is an isomorphic relation between the set of whole numbers and the set of non-negative numbers, because when $a + b = c$, then $a^1 + b^1 = c^1$; and when $a \times b = d$, then $a^1 \times b^1 = d^1$. Even though both of these sets behave identically under the same operation, it is probably best to have the child make this discovery rather than have you make the statement that the non-negative numbers *are* the set of whole numbers.

14.2. *Introducing the Concept of Integers*

It is a primary responsibility of the teacher to help the child recognize a need for integers. This need is not only mathematical—for example, we need a number that satisfies the equation $\square + 5 = 0$—but is also practical. For example, we have occasions when "5 being the number property of a set" does not fully convey the number property of the set. A bill for five dollars and a check for five dollars are entirely different uses of fiveness.

In grades after the elementary grades, it is a simple matter to define directed numbers and proceed to establish their place in the hierarchy of number systems. At the elementary level, we must proceed in a more intuitive manner in order to transit smoothly from the set of whole numbers to the set of integers.

Let us consider how one might intuitively introduce the integers via a map. Assume that John lived in the house labeled (*a*) in Figure 14.1. What would the students immediately notice if you were to say that Mary lives in the second house from John's house? The children would immediately say that you could not tell which house Mary lives in from those directions. What you have done is create a need for conveying more information.

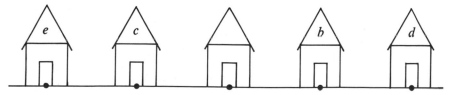

FIGURE 14.1

Discuss with the children various ways that we can communicate to someone which house Mary lives in, if she lives in the house labeled (*d*). For example, you might say that she lives in the second house to the right of John's house, if you are facing John's house. Or you might write $\overrightarrow{2}$ where the arrow tells us which way to go from John's house and the 2 tells us how many houses from John's house. Or you might write *r*2 where the *r* tells us to go right and the 2 tells us to go two houses, and so on. Let the children discuss how to symbolize directions for going to various houses from John's house.

Let us now settle on one type of symbolism and rename all of the houses in terms of their location with respect to John's house. (See Figure 14.2.)

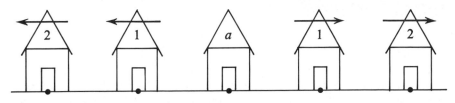

FIGURE 14.2

We are left with the problem of telling everyone where John's house is. Obviously, John's house is neither to the right nor left of John's house. Therefore, we use neither a ← symbol nor a → to mark the location of John's house. This is a very important principle relating to what we shall come to call the zero of the set of integers. This zero is neither positive nor negative, although there will be times when it will be desirable to define it either as positive or negative, such as when programming a computer. Because we go zero houses from John's house to get to John's house, it is appropriate that we name the location of John's house zero.

Having established a zero and the sets of numbers that will be related to zero, we are at a point where we can explore operations on this new set of numbers.

14.3. *Addition on the Set of Integers*

Where would we be if we went to $\overrightarrow{2}$ and then went 3 houses to the right of this house? Symbolically, we might express this idea as $\overrightarrow{2}$ followed by $\overrightarrow{3} = \square$. Extending our map, we see that this would take us to house $\overrightarrow{5}$. Therefore, we will say that $\overrightarrow{2}$ followed by $\overrightarrow{3} = \overrightarrow{5}$. Similarly, we could ask where we would be if we went to $\overrightarrow{2}$ and then went 3 houses to the left. Symbolically, we might express this idea as $\overrightarrow{2}$ followed by $\overleftarrow{3} = \square$. We see that this would take us to house $\overleftarrow{1}$. Therefore, we say that $\overrightarrow{2}$ followed by $\overleftarrow{3} = \overleftarrow{1}$.

We are now at a position where we can explore certain properties attributable to the operation "followed by" on the set of directed numbers.

E X E R C I S E S (1)

1. What relationship might the student discover if (using the map) he found solutions to the following problems and then studied the patterns that brought about these solutions?

a. $\vec{3}$ followed by $\overleftarrow{3}$ = □   c. $\vec{5}$ followed by $\overleftarrow{5}$ = □

b. $\overleftarrow{2}$ followed by $\vec{2}$ = □   d. 0 followed by 0 = □

2. What property might the student discover if he found solutions to the following problems and then studied the patterns that brought about these solutions?

a. $\vec{3}$ followed by 0 = □   c. 0 followed by $\overleftarrow{4}$ = □

b. $\overleftarrow{2}$ followed by 0 = □   d. 0 followed by $\vec{1}$ = □

3. What property might the student discover if he found solutions to the following problems and then studied the patterns that brought about these solutions?

1a. $\vec{3}$ followed by $\overleftarrow{2}$ = □   3a. $\vec{1}$ followed by $\vec{2}$ = □

 b. $\overleftarrow{2}$ followed by $\vec{3}$ = □   b. $\vec{2}$ followed by $\vec{1}$ = □

2a. $\overleftarrow{4}$ followed by $\overleftarrow{2}$ = □   4a. $\vec{2}$ followed by $\vec{4}$ = □

 b. $\overleftarrow{2}$ followed by $\overleftarrow{4}$ = □   b. $\vec{4}$ followed by $\vec{2}$ = □

4. What property might the student discover if he found solutions to the following problems and then studied the patterns that brought about these solutions?

1a. ($\vec{2}$ followed by $\vec{3}$) followed by $\overleftarrow{1}$ = □

 b. $\vec{2}$ followed by ($\vec{3}$ followed by $\overleftarrow{1}$) = □

2a. $\overleftarrow{3}$ followed by ($\overleftarrow{4}$ followed by $\vec{5}$) = □

 b. ($\overleftarrow{3}$ followed by $\overleftarrow{4}$) followed by $\vec{5}$ = □

3a. ($\overleftarrow{2}$ followed by $\vec{1}$) followed by $\overleftarrow{4}$ = □

 b. $\overleftarrow{2}$ followed by ($\vec{1}$ followed by $\overleftarrow{4}$) = □

As you have probably surmised, the operation "followed by" is equivalent to addition. Therefore, let us replace the words "followed by" by the symbol +.

Thus, we have established the meaning behind an operation before we have introduced the symbol for it. This is consistent with the sequence we should employ generally in introducing symbolism.

After establishing the arbitrariness of the symbol chosen to depict our new set of numbers, we can proceed to the more standard symbols for integers. By convention, man has decided to affix − to all numerals to the left of zero on the number line and + to all numerals to the right of zero on the number line. (While some series affix only the −, this author believes that in early activities with integers an effort should be made to distinguish the positive integers from the nonzero whole numbers. After the isomorphic relationship between the sets of non-negative integers and the set of whole numbers has been established, the + may be dropped.) Thus we see that $\overrightarrow{3} + \overleftarrow{2}$ translates to $^{+}3 + {}^{-}2$ (read "positive three plus negative two").

14.4. *Subtraction on the Set of Integers*

We can lay the groundwork for the development of subtraction by having the students investigate patterns such as "$^{-}3 + {}^{+}3 = 0$," "$^{+}7 + {}^{-}7 = 0$," "$^{-}2 + {}^{+}2 = 0$," and so on. Because of this relationship, we say that $^{-}3$ is the opposite of $^{+}3$, $^{+}7$ is the opposite of $^{-}7$, $^{-}2$ is the opposite of $^{+}2$, and so forth.

We are now ready to look at an operation we shall call "followed by the opposite of." We see that

> $^{+}7$ followed by the opposite of $^{-}2$ means
> $^{+}7$ followed by $^{+}2$, and
> $^{-}3$ followed by the opposite of $^{+}4$ means
> $^{-}3$ followed by $^{-}4$.

Returning to our number line, we discover that

> $^{+}7$ followed by the opposite of $^{-}2 = {}^{+}9$, and
> $^{-}3$ followed by the opposite of $^{+}4 = {}^{-}7$.

After having thus established the meaning behind our operation, we introduce the symbol − for "followed by the opposite of." We now explore the following related number sentences:

$$
\begin{array}{lcl}
^{-}3 - {}^{-}2 = {}^{-}1 & \text{and} & ^{-}1 + {}^{-}2 = {}^{-}3 \\
^{-}4 - {}^{+}2 = {}^{-}6 & \text{and} & ^{-}6 + {}^{+}2 = {}^{-}4 \\
^{+}8 - {}^{+}3 = {}^{+}5 & \text{and} & ^{+}5 + {}^{+}3 = {}^{+}8 \\
^{+}5 - {}^{-}3 = {}^{+}8 & \text{and} & ^{+}8 + {}^{-}3 = {}^{+}5
\end{array}
$$

Thus we see that the operations of addition and subtraction for integers are related in the same way that addition and subtraction were related for the set of whole numbers. We can also explore the concept that for every integer x and y, $(x - y)$ equals an integer. In other words, the set of integers is closed under subtraction.

EXERCISES (2)

1. What property is being investigated by the following set of paired problems? What discovery do we hope the children will make by working these problems?

   a. $^+6 - {}^+3 = \square$ c. $^-3 - {}^-2 = \square$ e. $^-4 - {}^+3 = \square$
   b. $^+3 - {}^+6 = \square$ d. $^-2 - {}^-3 = \square$ f. $^+3 - {}^-4 = \square$

2. What conclusion would the child draw about the associative property for subtraction by working the following pairs of problems?

   a. $(^+3 - {}^-2) - {}^+4 = \square$ c. $(^-5 - {}^+4) - {}^-1 = \square$
   b. $^+3 - (^-2 - {}^+4) = \square$ d. $^-5 - (^+4 - {}^-1) = \square$

3. What relationship that we have previously discussed are we attempting to reestablish with the following sets of paired problems?

   a. $^+6 - {}^+2 = \square$ c. $^-3 - {}^+2 = \square$ e. $^-4 - {}^-5 = \square$
   b. $^+6 + {}^-2 = \square$ d. $^-3 + {}^-2 = \square$ f. $^-4 - {}^+5 = \square$

4. What property of subtraction on the set of whole numbers does the following pattern relate to?

   a. $^+3 - {}^-6 = \square$ c. $^-3 - {}^-9 = \square$
   b. $(^+3 - {}^-4) - (^-6 - {}^-4) = \square$ d. $(\ 3 + {}^+7) - (^-9 + {}^+7) = \square$

14.5. *Teaching Multiplication and Division of Integers*

The topic of multiplication of integers is not developed extensively at the elementary school level. However, if we are ready to make a few assumptions about the isomorphic relationship that exists between operations on the set of non-negative integers and the operations on the set of whole numbers, the operation of multiplication on the set of integers offers the elementary teacher a real opportunity to introduce the child to mathematical proof.

In order to illustrate this, let us make the following assumptions:

> If a, b, and c are whole numbers, and a^1, b^1, and c^1 are their corresponding non-negative integers, then $a \times b = c$ implies $a^1 \times b^1 = c^1$. For example, if $3 \times 4 = 12$, then $^+3 \times {}^+4 = {}^+12$. The distributive property for multiplication over subtraction behaves in exactly the same manner for the set of integers as it does for the set of whole numbers. For example, if $6 \times (4 - 2) = (6 \times 4) - (6 \times 2)$, then $^+6 \times (^+4 - {}^+2) = (^+6 \times {}^+4) - (^+6 \times {}^+2)$.

With these assumptions, we can now proceed to establish that a positive integer times a negative integer gives a product that is a negative integer. Consider the following:

$^+6 \times {}^-3 = {}^+6 \times (^+1 - {}^+4)$	renaming
$^+6 \times (^+1 - {}^+4) = (^+6 \times {}^+1) - (^+6 \times {}^+4)$	distributive property of multiplication over subtraction
$(^+6 \times {}^+1) - (^+6 \times {}^+4) = {}^+6 - {}^+24$	multiplication of positive integers
$^+6 - {}^+24 = {}^-18$	

Thus, we have established that $^+6 \times {}^-3 = {}^-18$. By a similar proof we could establish for each pair of integers (one negative and one positive) that the product is negative. We can now proceed to "prove" that a negative integer times a negative integer is a positive integer. Consider the following:

$^-6 \times {}^-3 = {}^-6 \times (^+1 - {}^+4)$	renaming
$^-6 \times (^+1 - {}^+4) = (^-6 \times {}^+1) - (^-6 \times {}^+4)$	distributive property of multiplication over subtraction
$(^-6 \times {}^+1) - (^-6 \times {}^+4) = {}^-6 - {}^-24$	previously proved relationship (negative times positive equals negative)
$^-6 - {}^-24 = {}^+18$	

After the rules of multiplication have been established via the distributive property of multiplication over addition, the basic properties for the operation of multiplication can be explored. The following set of problems is typical of those you might use to get children to discover the commutative property of multiplication:

a. $^-3 \times {}^+5 = \square$ a. $^-7 \times {}^-6 = \square$ a. $^+2 \times {}^+4 = \square$
b. $^+5 \times {}^-3 = \square$ b. $^-6 \times {}^-7 = \square$ b. $^+4 \times {}^+2 = \square$

Notice that these problems have included each possible combination of negative and positive integers. It is not sufficient to structure the discovery exercises so that the child discovers that the commutative property holds for just one of the cases, such as a negative times a negative. All the combinations should be explored. In a like manner, the associative property can be explored with your class. The following problems are representative of the cases you may want to include in the exploration exercises:

$$(^+6 \times {}^+4) \times {}^+5 = \square \qquad {}^-2 \times (^-5 \times {}^+6) = \square$$
$$^+6 \times (^+4 \times {}^+5) = \square \qquad (^-2 \times {}^-5) \times {}^+6 = \square$$

$$(^-3 \times {}^+2) \times {}^+6 = \square \qquad (^-7 \times {}^+9) \times {}^-8 = \square$$
$$^-3 \times (^+2 \times {}^+6) = \square \qquad {}^-7 \times (^+9 \times {}^-8) = \square$$

$$^+2 \times (^-4 \times {}^+7) = \square \qquad (^+3 \times {}^-9) \times {}^-4 = \square$$
$$(^+2 \times {}^-4) \times {}^+7 = \square \qquad {}^+3 \times (^-9 \times {}^-4) = \square$$

$$(^+3 \times {}^+5) \times {}^-2 = \square \qquad {}^-2 \times (^-3 \times {}^-8) = \square$$
$$^+3 \times (^+5 \times {}^-2) = \square \qquad (^-2 \times {}^-3) \times {}^-8 = \square$$

Having established the multiplication of integers, it is a simple matter for you to define division as the inverse operation of multiplication and to proceed to establish the rules of signs for division. For example, $^+8 \div {}^-2 = {}^-4$, because $^-4 \times {}^-2 = {}^+8$.

EXERCISES (3)

1. Assuming $a \div b = c$ if $b \times c = a$, establish the following:

   a. $^+6 \div {}^-3 = {}^-2$ b. $^-6 \div {}^-3 = {}^+2$ c. $^+6 \div {}^+3 = {}^|2$

2. Create pairs of problems that could be used to help the child discover the compensation property for division of integers.
3. Create pairs of problems that could be used to aid the child in discovering the right distributive property of division over addition of integers.
4. Create pairs of problems that could be used to help the child discover the right distributive property of division over subtraction of integers.

14.6. *Ordering the Integers*

After introducing the child to integers, the teacher is in a position to develop several important inequality relationships. (We shall define an integer x as being less than an integer y if there exists a positive z such that $x + z = y$.)

We shall explore ways to develop intuitively some of the inequality relationships at the elementary level. The first of those we might develop is that for x, y, and z that are elements of the integers, if $x < y$, then $x + z < y + z$. This idea can be promoted by having the children explore the following types of problems:

Put a $<$ or $>$ in each of the following:

If $^+3 < {}^+5$, then $^+3 + {}^-2 \bigcirc {}^+5 + {}^-2$
If $^+3 < {}^+5$, then $^+3 + {}^+2 \bigcirc {}^+5 + {}^+2$
If $^+3 < {}^+5$, then $^-3 + {}^-2 \bigcirc {}^+5 + {}^-2$
If $^-3 < {}^+5$, then $^-3 + {}^+5 \bigcirc {}^+5 + {}^+5$
If $^-5 < {}^-3$, then $^-5 + {}^-2 \bigcirc {}^-3 + {}^-2$
If $^-5 < {}^-3$, then $^-5 + {}^+5 \bigcirc {}^-3 + {}^+5$

Although no number of such examples serves to prove the suspected relationship, it is sufficient in the elementary school to promote the suspicion that such a relationship exists for all integers.

Another relationship to which the children can be "exposed" is the following: For every x, y, and z that are elements of the integers, if $x < y$, then $x - z < y - z$. This idea can be promoted by having the children explore the following types of problems:

Put a $<$ or $>$ in each of the following:

If $^+3 < {}^+5$, then $^+3 - {}^+6 \bigcirc {}^+5 - {}^+6$
If $^+3 < {}^+5$, then $^+3 - {}^-6 \bigcirc {}^+5 - {}^-6$
If $^-3 < {}^+5$, then $^-3 - {}^+6 \bigcirc {}^+5 - {}^+6$
If $^-3 < {}^+5$, then $^-3 - {}^-6 \bigcirc {}^+5 - {}^-6$
If $^-5 < {}^-3$, then $^-5 - {}^+6 \bigcirc {}^-3 - {}^+6$
If $^-5 < {}^-3$, then $^-5 - {}^-6 \bigcirc {}^-3 - {}^-6$

14.7. *Negative Exponents and Scientific Notation*

A useful technique for introducing the child to negative exponents is to do it via a pattern. For example, consider the following:

$$1000 = 10^3$$

$$\frac{1000}{10} = 100 = 10^2$$

$$\frac{100}{10} = 10 = 10^1$$

$$\frac{10}{10} = 1 = 10^0$$

Notice that in going from 1000 to 100 we have divided the 1000 by 10, and in going from 100 to 10 we have divided the 100 by 10, and so on. If we maintain this pattern to go from 1 to the next number, we shall divide the 1 by 10, giving us a quotient of $\frac{1}{10}$. At this point, we could ask the children to study the pattern 10^3, 10^2, 10^1, 10^0 and see what might be a logical exponent to affix to the 10 in order to maintain the pattern. A negative 1 would be the logical choice.

Continuing in this manner we can establish:

$$1 \div 10 = \tfrac{1}{10} = 10^{-1} = .1$$

$$\tfrac{1}{10} \div 10 = \tfrac{1}{100} = 10^{-2} = .01$$

$$\tfrac{1}{100} \div 10 = \tfrac{1}{1000} = 10^{-3} = .001$$

etc.

Having introduced scientific notation, you can have the children explore some simple translations into scientific notation where a negative exponent results.

Consider the following translations:

$$.004 \to 4 \times \tfrac{1}{1000} \to 4 \times 10^{-3}$$

$$.00009 \to 9 \times \tfrac{1}{100,000} \to 9 \times 10^{-5}$$

Notice that we have introduced an intermediate translation in order to highlight the meaning behind the negative power of 10. These intermediate steps are especially useful when the translation involves problems such as the following:

$$.014 \to 14 \times \tfrac{1}{1000} \to 1.4 \times 10 \times \tfrac{1}{1000} \to 1.4 \times \tfrac{1}{100} \to 1.4 \times 10^{-2}$$

$$.00127 \to 127 \times \tfrac{1}{100,000} \to 1.27 \times 100 \times \tfrac{1}{100,000} \to 1.27 \times \tfrac{1}{1000} \to 1.27 \times 10^{-3}$$

EXERCISES (4)

1. Create a set of problems that would lead the child to suspect that the following relationships are true:

   If $x > 0$ and $y < z$, then $y \cdot x < z \cdot x$, and if
   $x < 0$ and $y < z$, then $y \cdot x > z \cdot x$.

2. Create a set of problems that would lead the child to suspect that the following relationships are true:

   If $x > 0$ and y and z are divisible by x, and $y < z$, then $y \div x < z \div x$. Also, if $x < 0$ and y and z are divisible by x, and $y < z$, then $y \div x > z \div x$.

3. Translate each of the following to scientific notation:

    a. .3   c. .0034
    b. .003   d. .00471

4. Translate each of the following from scientific notation to decimal notation:

    a. 4×10^{-2} b. 3.4×10^{-9} c. 6.47×10^{-11}

5. Find three standard measures that can be expressed with scientific notation involving negative exponents.

REFERENCES

BANKS, J. HOUSTON, *Learning and Teaching Arithmetic*, Boston: Allyn & Bacon, 1964, pp. 206–212.

BELL, CLIFFORD, CLELA HAMMOND, and ROBERT HERRERA, *Fundamentals of Arithmetic for Teachers*, New York: John Wiley & Sons, Inc., 1962, pp. 296–298.

CROUCH, RALPH, GEORGE BALDIN, and ROBERT J. WISNER, *Preparatory Mathematics for Elementary Teachers*, New York: John Wiley & Sons, Inc., 1965, pp. 182–219.

LOVELL, K., *The Growth of Basic Mathematical and Scientific Concepts in Children*, New York: Philosophical Library, 1962, pp. 128–132.

PAGE, DAVID A., *Number Lines, Functions, and Fundamental Topics*, New York: The Macmillan Company, 1964, pp. 49–54.

PETERSON, JOHN A., and JOSEPH HASHISAKI, *Theory of Arithmetic*, New York: John Wiley & Sons, Inc., 1963, pp. 112–150.

SHIPP, DONALD E., and SAM ADAMS, *Developing Arithmetic Concepts and Skills*, Englewood Cliffs, N.J.: Prentice-Hall, Inc., 1964, pp. 169–176.

SMITH, SEATON E., JR., *Explorations in Elementary Mathematics*, Englewood Cliffs, N.J.: Prentice-Hall, Inc., 1966, pp. 67–76, 106–108.

STEWART, B. M., *Theory of Numbers*, 2nd ed., New York: The Macmillan Company, 1964, pp. 162–174.

VAN ENGEN, HENRY, MAURICE L. HARTUNG, and JAMES E. STOCHL, *Foundations of Elementary School Arithmetic*, Chicago: Scott, Foresman and Co., 1965, pp. 300–301.

WARD, MORGAN, and CLARENCE HARDGROVE, *Modern Elementary Mathematics*, Reading, Mass.: Addison-Wesley, 1964, pp. 271–294.

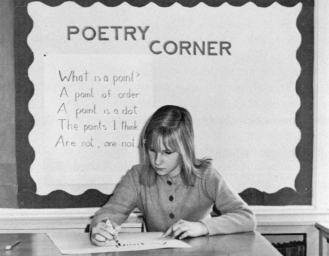

Language arts can motivate a child to learn mathematics.

POETRY CORNER

What is a point?
A point of order
A point is a dot
The points I think
Are not, are not

15

Geometry

15.1. *Introduction*

THE NATURE of the geometry appropriate for the elementary school is essentially informal as opposed to the geometry of the secondary school, which is based on proof. This informal approach is developed through "picture models," together with objects in the child's environment that serve as models. To a large extent, we might describe this geometry as one of classification and exploration.

The inclusion of more geometry in the curriculum helps give mathematics a broader and more flexible base than was possible under traditional programs that were oriented almost exclusively toward arithmetic. The nature of this geometry is such that it often complements and strengthens the arithmetic program. For example, by establishing a unit segment on a line, we can construct a number line that serves as a useful model with which to explore operations on the sets of whole numbers, fractional numbers, and integers.

15.2. *Points, Space, and Planes*

Geometry can be defined as the study of sets of points. This definition contains the undefined word *points*. In our study of geometry, we shall have many undefined words. Although we shall leave these words undefined and develop the concepts intuitively, it still will be possible to talk about properties that these "things" possess.

One of the properties we can attribute to a point is that it has no dimension (size). This property has implications for the teacher. If points have no size, and we choose to make a dot on a piece of paper to be our model of a point, then the smaller the dot, the better the representation. We must be careful that we do not give children misconceptions of geometrical ideas through grossly imperfect models. We shall use small dots to be pictures of points. These dots will give us a rough idea of the location of the point to which we are referring. Sometimes we shall want to make it clearly understood to which of the many points we are referring. In such cases, it will be convenient for us to name the point. We do this by placing a capital letter of the alphabet in close proximity to the dot picturing the point. In Figure 15.1, several points have been named.

$B \bullet$ R $K \bullet$

    $\bullet$ $\bullet Z$

        $\bullet A$

FIGURE 15.1

The set of all points constitutes space. This space goes on and on in all directions forever and ever. It is everywhere dense, which means that there are no locations in space where there are no points. There is nothing especially interesting about space per se; it is really the properties of particular subsets of space that are of prime interest to us.

The first subset of space on which we shall focus our attention is that set of points identified as a plane. Intuitively, we might imagine a plane as being like the surface of a very smooth table (or wall or ceiling) that goes on and on forever. A plane has infinite length and width, without "thickness." One of the properties we can attribute to a plane is that it is everywhere dense. In other words, there are no locations in the plane where there are no points. The teacher has many models available to him for conveying the idea of a plane to his students. Statements such as the following will help in developing the idea of a plane:

> "If we were to consider the surface of this desk to be extended right and left and front and back forever and ever, this surface would be a good model of what a plane is like."
>
> Or, "If we were to consider the surface of this wall to be extended up and down and right and left forever and ever, this surface would be a good model of a plane."

Any three points in space determine one plane. This basic idea of planes can be demonstrated to children by the following:

1. Have three children standing fairly close together select three points in space by letting the end of a finger of each mark the approximate location of one of these points.
2. Place a piece of masonite or plastic or other firm material on the tips of the fingers.
3. Have the children shift their fingers to determine another point.
4. Lead the children to see that two points would not fix a plane but, on the contrary, would allow an infinite set of planes to pass through the two points.
5. Lead the children to see that four points may or may not determine one plane.

Some or all of the following concepts can be investigated as one studies planes:

1. A set of points is coplanar if every point of the set lies in the same plane.
2. The intersection of two planes is a line.
3. When two planes do not have points in common, the planes are said to be parallel.

We shall be especially concerned in this chapter with subsets of this plane. Unless otherwise noted, all figures referred to in the next section will be understood to be subsets of this plane.

15.3. *Curves*

The simplest of all geometric figures is the curve. Curves can be classified as those finite in length (in other words, those whose length could be measured if we so wished), and those infinite in length (or nonmeasurable).

Let us see how we might introduce this concept to children. The following dialogue might be used to give children an intuitive "feel" for the variety of figures that comprises the curve that is finite in length.

"Draw two dots on your paper."
"Place the lead of your pencil on top of one of the dots."
"I am going to have you close your eyes and draw around the paper. When I tell you to open your eyes, either draw back to the dot from which you started, or draw to the other dot."
"Close your eyes. Draw around on your paper. Now open your eyes and draw to one of the dots."

(You may wish to have different children display their pictures at this time.) "You have each drawn a picture of a curve. How many different curves do you suppose there are?" (Many; so many you can't count them; etc.)

"Which of you drew over to the dot you started with? You have drawn a picture of what we call a closed curve. If you draw back to the dot you started from, you will always draw a picture of a closed curve."

At this point, you will wish to classify some pictures on the basis of their using one point or two points. In Figure 15.2, we see several curves classified on the basis of either one- or two-point derivations. Notice that it is possible to draw the figures in (a) with two points and the figures in (b) with one point.

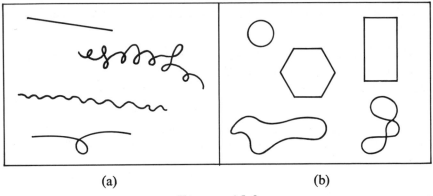

(a)   (b)

FIGURE 15.2

After the children have progressed to the stage where they can classify curves on the basis of one- or two-point origins, and thus can classify these paths into closed and nonclosed curves, they are ready to learn further techniques of classification.

Before undertaking this classification, we will introduce the child to two properties that may or may not be properties of a particular curve. The first of these properties is that a path may have endpoints. This concept could be developed intuitively as follows:

"Pretend that Curve A (Figure 15.3) is a narrow road along which you could ride a bicycle. You are not allowed to turn your bicycle around in the road. If you kept on riding in the direction shown, what would happen?" (You would come to the end of the road.)

"We call the point where the curve ends the endpoint. How many endpoints does Curve A have?" (Two.)

"Pretend that Curve *B* is a narrow road. If you kept riding on the curve, would you come to the end?" (No.) "We say that Curve *B* has zero endpoints."

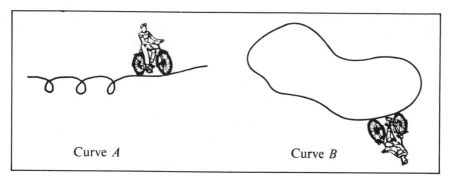

Curve *A*   Curve *B*

FIGURE 15.3

A second property is that a curve may have crosspoints.

"Pretend that you are riding your bicycle along a curve. If you reach a point on the curve where you have a choice of *which way* you would go, you call this type of point a crosspoint. We could also call these points 'decision points' or 'which way' points. This drawing (Figure 15.4) shows some cross-points in various curves."

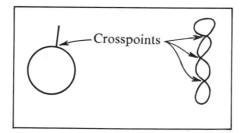

Crosspoints

FIGURE 15.4

So far, we have classified the set of curves as two subsets—those that are infinite in length and those that are finite in length. We have then classified the set of finite curves into two subsets consisting of closed curves and non-closed curves. We have identified the two properties which a curve can have. Now, on the basis of the property of crosspoints, we shall classify the set of closed curves into two subsets.

15.4. *Simple Closed Curves*

When a closed curve has zero crosspoints, we name this type a *simple closed curve*. Figure 15.5 shows sets of closed curves classified on the basis of having or not having crosspoints.

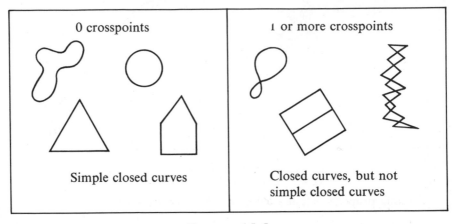

FIGURE 15.5

The simple closed curve partitions every plane into three disjoint sets of points. Let us examine how we might explore this concept with children. Pretend that a farmer has run one strand of wire around a field. In the field is a cow. The cow has learned that she cannot eat the grass directly under the wire, because every time she tries to do so, the wire gives her a shock. The cow has also learned that every time she tries to eat the grass on the other side of the wire, she gets a shock. The set of points that corresponds to where the cow can eat grass is called the interior region. The set of points corresponding to the grass directly under the fence (or, in other words, the simple closed curve) will be called the boundary. The set of points that is not the interior region and not the boundary is called the exterior region.

We say that the simple closed curve bounds a set of points. This set of points that is bounded is referred to as the interior region. Occasionally, we are interested in classifying the set of interior regions into two disjoint subsets consisting of convex regions and concave regions.

Let us see how we can distinguish a concave region from a convex region. A simple closed curve is pictured in Figure 15.6(a). Pretend that we stick pins all around the boundary of this curve, as in Figure 15.6(b). If we were to put a rubber band around our pins, as in Figure 15.6(c), we would find that it would not follow the boundary of our simple closed curve. When the path is such that the rubber band will not follow the boundary, we describe the figure as concave.

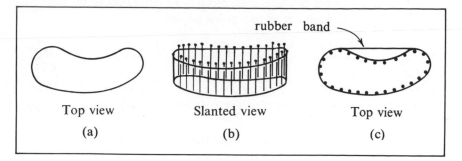

FIGURE 15.6

Figure 15.7 shows several concave figures paired with the pictures that would result if we did the same thing with the rubber band.

When the rubber band follows the *same* curve as the simple closed curve, we say the interior region represents a convex set of points.

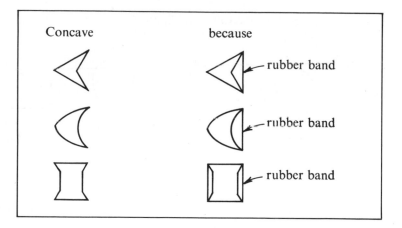

FIGURE 15.7

EXERCISES (1)

1. Review the properties of points. Which would be a better picture of a point, a large dot, or a small dot?
2. Select a point on your paper. Place a dot to mark the location of your point and give it a name.
3. Name five models that could be used to develop the idea of a plane.

4. Identify whether the following pictures of curves could be constructed via one-point or two-point origins.

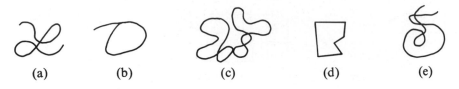

(a)   (b)   (c)   (d)   (e)

5. Identify the properties that each of the following curves have that prevent their being called simple closed curves.

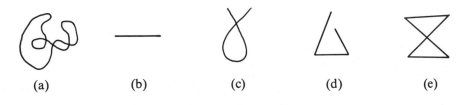

(a)   (b)   (c)   (d)   (e)

6. Tell whether each of the following figures bounds a convex or a concave region:

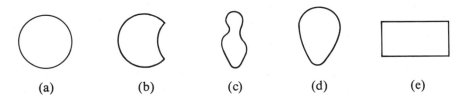

(a)   (b)   (c)   (d)   (e)

15.5. *Line Segment*

Before exploring other concepts relative to the simple closed curve, it will be necessary to develop the concept of a line segment.

If you were to take a very small pebble and let it drop to the floor, the path the pebble took would be like a line segment. Or, if two people were to pull tightly on the ends of a very fine wire, the path that the wire formed would be like a line segment. A line segment has the properties of being finite in length, without thickness, and with two endpoints.

We shall have occasion to refer to a line segment among many line segments.

$$R \qquad K$$

(a)   (b)

FIGURE 15.8

For this reason, it will be desirable to be able to give a name to a line segment. In Figure 15.8(a) we have pictured a line segment. In Figure 15.8(b), we have given letter names to the two endpoints. We can now refer to this line segment as $\overline{RK}$ (read line segment RK) or $\overline{KR}$ (read line segment KR).

15.6. *Polygons*

Line segments serve as the building blocks for a special subset of simple closed curves. When a simple closed curve is composed of line segments only, we call this curve a *polygon*. Figure 15.9 depicts a few members of the class of polygons.

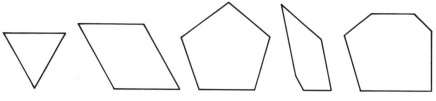

FIGURE 15.9

When two line segments are joined together in such a way that the joining forms an endpoint common to the two line segments, we refer to this common endpoint as a *vertex*. When more than two line segments are involved and more than one common endpoint is formed, these endpoints are referred to as *vertices*.

In Figure 15.10, the vertices of the polygons have been given names.

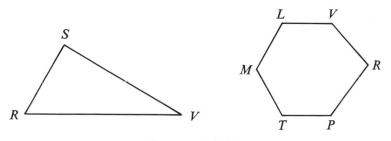

FIGURE 15.10

The line segments of the polygon are designated *sides* of the polygon. It is on the basis of the number of sides that a polygon has that we are able to classify further the polygons. Three-sided polygons are called *triangles*, four-sided polygons are called *quadrilaterals*, five-sided polygons are called *pentagons* and so on.

We shall not be able to classify these polygons further until we have explored the relationship called congruency that can exist between two line segments. Two line segments will be said to seem congruent if each measures the same length. For this to be a usable definition for children, we need to create a technique whereby they can determine when two pictured line segments measure the same length and, hence, seem congruent. Figure 15.11 shows how the edge of a piece of paper can be used to demonstrate that two line segments are congruent.

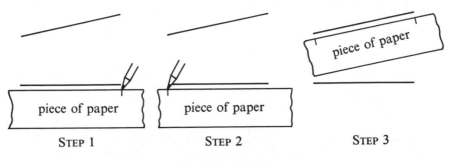

STEP 1   STEP 2   STEP 3

FIGURE 15.11

If we compare the sides of a triangle for the relationship of congruency, we can further classify the set of triangles. When we find a triangle in which no two sides are congruent, we call it a *scalene triangle*. When at least two sides of the triangle are congruent, it is classified as an *isosceles triangle*. When all three sides are congruent, we classify it as an *equilateral triangle*. If we compare the sides of a quadrilateral and discover that opposite sides are congruent, we classify this quadrilateral as a *parallelogram*. When a parallelogram has congruent adjacent sides, we classify this figure as a *rhombus*.

EXERCISES (2)

1. Draw a picture of a line segment. Name the line segment.
2. What properties in the following figures prevent their being called polygons? Answer for each figure.

(a)   (b)   (c)   (d)   (e)

3. What properties in the following figures prevent their being called triangles? Answer for each figure.

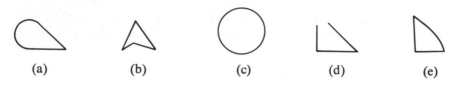

(a)   (b)   (c)   (d)   (e)

4. What properties in the following figures prevent their being called quadrilaterals? Answer for each figure.

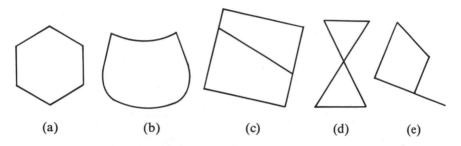

(a)   (b)   (c)   (d)   (e)

5. What properties in the following figures prevent their being called parallelograms? Answer for each figure.

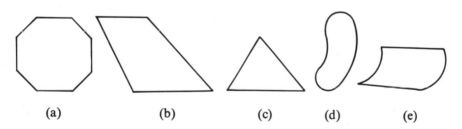

(a)   (b)   (c)   (d)   (e)

6. Tell whether each figure is a scalene triangle or an isosceles triangle or an equilateral triangle. (Remember, to be an isosceles triangle, the triangle must have at *least* two congruent sides.)

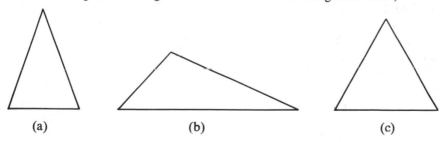

(a)   (b)   (c)

We need only one further concept in order to complete our classification of the polygons. We need to develop the concept of a diagonal of a polygon. Any line segment that connects a vertex of a polygon with a vertex not belonging to either of the two line segments forming the first vertex will be said to be a diagonal. Figure 15.12 illustrates various polygons with and without diagonals.

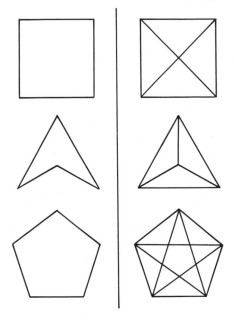

FIGURE 15.12

The relationship that exists between the number of diagonals of a polygon and the number of sides of the polygon is an interesting one. We find that a polygon with three sides can only have zero diagonals; one with four sides can only have two diagonals; one with five sides can only have five diagonals, and so on. Can you find the pattern? (Start with a quadrilateral. Construct the diagonals. Add a point in the exterior region such that going from this point to two adjacent vertices with line segments forms a pentagon. How many diagonals will this new vertex contribute? Continue this process of adding a dot to form a new vertex.)

We are now in a position to classify the parallelograms further on the basis of their having or not having congruent diagonals. If a parallelogram has congruent diagonals, then we call this parallelogram a *rectangle*. The set of all rectangles for which all sides are congruent is classified as *squares*. Figure 15.13 summarizes how we have classified the closed curve.

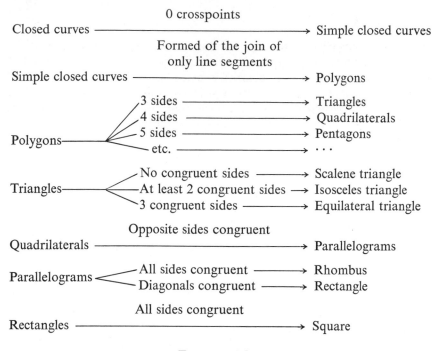

FIGURE 15.13

15.7. *Circle*

One other planar figure of general interest that is a simple closed curve but not a polygon is the *circle*. We might define a circle as a simple closed curve with the property that there exists a point in the interior region of the circle such that all line segments that could be considered with one endpoint as a boundary point and one endpoint as this point would be congruent. In more sophisticated language, the circle is a simple closed curve such that each boundary point is equidistant from some fixed point in the interior. This fixed point, which is equidistant from any point of the boundary, is the *center* of the circle.

A line segment from the center to the boundary is identified as a *radius*. Any line segment that has as endpoints two boundary points and also contains the center point is called a *diameter*. Any line segment with endpoints consisting of boundary points is identified as a *chord*. The diameter satisfies these requirements and can also be called a chord. The set of boundary points between two boundary points is referred to as an *arc*.

15.8. *Rays*

We have discussed how some of the curves of finite length are classified. Now we shall study the properties used to classify curves of infinite length.

Let us imagine that a line segment is extended forever and ever in one direction. A geometric figure of this type is called a *ray*. (See Figure 15.14.) The arrow denotes that the ray goes on in that direction forever and ever. An endpoint and one other point on the ray have been named. We name this ray $\overrightarrow{AK}$ (read ray *AK*).

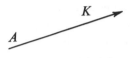

FIGURE 15.14

15.9. *Angles*

Just as the line segment served as the building block for the polygon, so the ray will serve as the building block for the figures we call *angles*. When two rays are joined (or the union of the two rays is taken) in such a way that a common endpoint is formed, we define the resultant figure as an angle.

Figure 15.15 depicts an angle. The endpoint common to the two rays is named the *vertex* of the angle. Notice that the vertex and one other point on each of the two rays has been given a name. With three such points named, we can name the angle. This angle is named $\angle$ *RKZ* (read angle *RKZ*).

FIGURE 15.15

Notice that the name of the vertex point is always placed between the names of the points on the ray that are not endpoints. (When there is no chance of ambiguity, it is permissible to refer to the angle by only its vertex name. For example, the previous angle could be designated $\angle$ *K*.)

It will be convenient to define a measure of an angle. Consider an angle that has a vertex corresponding to the center point of a circle. (See Figure 15.16.) This circle has been partitioned into 36 arcs of equal length. Each of these arcs will be said to be one degree in length and is indicated as follows: 10° (read one degree).

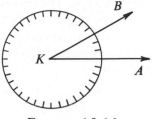

FIGURE 15.16

The measure of ∠ BKA is defined as the number of the 360 arcs between points A and B on the circle, if the number is less than 180. (A figure formed of the join of two rays, which has a measure of 180, will be defined as a line and not an angle.) In order to facilitate the determination of the measure of an angle, we use an instrument called a *protractor*, which has the measure of these arcs named. Figure 15.17 depicts how a protractor can be used to determine the measure of ∠ MAT. (Notice that one ray is placed along the radius defined by $\overline{AM}$.) The measure of this angle is 30°.

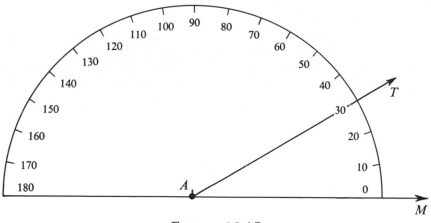

FIGURE 15.17

If the measure of an angle is 90°, this angle is named a *right angle*. If the measure is less than 90°, the angle is defined as an *acute angle*. If the angle's measure is greater than 90° and less than 180°, the angle is defined as an *obtuse angle*.

15.10. *Line*

If we consider a line segment as a subset of a set of points that goes on and on in both directions forever and ever, the line segment is a subset of a figure called a line. Figure 15.18 depicts a line. The arrows indicate that the line goes on and on in both directions without end. Notice that two points on the line have been named. Using these two named points, we give the line a name $\overleftrightarrow{XL}$ (read line *XL*). The line has the properties of being infinite in length, without thickness, and without endpoints.

FIGURE 15.18

Two lines will be said to be intersecting if they have one point in common. Two lines will be said to be parallel if they have no points in common. (Remember that we have specified that all of the figures we are considering are in a plane.) We now have new properties that will enable us to reclassify some of our polygons.

15.11. *Triangles Reclassified*

When children have been acquainted with an angle and its measure, they are in a position to further refine their techniques of classification.

We have classified triangles on the bases of the congruency or noncongruency of pairs of sides. Now, if we consider each pair of sides as *determiners* of an angle, we shall be able to reclassify our triangles on the basis of the measure of an angle. Notice that we are not saying that these sides are an angle; we are saying only that if each of the sides were extended in a direction away from the common vertex, an angle would result. Notice in Figure 15.19 that when sides *AK* and *KG* are extended, they form the angle ∠ *AKG*.

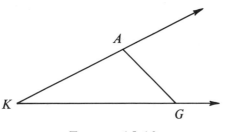

FIGURE 15.19

If we were to take the measure of this angle, we would find that it is an acute angle. If we find the measure of the angle determined by *AK* and *AG*, we find that this is an obtuse angle. If every angle determined by a triangle is an acute angle (remember that we have defined a measure of an angle as that part of the boundary of the circle that is less than a measure of 180°), the triangle is called an acute triangle.

Figure 15.20 depicts some acute triangles. If we were to take a protractor and measure the angles determined by each pair of sides, we would discover that each angle measures less than 90°.

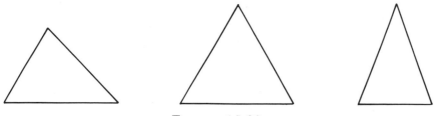

FIGURE 15.20

If the measure of one angle determined by the sides of the triangle is greater than a right angle, the triangle is classified as an obtuse triangle. Figure 15.21 depicts some obtuse triangles.

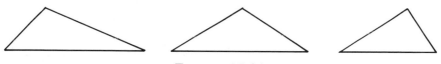

FIGURE 15.21

If the measure of one of the angles determined by the sides of the triangle is equal to a right angle, then the triangle is classified as a right triangle. (See Figure 15.22.)

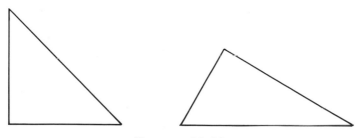

FIGURE 15.22

If two triangles determine angles with the same measure, the triangles are said to be similar. Figure 15.23 depicts similar triangles. We can symbolize this relationship as follows: $\triangle CEF \sim \triangle RKZ$ (read triangle *CEF* is similar to triangle *RKZ*).

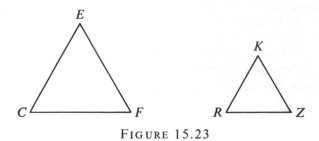

FIGURE 15.23

If we have two triangles in which one of the sides of one of the triangles is congruent to one of the sides of the other triangle, in which the triangles are similar, and in which the sides that are congruent are oriented the same way with respect to the angles determined by the triangles, then we say the triangles are congruent. Figure 15.24 depicts congruent triangles. We can symbolize this relationship as follows: $\triangle ABC \cong \triangle DEF$ (read triangle ABC is congruent to triangle DEF).

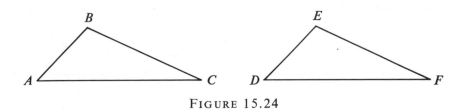

FIGURE 15.24

15.12. *Quadrilaterals Reclassified*

The concepts of the measure of an angle and parallelism permit us to refine further our techniques for classifying the set of quadrilaterals. Previously, we have classified a parallelogram as a quadrilateral with congruent opposite sides. Now, if we consider each of these sides as determining a line, we can say that a parallelogram is a quadrilateral with two pairs of sides, each pair of which determines a set of parallel lines. We can reclassify our rectangle as being a parallelogram with sides that determine four right angles.

EXERCISES (3)

1. What is the name of the longest possible chord a circle can have?
2. Draw a picture of a ray and name it $\overrightarrow{ZM}$.
3. Draw a picture of a triangle and name it $\triangle ACE$.

4. Using a protractor, find the sum of the measure of the three angles determined by various triangles.
5. Can you have an obtuse isosceles triangle?
6. Can you have an obtuse equilateral triangle?
7. Why can't you have a right equilateral triangle?
8. What is the name of the line pictured?

9. Describe a rhombus in terms of its sides determining parallel lines and congruent sides.
10. What would be the best name you could give to a quadrilateral whose opposite sides determine parallel lines and in which one pair of sides determined a right angle?

15.13. *Three-Dimensional Figures*

Until now we have been referring to geometric figures in a plane, or, in other words, two-dimensional figures. In this section, we shall explore some of the common three-dimensional figures taught at the elementary level. To do this, we shall introduce the term *join*. A join will be defined as the set of points that constitutes line segments connecting a set of points in a plane and a set of points that does not lie in this plane. For example, consider the point A above the plane in Figure 15.25 and also the set of points in the plane consisting of the circle and its interior region.

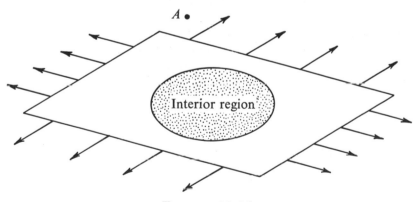

FIGURE 15.25

Figure 15.26 illustrates the resulting three-dimensional figure after we consider the join. The resulting figure is called a *cone* and its interior region.

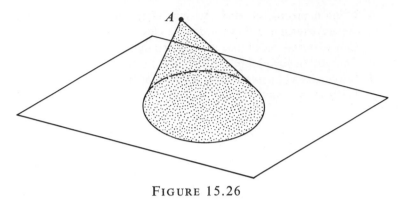

FIGURE 15.26

By using other simple closed paths in a plane, we can form the join of other three-dimensional figures. For example, in Figure 15.27, we see a perspective view of a square and its interior region in a plane and a point not on this plane. When we consider the join, we call the resulting figure a *square pyramid* and its interior region.

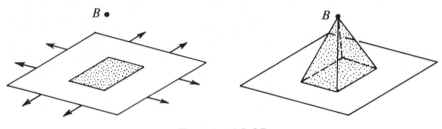

FIGURE 15.27

By choosing other polygons, we can construct various types of pyramids and their interior regions. For example, a triangular pyramid can be thought of as the join of a triangle and its interior region and a point not on the plane. (See Figure 15.28.)

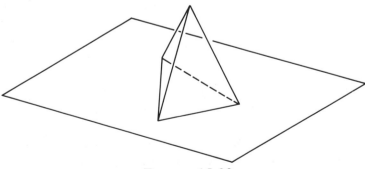

FIGURE 15.28

By considering the join of two sets of points in two planes, we can investigate some very interesting three-dimensional figures. For example, suppose we consider the join of two circles having radii of equal measure, but on parallel planes. We shall consider the join of these two circles and their interior regions. The resulting figure is called a *cylinder*. (See Figure 15.29.)

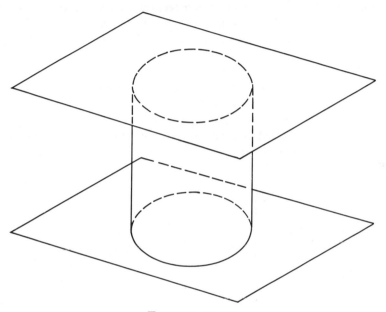

FIGURE 15.29

If, instead of using circles, we had chosen to form the join of quadrilaterals and their interior regions, we would have called the resulting figure a *quadrilateral prism*.

We have been considering *polyhedrons* (many-faced solids). Figure 15.30 identifies the names we give to various parts of the polyhedrons.

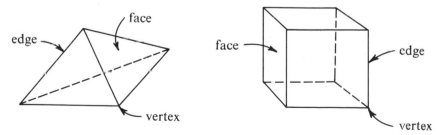

FIGURE 15.30

15.14. *Coordinates*

We have discussed already how to construct a number line. This number line provided a useful model with which to identify points in the line. By using two of these number lines, we would be able to identify points in a plane.

Let two lines intersect in a plane such that four right angles are determined by the lines. We shall call the point of intersection the *origin*. For convenience, we shall orient one of the lines in a horizontal manner and the other in a vertical manner. In order to be able to refer to these lines without having to say "horizontal" and "vertical" each time, we shall call the horizontal line the △ axis and the vertical line the □ axis.

Starting at the origin, we shall mark off a number line to the right of the origin along the △ axis. (When negative numbers have been introduced, these will be designated to the left of the origin.) We shall also mark off a number line starting from the origin and moving in an upward direction along the □ axis. Figure 15.31 illustrates our resulting figure.

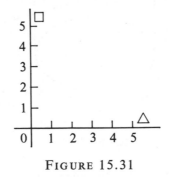

FIGURE 15.31

It will facilitate our future discussion if we construct a grid using the points named on the two axes. Figure 15.32 illustrates such a grid.

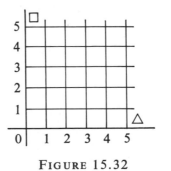

FIGURE 15.32

We shall name points in the portion of the plane that has the grid by naming a pair of numbers. The first number named will refer to a column named on the △ axis; the second number will refer to the row named on the □ axis. The intersection of the column identified by the first number and the row identified by the second number is the point named by the ordered pair. In Figure 15.33, point *A* can also be named by the ordered pair of numbers (5, 4) and point *B* by the ordered pair (1, 3).

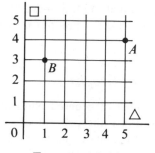

FIGURE 15.33

We shall treat as exercises some of the relationships that can be explored on our grid.

EXERCISES (4)

1. Is point (2, 3) the same point as (3, 2)?
2. The ordered pairs (1, 5), (2, 4), and (3, 3) are said to satisfy the equation △ + □ = 6 because:

$$\triangle{1} + \boxed{5} = 6$$
$$\triangle{2} + \boxed{4} = 6$$
$$\triangle{3} + \boxed{3} = 6$$

Copy the following coordinate grid and plot these three points:

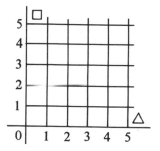

3. If the three points designated in Exercise 2 are connected via line segments, would these line segments determine one line?

4. Find four pairs of numbers that satisfy the equation $\triangle + \square = 5$ such that ordered pairs could be recorded on our grid in Exercise 2. (Fractional numbers are permissible.)

5. If the rule for adding these ordered pairs is as follows: $(a, b) + (c, d) = (a + c, b + d)$

   a. Is $(3, 4) + (5, 9)$ equal to $(5, 9) + (3, 4)$?
   b. Is $(3, 4) + (5, 0)$ equal to $(4, 3) + (0, 5)$?
   c. Is $(3, 4) + (2, 5) + (3, 1)$ equal to $(3, 4) + (2, 5) + (3, 1)$?

15.15. *Construction of Graphs*

Having established the idea of ordered pairs of numbers, the teacher is now in a position to introduce the concept of "line" graphs. Let us give some applied meaning to our pairs of numbers. For example, let us specify that the numbers along the $\triangle$ axis refer to miles and that the numbers along the $\square$ axis refer to hours. Now we can create a "picture" showing various types of rate situations. Consider the following:

John walks 2 miles per hour.
In 2 hours he will have walked 4 miles.
In 3 hours he will have walked 6 miles.

Figure 15.34 depicts this information as a graph.

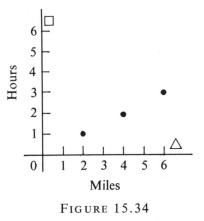

FIGURE 15.34

If we write a mathematical sentence depicting this relation, we obtain $\triangle = 2 \times \square$, or $\square = \frac{1}{2}\triangle$. We can obtain the ordered pairs $(0, 0)$ and $(2, 1)$

using this equation. Noting that all of the points lie on a straight line, we connect points (0, 0) and (6, 3) with a line segment.

We are now ready to explore with the children how graphs are used. You should demonstrate to them that, given either the hours or the miles traveled, how far John had traveled or how long John had traveled could be found out quickly. For example, suppose we wanted to know how far John had traveled after two and a half hours. Figure 15.35 shows how the answer can be read directly from the graph.

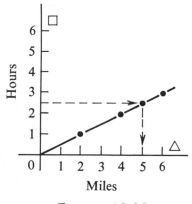

FIGURE 15.35

We can verify that 5 miles is the correct answer by showing that 5 is equal to 2 times $2\frac{1}{2}$. Having the children "read off" solutions to problems will help them understand one of the functions of line graphs.

You will also want to introduce the child to the "broken-line" graph. Although its function is not nearly as general as that of the line graph, it is nevertheless quite useful in conveying ordered relationships. This time, instead of comparing numerical relationships, we shall compare the ordered sequences of months with ordered sequences of numbers. In this case, the numerals will reflect the number of words that John spells correctly on each monthly spelling test of 100 words. Figure 15.36 depicts such a relationship.

We can use a broken-line graph to note trends. For example, we note that, except for John's January score, each month his score was better than that of the preceding month. The broken-line graph and the line graph are especially useful when the $\triangle$ variable has many increments. Line and broken-line graphs will be further developed with the exercises. If the number of increments of $\triangle$ is relatively small, a type of graph called a bar graph may be more appropriate than a line graph. The construction of a bar graph is not too dissimilar from the construction of a line graph. The first step in constructing a bar graph is to make dots on the graph to correspond to the ordered

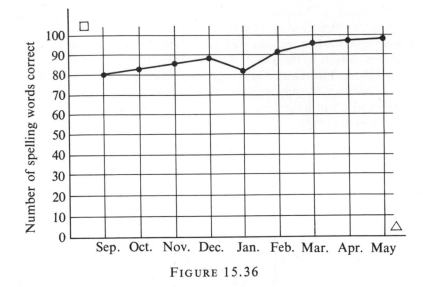

FIGURE 15.36

pairs. For example, suppose we were given the following table depicting John's performance on weekly 20-item mathematics tests. (See Figure 15.37.)

First week	10
Second week	19
Third week	11
Fourth week	18
Fifth week	10

FIGURE 15.37

We would first set up a graph with dots corresponding to the ordered pairs (1st, 10), (2nd, 19), (3rd, 11), (4th, 18), and (5th, 10). (See Figure 15.38.)

Then we would construct bars whose lengths correspond to a distance from the △ axis to the dot. (See Figure 15.39.)

We can construct the bar graphs in either a vertical manner as in Figure 15.38, or in a horizontal manner, shown in Figure 15.40.

Even though bar and line graphs serve to depict ordered relationships, sometimes we are interested in comparing fractional parts to a whole, and these types of graphs are not appropriate. For example, suppose we spend $\frac{1}{4}$ of our budget for food, $\frac{1}{4}$ for rent, $\frac{1}{8}$ for transportation, $\frac{1}{8}$ for medical fees, $\frac{1}{8}$ for entertainments, and $\frac{1}{8}$ for insurance. A circle graph would be appropriate

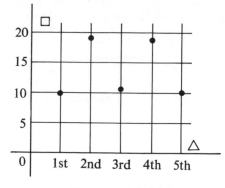

FIGURE 15.38

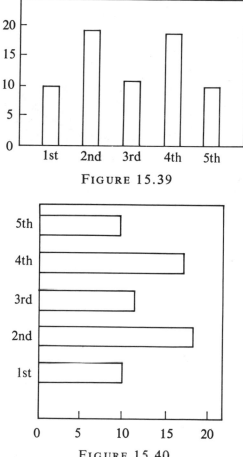

FIGURE 15.39

FIGURE 15.40

for depicting these relationships. In Figure 15.41, we can easily see that we spend twice as much for food as we do for transportation. Comparative expenditures for various things are easily noted when using a circle graph.

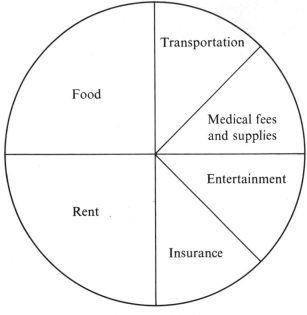

FIGURE 15.41

Sometimes we are not especially interested in very precise relationships, but only in more general relationships. In this case, the most appropriate graph to use might be the pictograph. In constructing a pictograph, we select some picture that will show a certain number of a given unit. For example,

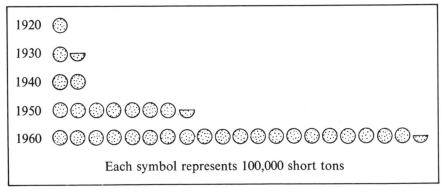

FIGURE 15.42

suppose we are interested in showing aluminum production from 1920 through 1960. We might let a picture of an aluminum ingot stand for 100,000 tons of aluminum. Figure 15.42 shows how our pictograph of aluminum production might look.

Notice that this type of graph gives only a gross comparison of the ratios involved. We can increase the usefulness of a graph of this type by accompanying the pictures with the numerical data.

EXERCISES (5)

1. Name three relationships for which a line graph could be constructed.
2. Using one of the following sources, construct a table that could be used to construct a broken-line graph:
   a. *World Almanac*　　c. Newspaper
   b. Business magazine　　d. Farm magazine
3. Using the same sources, construct a table that could be used to construct a bar graph.
4. Using the same sources, construct a table to show data for a pictograph that would be an appropriate graph.
5. List four sets of relationships that would lend themselves to description by circle graphs.

REFERENCES

ABBOTT, E., *Flatland*, New York: Dover Publications, Inc., 1953.

BRUMFIEL, CHARLES, ROBERT EICHOLZ, and MERRILL SHANKS, *Fundamental Concepts of Elementary Mathematics*, Reading, Mass.: Addison-Wesley, 1962, pp. 193–197, 237–252, 266–287, 353–370.

BRUMFIEL, CHARLES, ROBERT EICHOLZ, MERRILL SHANKS, and P. G. O'DAFFER, *Principles of Arithmetic*, Reading, Mass.: Addison-Wesley, 1963, pp. 272–292, 305–319.

BRUNE, I. H., "Geometry in the Grades," *The Arithmetic Teacher*, vol. 8, pp. 210–219, May, 1961.

D'AUGUSTINE, CHARLES HENRY, "Factors Relating to Achievement with Selected Topics in Geometry and Topology When Taught to Fifth-, Sixth-, and Seventh-Grade Pupils in a Programmed Text," *Dissertation Abstracts*, XXIV, pp. 4538–4539, May, 1964.

EVENSON, A. B., *Modern Mathematics: Introductory Concepts and Their Implications*, Chicago: Scott, Foresman and Co., 1962, pp. 75–140.

FLOURNOY, FRANCES, *Elementary School Mathematics*, Washington, D.C.: The Center for Applied Research in Education, 1964, pp. 49–51.

FREEMAN, MAE (BLACKER), *Fun with Figures*, New York: Random House, Inc., 1946.

HACKER, SIDNEY G., WILFRED E. BARNES, and CALVIN T. LONG, *Fundamental Concepts of Arithmetic*, Englewood Cliffs, N.J.: Prentice-Hall, Inc., 1963, pp. 89, 113.

HARTUNG, MAURICE, et al., *Charting the Course for Arithmetic*, Chicago: Scott, Foresman and Co., 1960, pp. 131–133.

HAWLEY, N. S., "Geometry for Primary Grades," *The Arithmetic Teacher*, vol. 8, pp. 374–376, November, 1961.

HEDDENS, JAMES W., *Today's Mathematics, A Guide to Concepts and Methods in Elementary School Mathematics*, Chicago: Science Research Associates, Inc., 1964, pp. 357, 379–398, 417–429.

JOHNSON, DONOVAN A., and WILLIAM H. GLENN, *Adventures in Graphing*, St. Louis, Mo.: Webster, 1961.

JOHNSON, DONOVAN A., *Curves in Space*, St. Louis, Mo.: Webster, 1963.

JOHNSON, DONOVAN A., and W. H. GLENN, *Geometric Constructions*, St. Louis, Mo.: Webster, 1963.

JOHNSON, DONOVAN A., "Geometry for the Primary," *The Grade Teacher*, vol. 79, p. 52, April, 1962.

JOHNSON, DONOVAN A., *Topology, The Rubber-Sheet Geometry*, St. Louis, Mo.: Webster, 1960.

LOVELL, K., *The Growth of Basic Mathematical and Scientific Concepts in Children*, Great Britain: Philosophical Library, Inc., 1961, pp. 114–126.

MILLER, G. H., "Geometry in the Elementary Grades: A Comparative Study of Greek Mathematics Education," *The Arithmetic Teacher*, vol. 11, pp. 85–88, February, 1964.

NATIONAL COUNCIL OF TEACHERS OF MATHEMATICS, *Enrichment Mathematics for the Grades, Twenty-seventh Yearbook*, Washington, D.C.: The National Council of Teachers of Mathematics, 1963, pp. 134–164, 302–311.

NATIONAL COUNCIL OF TEACHERS OF MATHEMATICS, *Insights into Modern Mathematics, Twenty-third Yearbook*, Washington, D.C.: The National Council of Teachers of Mathematics, 1957, pp. 82–110.

NATIONAL COUNCIL OF TEACHERS OF MATHEMATICS, *Instruction in Arithmetic, Twenty-fifth Yearbook*, Washington, D.C.: The National Council of Teachers of Mathematics, 1960, pp. 65–66, 85–87.

NORTON, M. SCOTT, *Geometric Constructions*, New York: McGraw-Hill Book Company, Inc., Webster Division, 1963.

PINCUS, MORRIS, "An Adventure in Discovery," *The Arithmetic Teacher*, vol. 2, pp. 28–29, January, 1964.

RANUCCI, ERNEST R., "Discovery in Mathematics," *The Arithmetic Teacher*, vol. 12, pp. 14–18, January, 1965.

RANUCCI, ERNEST R., "Introduction to Symmetry," *Updating Mathematics*, sect. 3, vol. 1, no. 8, 1959.

RUTLAND, L., and M. HOSIER, "Some Basic Geometric Ideas for the Elementary Teacher," *The Arithmetic Teacher*, vol. 8, pp. 357–362, November, 1961.

SISTER JOSEPHINA, "A Study of Spatial Abilities of Preschool Children," *The Arithmetic Teacher*, vol. 11, pp. 557–560, December, 1964.

SPENCER, PETER LINCOLN, and MARGUERITE BRYDEGAARD, *Building Mathematical Competence in the Elementary School*, New York: Holt, Rinehart and Winston, Inc., 1966, pp. 305–342.

SWAIN, ROBERT L., and EUGENE D. NICHOLS, *Understanding Arithmetic*, New York: Holt, Rinehart and Winston, Inc., 1965, pp. 257–276.

THORPE, CLEATA B., *Teaching Elementary Arithmetic*, New York: Harper & Row, Publishers, Inc., pp. 233–243, 257–260.

VAN ENGEN, HARRY, MAURICE L. HARTUNG, and JAMES E. STOCHL, *Foundations of Elementary School Arithmetic*, Chicago: Scott, Foresman and Co., 1965, pp. 360–393.

WARD, MORGAN, and CLARENCE HARDGROVE, *Modern Elementary Mathematics*, Reading, Mass.: Addison-Wesley, 1964, pp. 166–204.

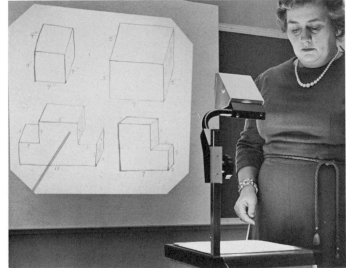

Visual aids can be used to motivate a child to learn mathematics.

16

Teaching Measurement

16.1. *Introduction*

THE METHODS of teaching measure are quite distinct from those employed in teaching number and numeration systems. Whereas we were concerned with such things as patterns, place value, properties, and computation in teaching measure, we shall be concerned with such things as standards, precision, approximations, scientific notation, accuracy, and special measurement systems.

The study of measurement offers the elementary teacher a much greater opportunity to be creative than does the teaching of numeration and number systems. For example, any time we touch an object that is mass-produced in our society, we can be sure that there is one or more standard measure associated with it. For example, a shirt (sleeve length, neck size), light bulb (wattage, voltage), cardboard box (volume, breaking strength), ink (color, amount), air conditioner (Btu., horsepower, amperage, voltage), pump (water pressure, gallons per minute), gasoline (octane, cost), and so on, all involve measure. There are few things with which man comes in contact for which standards of measure have not been created. The teacher is in a position to act as a connoisseur, selecting and developing basic principles of measure from those types of measure promising the greatest chance to reflect creative effort at problem solving.

16.2. *Principles of Teaching Measure*

What are some basic principles of teaching measure that are applicable in some form to all types of measure? The first of these is that the earliest activity in which individuals should be engaged is that of making gross comparisons of the type of measure under consideration. A common mistake teachers make in introducing a new measure is to start at the point where a standard has been devised; they thus deprive the student of learning some of the inherent properties of measure (that is, the basic nature of measure is the comparison of something with something else; a standard is needed only to communicate information about the comparison, and not when only one individual is involved in the comparison; the number one is assigned to one of the things being compared and this serves as a unit against which all further comparisons are made).

This first gross comparison takes many forms. It may take the form of a direct perceptual observation, such as looking at two pencils and *seeing* that one is longer than another, or listening to two sounds and *hearing* that one is louder than another, or *feeling* that it is hotter in the sun than in the shade, or *smelling* two liquids and observing that one has a "stronger" odor than another, or *tasting* two liquids and observing that one tastes more bitter than another. It may take the form of indirect comparison, such as observing that John is heavier than Mary because the teeter-totter stays down on John's side, or observing that one battery has more voltage than another because a bulb burns brighter when one battery is used than when another is used, or that the car has less gas than it had an hour ago because the gauge needle is not as far over.

The second principle of teaching measure is that we must establish a means of being able to tell when two measures are equal. (We shall use the symbol $\underset{=}{m}$ to refer to the relation of two things equal in measure. Because we already have used the symbol $=$ to mean exactly equal, and because measurement is always approximate and never exact, it will not be appropriate to use $=$ to represent the idea of "equal in measure." Some elementary series do not make this distinction.)

Sometimes we can establish that two things are equal in measure by direct means. For example, when we have two pieces of string, we can establish that they are equal in length by pulling them "apart" and matching them "end to end" and observing that they "match in length." Sometimes our establishment of equal in measure must be indirect. For example, if we observe that the liquid in a thermometer rises to the same height when immersed in two boiling liquids, we say that the temperatures of the liquids are equal in measure.

Some instruments are designed to establish when two objects are equal in measure. For example, a balance can be established when two objects have the same weight, and calipers can be used to determine when two objects have the same width. This idea of establishing equal measures plays an important role in the development of the concepts of measure. Each time a new measure is studied, this basic idea should be explored, and the children should be encouraged to suggest techniques of establishing when the things they are comparing are equal in measure. (Later it will be important to extend this concept to the selected standard, the method of mastering this standard, and how to check a model of the standard of measure against the "master" standard of measure.)

The third basic principle of measure involves selecting a unit of measure. Children should be given the opportunity to appreciate the complete arbitrariness of this selection. They should also be given the opportunity to appreciate the fact that allowing everyone to select his own unit of measure leads to chaos when each attempts to communicate using his own standard. Such discussion questions as the following will prove useful in promoting this concept:

> "What would happen if everyone were allowed to select his own units and you wanted to buy a shirt, or cereal, or milk, or a tire for the car, etc.?"
>
> "What would happen if each state selected its own units of money?"
>
> "What would happen if each gas station had its own unit of measure for selling gasoline or oil or batteries?"

As the students experiment with the selection of various units of measure, you have an obligation to develop the principle that precision of measure increases as our size of unit is decreased. Experimenting with units of various sizes also provides an opportunity to develop the principle that the greatest possible error is equal to one-half the unit of measure. In other words, if we are measuring a rope to the nearest pencil length, our answer will not be more than $\frac{1}{2}$ a pencil length from the correct length of the rope. (At the junior high level, this concept is extended to include the idea of relative error.)

As students are selecting units, the teacher should give guidance to them in selecting a measure to fit the thing being measured. For example, we would not use a linear measure to describe or compare the volume of two things, nor would we select a measure larger than a typical member of the set we are measuring. For example, we would not choose a rake length to measure the length of a beetle. Nor would we choose a measure disproportionately smaller than the thing being measured. For example, we would not measure the circumference of the earth with widths of a hair, nor the distance to the sun in inches.

As the children are exploring different units, the teacher should establish the need for a standard unit. This can be accomplished by forced communication situations. For example, you want to let a friend living in another state know how tall you are, how much you weigh, how long you can hold your breath, how hot it was yesterday, and so forth. Or you want to order a part for your bicycle or a dress or some potatoes. Or you want your milkman to deliver some milk or butter or cream. Situations that create the need for a standardized unit will give students an appreciation for our standards.

One of the last principles of teaching measure involves leading the class to make certain generalizations with regard to measure. In their simplest form, these may lead to such formulae as "area of a square $\overset{m}{=} S^2$," "area of a trapezoid $\overset{m}{=} \frac{1}{2}(b_1 + b_2)h$," or "perimeter of a rectangle $\overset{m}{=} 2 \times$ (length + width)." Other generalizations of a more complex nature involve such things as "conversion from one system to another," "knowledge of significant digits," "knowledge that there exist frontiers of measure" (for example, measurement of atomic particles or the size of the universe, the measurement of trajectories of bodies in relation to other moving bodies, or the measurement of the size of distant stars, and so on).

Each type of measure has its own special generalizations that pertain to it. It is important that the teacher encourage the children to seek these generalizations.

In this chapter we shall present techniques of teaching some classical measures traditionally included in elementary series. We shall also look at a more exotic type of measure in order to highlight the possibilities for developing creative solutions for establishing the measure of various things.

16.3. *Teaching Time*

A child entering school for the first time comes with a great many misconceptions about time. He has heard his mother say, "In a minute we will do such and such," or "Wait a second," followed by varying degrees of passing time before an event. A minute and a second do not represent a fixed unit of time to the child, but represent ideas synonymous with "a little while."

The teacher will need to develop a child's perception of a minute, an hour, and a day, along with the establishment of a unit. A child's first experiences with measures of time should be via gross comparison. Comparing the length of time it takes to empty two containers or comparing the length of time it takes two people to run the same distance are activities that lend themselves to comparison of a gross nature. Similar activities can be used to establish the same length of time.

The teacher can exercise his creativity in the manner in which he promotes the selection of a unit of time. An excellent motivational device is to display some of ancient man's attempts to arrive at a unit of time, such as the water clock, candle clock, rope clock, hourglass, and sun dial. Let the class suggest other means of arriving at a unit and try as many of these as is feasible. Although some of these may not be the right type of unit to measure time, it is probably best to allow the children to come to this conclusion through experimentation, rather than serve as the rulemaker with your adult perceptions.

With the derivation of a unit of time, the need to associate a number with this unit becomes obvious. For example, we did something four fleegens* ago, or John can run to the tree in five goops. A question such as the following will motivate the need for a standard unit of measure: "Mary can hold her breath eight tingles; John can hold his breath three wintles; who can hold his breath longer?"

Early experiences with standard measure not only should teach the child to "read" measures (such as looking at a clock and being able to announce the time), but also should help him gain a "feel" for the standard being taught. For example, to help him relate to the one-hour idea, you might say, "The clock now says ten o'clock; in one hour we shall go out to the playground." Or, to help give him the feel of one minute, you might say, "The bell will ring in one minute."

Generally, the child is first taught to read a clock by hours. This learning experience should be cyclic. That is, not only is it desirable that the child be able to read a clock, but it is also necessary that he be able to construct or draw or set a clock showing a designated time. Half hours, quarter hours, five-minute intervals, minutes, minutes to, minutes after—all these sequentially follow the introduction of the concept of an hour. Certain generalizations such as "any 15 consecutive minutes constitute a quarter of an hour," or "any 30 consecutive minutes constitute a half hour," should be taught.

The child's concepts of time are gradually extended to the idea of days, weeks, months, years, and so on. Gradually, his concepts of measure are extended to include the incorporation of measures of time. For example, he will learn that a light year (the distance light travels in a year) is a standard for measuring distances, or that miles per hour is a standard for measuring velocity, or that foot pounds per second is a measure of rates of work, or that particle bombardments per second is a measure of radiation intensity.

You, as the teacher, will find some of the following motivational devices useful in the exploration of the concept of the measure of time.

* Along with the creation of a unit, we also create a name for the unit.

1. A collection of various types of timepieces
2. Demonstrations of how timepieces are used
3. A play where there is an attempt to identify the role of measure during some period in history
4. Exhibits the students have prepared that represent novel ways they have created to tell time
5. Student-created games involving time as a measure
6. Bulletin board displays that depict, with cutouts from newspapers and magazines, the role that measurement of time plays in our society
7. Creative writing experiences, such as a science-fiction story about measures of time on a nonrotating planet with two suns
8. Students' research into the history of the measurement of time.

16.4. *Teaching Linear Measure*

The child comes to school with certain conceptions about length. The preschool child has many experiences with gross discriminations that involve discrimination in terms of length or one of its related concepts. He already has command of such concepts as taller than, shorter than, bigger than (in height), smaller than (in height), nearer than, farther than, and so on.

Even though he has had certain experiences in gross discrimination of length, he will need help in refining these concepts. For example, you will need to demonstrate refined techniques of comparing lengths, such as a side-by-side comparison or the construction of a movable model of one of the lengths. For example, in order to compare lengths you might use a picture of a line segment that corresponds in length to one of the objects being compared.

Comparison of lengths of objects such as pencils, children, shoes, fingers, strips of paper, plants, leaves, and ropes provides a natural environment for building readiness for the concept of "less than" in measure, "greater than" in measure, "the same" in measure.

Following experiences with gross comparisons, it is the teacher's responsibility to define what will be meant when we say two objects are the same in length. This is not a trivial concept, but requires careful development. Children start comparing heights and lengths on a visual basis, and such factors as color and nearness of objects play a role in distorting their perception of length. Such concepts as "the shortest distance between two points is the measure of a line segment whose endpoints are the two points" and the "necessity of a strictly vertical comparison for comparing heights" must be developed by the teacher.

These techniques are best taught through demonstrations using proper measurement techniques. Such concepts as the shortest distance between

FIGURE 16.1

two points can easily be demonstrated with string, where the nonextended piece of string is compared with itself extended. Figure 16.2 depicts how the edge of a piece of paper can be used to compare the lengths of two line segments. Our conclusions about two line segments having the same length are limited by our ability to perceive and our ability to master the skills of measurement.

Following gross comparisons and the establishment of what will be meant by saying that two objects have the same length, it is necessary to develop the concept of unit and scale. Children again should be encouraged to see the arbitrariness of the unit we select. At this point, they should be given measuring experiences to point out that precision is increased as we decrease the size

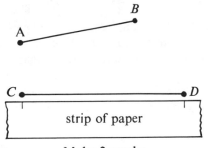

Make 2 marks

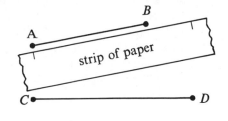

Compare lengths of the two line segments against the marks on the strip of paper.

STEP 1   STEP 2

FIGURE 16.2

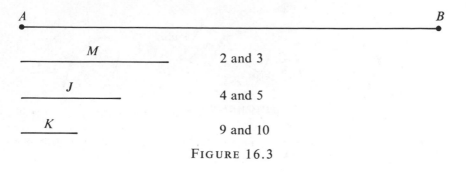

FIGURE 16.3

of our unit. For example, suppose we measure $\overline{AB}$ in Figure 16.3 with units M, J, and K. We find that the measure is between 2 and 3 measures of M, and between 4 and 5 measures of J, and between 9 and 10 measures of K. It is quite easy to see that if we are to be "off," at most, by one-half a unit of measure, the smaller unit of measure gives us the greatest precision.

In teaching children how to measure things of a "nonstraight" nature (such as the circumference of a circle), the teacher has a wonderful opportunity to develop their ability to attack real problems creatively. The teacher should encourage the children to suggest techniques of finding the measure. Several "promising suggestions" should be tried. The following represent a few of the creative solutions to linear measurement problems suggested by children:

> *Problem:* to find the length of a tangled fishline. Cut off a unit length and weigh this piece. Weigh the rest of the fishline. Divide the weight of the tangled fishline by the weight of a unit in order to derive the number of units.
>
> *Problem:* to measure the distance around a lake that is very marshy around the edge. This solution was suggested by a sixth-grade class. Take a picture of the lake from the air. Mark off a unit on the picture. See how long this unit is at the lake. Find out how many of these units it takes to go around the picture of the lake. Multiply this number times the number of the length one unit corresponds to in terms of the lake.
>
> *Problem:* to measure the depth of water in a well. Let out a string with a rock attached until the rock touches the bottom. Measure the length of wet string.

The creation of a wheeled measuring device is appropriate at this stage of developing a measure. Even though devices of this nature are generally circular, noncircular ones are also suitable. Let the children create various devices to speed up the measuring process. Figure 16.4 depicts some devices that might be created for this purpose.

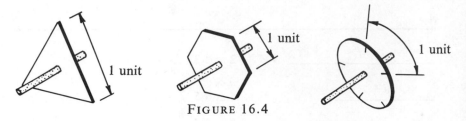

FIGURE 16.4

Devices such as an odometer, pedometer, and cyclometer will stimulate discussion. These devices will also underscore the advantage of creating a scale.

Measurement of distance and length in everyday situations is rarely of the "put the ruler down and measure it off" variety. Such things as radiation, radio waves, and sound waves are some of the more exotic things that are used to measure distance and height. The student should be made aware that in mastering the use of a tape measure or a ruler he has only reached the threshold of determining linear measure, and that man strives always for more and better ways to measure things linearly. The teacher should promote creative effort in the search for such devices and standards.

Until now we have not identified which or what standards of linear measure will be taught. Certainly the child needs to be familiar with inches, feet, yards, and so on. This need involves not only knowing that 12 inches is equal in measure to one foot, but also involves the child's gaining a "feel" of what an inch is and what a foot is. The development of this feel involves his measuring things in inches, feet, and so forth.

Development of a feel for larger units can be accomplished by relating these measures to the experiences a child has had. For example, a mile might be described as being about as far as walking around the school grounds five times. A similar feel can be developed for smaller measures. For example, you might compare $\frac{1}{128}$ of an inch to the width of a hair.

Although we have an obligation to introduce the child to our common linear measures, we have an equal, if not greater, obligation to introduce him to the measures of science, and for that matter the measure used by a large proportion of the civilized world. In other words, we need to familiarize him with the metric system of linear measure, along with pointing out its advantages as a measuring system.

The following designate the decimal multiples of the meter. (The meter is the basic unit of measurement of length in the metric system.)

Myriameter $\overset{m}{=}$ 10,000 meters
Kilometer $\overset{m}{=}$ 1000 meters
Hectometer $\overset{m}{=}$ 100 meters

Decameter $\overset{m}{=}$ 10 meters

One meter

Decimeter $\overset{m}{=} \frac{1}{10}$ meter, or .1 meter

Centimeter $\overset{m}{=} \frac{1}{100}$ meter, or .01 meter

Millimeter $\overset{m}{=} \frac{1}{1000}$ meter, or .001 meter

In the development of concepts relative to the metric system, it is important to establish a feel for a meter, centimeter, or kilometer in terms of lengths of common objects in the child's environment.

Some experience in converting from our system of measure to the metric system and back serves to establish a feel for the various types of units. A ratio approach offers a convenient means to translate between systems of measure that have the same "zero" and that both employ a multiple-unit approach to measure. (This is in contrast to such measures as temperatures, which have different zeros and scales of measure, or such measures as atomic half-life measures, which use an exponentially derived scale.)

In Figure 16.5, we see several ratios that will prove useful either in converting from our system to the metric system or from the metric system to our system.

2.54 centimeters: 1 inch $\overset{\cdot \cdot}{\cdot \cdot}$ □ centimeters: △ inches, or $\frac{2.54}{1} = \frac{\square}{\triangle}$

.3048 meter: 1 foot $\overset{\cdot \cdot}{\cdot \cdot}$ □ meters: △ feet

.9144 meter: 1 yard $\overset{\cdot \cdot}{\cdot \cdot}$ □ meters: △ yards

5.029 meters: 1 rod $\overset{\cdot \cdot}{\cdot \cdot}$ □ meters: △ rods

1.6093 kilometers: 1 mile $\overset{\cdot \cdot}{\cdot \cdot}$ □ meters: △ miles

FIGURE 16.5

It is important that the teacher stress the ease of converting within the system. For example, 3.5 meters easily translates to $3.5 \times 100 \overset{m}{=} 350$ centimeters.

As the children are developing feel for linear measure, you will want to be developing the generalizations that relate to linear measure. A useful technique to employ is to record measures in tabular forms and request the children to look for a number pattern that might be useful in determining a linear measure. For example, suppose we have measured the sides of several rectangles in order to determine the perimeter. (See Figure 16.6.) A question such as "What would be the fewest number of sides of a rectangle that we could measure and still determine the perimeter of a rectangle?" will lead the children to the generalization that $P \overset{m}{=} 2 \times (l + w)$.

By similar activities, it could be discovered that the perimeter of a square is equal in measure to four times the measure of one side.

Rectangle	w_1	l_1	w_2	l_2	Perimeter
A	3	5	3	5	16
B	1	8	1	8	18
C	14	26	14	26	80

FIGURE 16.6

16.5. *Teaching Area Measure*

Techniques of determining a number to assign to a surface have been with us since antiquity. The Egyptians of the pre-Christian era used area measure to reassign land to the farmers after the flooding Nile had obliterated the previous year's boundary markers.

Unlike linear measure, area measure is a concept about which the pre-school child has had few opportunities to develop misconceptions. His first experiences with area measure, then, should involve activities requiring him to make gross discriminations involving surface. Such questions as the following will help him focus on the nature of area measure:

"If we painted this wall and that wall, which wall would take the most paint?"

"Can I cover all the glass on the window with this sheet of paper?"

"Could I write more on this piece of paper (very small piece), or on this piece (very large piece)?"

Comparison of areas such as lawns, sidewalks, floors, ceilings, and walls will help develop an intuitive awareness of "less than," "greater than," and "the same as" in measure.

In early work with selecting a unit of measure for area, it is suggested that the children be allowed to try a variety of units, including circular regions for units, polygonal regions for units, and nonsymmetric regions for units. The teacher should lead them to see that the circular region would not be a wise choice, because it leaves some surface uncovered, even when the circles are touching. Figure 16.7 illustrates the derivation of the surface area using various shaped units areas.

When we were concerned with linear measure, we could assert that our measurement was correct to the nearest one-half unit. However, when finding the area of a certain surface, we can assert only that the measure of area is between the number of units that is completely within the figure being measured and the number of units required to completely cover the region. This idea is illustrated by Figure 16.8, where we find that there are 12

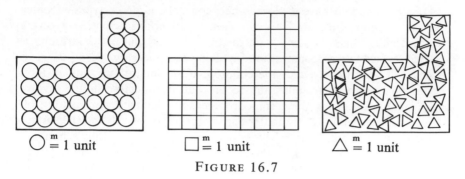

$\bigcirc \overset{m}{=} 1$ unit $\square \overset{m}{=} 1$ unit $\triangle \overset{m}{=} 1$ unit

FIGURE 16.7

units completely within the region, but that it took 28 units to completely cover the region. If we were to decrease the size of our units, we would find the precision of our measure would increase accordingly.

A useful teaching aid to incorporate when studying area is a grid printed on a sheet of clear acetate. This grid can be quickly superimposed over the regions of which you want to determine the area.

It is suggested that you encourage the children to determine novel ways of determining the areas of such things as:

1. A flat island of which you have only an aerial photograph
2. One face of an object, such as a coin
3. One surface of a roll of aluminum foil in which you are not allowed to unroll the foil more than one inch
4. The surface of a mountain

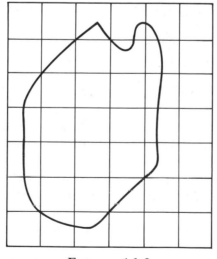

FIGURE 16.8

After the children have explored such concepts as units, types of units, and the creation of a scale, you will want to undertake activities involving standard units. Again you will want to stress the fact that a standard unit is selected to facilitate communication involving area measure.

You will want to introduce the children to the square inch, square foot, square yard, acre, square mile, and so on. This introduction should involve their gaining a feel for these standard measures, either by measuring off various surfaces with the unit under consideration, or by relating the surface to their environment. This might be done by saying that Billy's house is located on one acre of land, or that a football field is a little more than one acre of land.

Just as it was important to introduce linear metric measure, it is important that the children be given a feel for area measure based on metric units.

The following designate the decimal multiples of the square meter:

1 square meter $\overset{m}{=}$ 1 centare

100 square meters $\overset{m}{=}$ 1 are

10,000 square meters $\overset{m}{=}$ 1 hectare

Some experience in converting from our system of measure to the metric system and back serves to establish a feel for the various types of units. A ratio approach will prove helpful, because both systems have the same zero and both utilize a multiple-unit approach. In Figure 16.9, we see several ratios that prove useful either in converting from our system to the metric system or in converting from that system to ours.

6.45 square centimeters: 1 square inch $\because$ $\square$ square centimeters:
    $\triangle$ square inches
.093 square meter: 1 square foot $\because$ $\square$ square meters: $\triangle$ square feet
.405 hectare: 1 acre $\because$ $\square$ hectares: $\triangle$ acres

FIGURE 16.9

When teaching the metric system, stress the ease with which conversions can be made within the system. For example, 2.5 centares easily translates to $2.5 \times .01 \overset{m}{=} .025$ are.

You will want to have your students exploring such relationships as the area of a rectangle $= l \times w$, and the area of a triangle is equal to $\frac{1}{2} \times bh$. Even though tabular recordings can be used to focus the children's attention on these relationships, we shall explore an alternate approach to discovering these relationships.

If you mark off the unit squares on a rectangle, it is a simple matter to

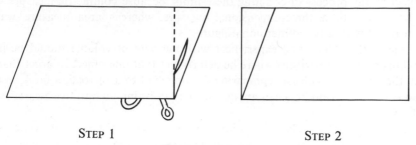

STEP 1   STEP 2

FIGURE 16.10

relate the array formed to the multiplication operation and hence to area of rectangle $\overset{m}{=} l \times w$ (or number of rows times the number in each row).

Figure 16.10 shows how a parallelogram can be partitioned and reconstructed to become a rectangle. In this way, the children can be led to see that the area of a parallelogram $\overset{m}{=} b \times h$.

Similarly, Figure 16.11 shows the relationship of the area of a triangle to the area of a parallelogram formed by using two triangles congruent to the original triangle.

Although we have concentrated on direct measures of area, the indirect measures of area offer a chance for the child to exercise creative solutions to area problems and to relate more closely to the means whereby he will derive area in social situations.

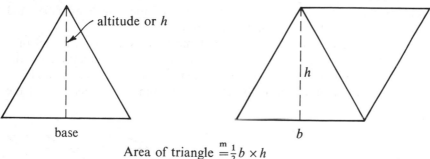

Area of triangle $\overset{m}{=} \frac{1}{2} b \times h$

FIGURE 16.11

16.6. *Teaching Measure of Volume*

It is generally not possible to measure the volume of an object directly. It is usually not feasible to examine the number of cubic units of a given object by the process of counting these units, because volumetric measure is concerned with a three-dimensional measure, whereas area measure was concerned with a two-dimensional figure.

One of the child's first experiences with measure of volume should be in making gross comparisons where he determines that one object is larger than another. Such activities as comparing a tennis ball to a softball, a book to a radio, or a tree trunk to a can are useful in establishing an intuitive awareness of volume.

It is important to relate the volume of an object to the space it occupies. One way to focus on this aspect might be to say, "Suppose you were packing a football and a marble; which object would take up more space in the box?"

A useful technique with which to develop this idea of a unit of volume is to do it through the vehicle of water displacement. For example, fill a jar about half full of water. Mark the level of the water on the side of the jar with a grease pencil. Add a marble to the water and mark the new level of water. Keep adding marbles and marking the new water levels. Remove the marbles from the water and add a few drops to return the level of the water to its starting point. Now you have a series of marks on the side of the jar that correspond to the volume of water displaced by various numbers of marbles.

By defining a unit of volume as the amount of water displaced by one marble, you can proceed to compare the volume of various objects with respect to marble units. This technique allows you to determine the volume of irregularly shaped objects such as jewelry, figurines, or rocks. By working with modeling clay, you can use other types of units such as cubes and rectangular boxes to establish units of displacement.

Another technique for establishing volume is to construct a model of a given object using unit cubes. In Figure 16.12, we can see that a model of the rectangular box has been constructed using unit cubes. After a model is constructed, the number of units used is determined in order to find the volume.

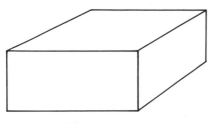
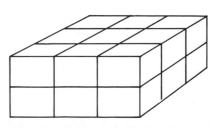

Object   Model constructed of unit blocks

FIGURE 16.12

Rectangular box	l	w	h	Volume
A	1	1	1	1
B	2	2	2	8
C	2	3	2	12
D	4	5	2	40

FIGURE 16.13

The technique of constructing models using unit cubes will prove useful in getting children to discover generalizations such as "the volume of a rectangular box is equal in measure to $l \times w \times h$."

The table in Figure 16.13 was derived using unit cubes to make up models for rectangular boxes. Ask the children to see if they can find the relationship between the length, width, and height, and the volume.

This type of activity will lead them to the technique of determining indirectly the volume of a rectangular solid, simply through determining the measure of length, width, and height, and then utilizing the generalization that the volume $\overset{m}{=} l \times w \times h$.

By exposing children to a great many techniques for determining volume, you will give them an opportunity to appreciate fully the complexity involved in the everyday application of volume determination. You may want to have them explore one or more of the following problems:

1. How can a lumberman estimate how much lumber one can get from a given tree?
2. How can a miner estimate the amount of gold a given mine will produce?
3. How can an astronomer estimate the size of a given star?
4. How can a car manufacturer determine how much steel will be used in a new car?
5. How can a mason estimate how many units of bricks will be needed for a building?
6. How can a road engineer estimate how many trucks of dirt he will need to fill a roadway?

While the children are exploring the nature of volume, the role of the standard units will need to be developed. One of the first experiences that a child will have with standard units is discovering that there is a wide variety of standards for volume, and that our selection of an appropriate standard depends on the nature of the object we are measuring. For example, we have measures such as ounce, pint, quart, gallon, liter, teaspoon, tablespoon, cup, and dram. All these are associated with liquid measure. Others, such as cord, board foot, bushel, peck, cubic inch, cubic foot, cubic yard, and so forth, are associated with solid measure.

It is important to develop general conversion techniques for the more common measures that will be encountered in everyday life. However, it is equally important that children view the measure of volume in its broader perspective so that in the future they will be able to interpret and translate from one standard to another, working with measures uncreated as of now.

Allow them to create their own units of measure. Let them describe the ratio of this new measure to one of the standard measures. Require them to determine various translations to and from their system to the standard system. It has been stressed all along that it is essential for children to get a feel for the various standard units. This is no less important for volumetric measure. It will be useful to display various containers holding standard units, such as quarts, pints, and cups. Allow the children to fill these containers and to transfer the material from container to container so that they gain a feel for relative capacities. It is also desirable to have a large number of cubic-inch blocks on hand so that relationships such as the following can be shown:

> 144 cubic inches $\underline{m}$ 1 cubic foot.
>
> Halving two of the dimensions of a rectangular solid decreases the volume to one-fourth the original volume.
>
> Doubling three of the dimensions of a rectangular solid makes the new volume eight times as large as the original volume.

16.7. *Teaching Measure of Water Pressure*

In order to illustrate the general applicability of the previously mentioned principles, the techniques of teaching a measure that is not normally taught in the elementary school will be developed. Although the measure of water pressure is not taught per se, it is so common that the concept of water pressure is within the experience of most people.

To develop our measure of water pressure, let us assume that we have several tin cans varying in height, each having a very small hole in the side, near the bottom. Let us further assume that each of the cans has had its top removed. Line up the five cans of varying heights along the edge of a table in such a way that the hole in each can faces away from the table. Have five children stand on the other side of the table. Let each child lean over, and, placing his hand around a can, place his finger over the hole in the can. Fill each can with water. On your signal, have all the children remove their fingers from the cans. Figure 16.14 illustrates how the resulting streams will look.

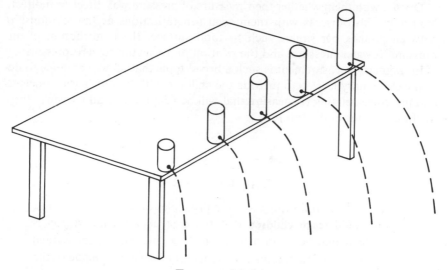

FIGURE 16.14

The following dialogue could be used to develop the idea of pressure and how to make gross comparisons of pressure:

"From which can did the water squirt out the farthest?" (The tallest can.) "We say the water from the tallest can had the most pressure and thus squirted out the farthest."

"Which can had the least pressure?" (The shortest can.) "Do you think that how wide a can is will affect the pressure?" (Demonstrate that the pressure is independent of the width of the can by filling to the same level two cans differing in diameter, and allow the children to observe that they both squirt out the same distance.)

"When two streams of water squirt out the same distance, we shall say the streams are under the same pressure." (This establishes the rule whereby the equality of two measures can be determined.)

Let the children suggest some ways a unit of pressure might be designated. Some possible suggestions are the height of the smallest can and the distance from the table that the water from the smallest can squirts. Let the children create a name for their unit of pressure. Construct a scale using the unit of measure they suggest. Discuss the fact that the smaller the unit selected, the more precise is the measurement of pressure.

Let the children investigate some of the standard units of measure—pounds per square inch, inches of mercury, grams per square centimeter, and so on. Let them discuss some of the uses of these standard units of measure—weather reports, pumping stations, and submarines.

Discuss with them whether their measure of pressure was direct or indirect. You might also discuss with them such generalizations as the relationship between pounds per square inch to total surface, the contribution of air pressure to water pressure, and the relation of a vacuum to zero pressure.

In summary, measurement is such a broad topic that all we can hope to do at the elementary level is to provide the children with certain basic concepts and principles relating to measure that will be adaptable to all measures they might encounter in the future.

EXERCISES

1. Outline how, following the basic principles of teaching measures, you would teach children that the area of a circular region is approximately equal in measure to $\frac{22}{7}$ × (measure of the radius) × (measure of the radius). Some mention should be made of the fact that $\frac{22}{7}$ is only an approximation, and that when our techniques for determining area are refined, we shall be able to come close to the real value of this factor.
2. Outline how you would develop a unit on weight around the basic principles.
3. Outline how you would develop a unit on money around the basic principles.
4. Outline how you would develop a unit on temperature around the basic principles.
5. Select one of the following and design an experiment that can be used to explore the principles of measurement:
   a. Atomic half-life   d. Breaking strength
   b. Intensity of magnetic field   e. Viscosity
   c. Smoothness   f. Brightness

REFERENCES

BANKS, J. HOUSTON, *Learning and Teaching Arithmetic*, Boston: Allyn & Bacon, 1964, pp. 342–357, 365–371, 383–403.

BELL, CLIFFORD, CLELA HAMMOND, and ROBERT HERRERA, *Fundamentals of Arithmetic for Teachers*, New York: John Wiley & Sons, Inc., 1962, pp. 238–247.

BOTTS, T., "Linear Measurement and Imagination," *The Arithmetic Teacher*, vol. 9, pp. 376–382, November, 1962.

BOWLES, D. R., "The Metric System in Grade 6," *The Arithmetic Teacher*, vol. 11, pp. 36–38, January, 1964.

CHURCHILL, EILEEN M., *Counting and Measuring*, Great Britain: Routledge & Kegan Paul, 1962, pp. 108–130.

CROUCH, RALPH, GEORGE BALDWIN, and ROBERT J. WISNER, *Preparatory Mathematics for Elementary Teachers*, New York: John Wiley & Sons, Inc., 1965, pp. 414–485.

DAVIS, P. J., *The Lore of Large Numbers*, New York: Random House, 1961.

DUTTON, WILBUR, and L. J. ADAMS, *Arithmetic for Teachers*, Englewood Cliffs, N.J.: Prentice-Hall, Inc., 1963, pp. 150–174.

EDUCATION RESEARCH COUNCIL OF GREATER CLEVELAND, *Key Topics in Mathematics for the Primary Teacher*, Chicago: Science Research Associates, Inc., 1962, pp. 73–76.

FLOURNOY, FRANCES, *Elementary School Mathematics*, Washington, D.C.: The Center for Applied Research in Education, 1964, pp. 47–49.

HEDDENS, JAMES W., *Today's Mathematics, A Guide to Concepts and Methods in Elementary School Mathematics*, Chicago: Science Research Associates, Inc., 1964, pp. 437–445.

KEEDY, M. L., "Informal Deduction in the Junior High School," *Updating Mathematics*, sect. 3, vol. 1, no. 5, 1959.

LOVELL, K., *The Growth of Basic Mathematical and Scientific Concepts in Children*, Great Britain: Philosophical Library, 1961, pp. 104–113.

MARKS, JOHN L., JAMES R. SMART, and IRENE SAUBLE, *Enlarging Mathematical Ideas*, Boston: Ginn and Company, 1961, pp. 25–27, 55–56.

MORRIS, DENNIS E., and HENRY D. TOPFER, *Advancing in Mathematics*, Chicago: Science Research Associates, 1963, pp. 259–270.

NATIONAL COUNCIL OF TEACHERS OF MATHEMATICS, *Enrichment Mathematics for the Grades, Twenty-seventh Yearbook*, Washington, D.C.: The National Council of Teachers of Mathematics, 1963, pp. 108–126.

NATIONAL COUNCIL OF TEACHERS OF MATHEMATICS, *The Growth of Mathematical Ideas, Grades K–12, Twenty-fourth Yearbook*, Washington, D.C.: The National Council of Teachers of Mathematics, 1959, pp. 182–201.

NATIONAL COUNCIL OF TEACHERS OF MATHEMATICS, *Instruction in Arithmetic, Twenty-fifth Yearbook*, Washington, D.C.: The National Council of Teachers of Mathematics, 1960, pp. 259–263, 341–343.

OLANDER, C., "A Model for Visualizing the Formula for the Area of a Circle," *The Mathematics Teacher*, vol. 48, pp. 245–246, April, 1955.

PAGE, DAVID, "Well-Adjusted Trapezoids," *Updating Mathematics*, sect. 11, vol. 4, no. 8, 1962.

RANUCCI, E. R., "The Shortest Distance from Here to There," *Updating Mathematics*, sect. 11, vol. 1, no. 1, 1958.

SANFORD, VERA, *A Short History of Mathematics*, Boston: Houghton Mifflin, 1930, pp. 353–377.

SCHAAF, WILLIAM L., *Basic Concepts of Elementary Mathematics*, New York: John Wiley & Sons, Inc., 1960, pp. 203–220.

SCHAEFFER, GRACE C., "An Informational Unit on Time," *Elementary School Journal*, vol. 38, pp. 114–117, October, 1937.

SHIPP, DONALD, and SAM ADAMS, *Developing Arithmetic Concepts and Skills*, Englewood Cliffs, N.J.: Prentice-Hall, Inc., 1964, pp. 142–144, 232–236, 263–265.

SPENCER, PETER LINCOLN, and MARGUERITE BRYDEGAARD, *Building Mathematical Competence in the Elementary School*, New York: Holt, Rinehart and Winston, Inc., 1966, pp. 316–344.

SWAIN, ROBERT L., and EUGENE D. NICHOLS, *Understanding Arithmetic*, New York: Holt, Rinehart and Winston, Inc., 1965, pp. 279–304.

SWENSON, ESTHER J., *Teaching Arithmetic to Children*, New York: The Macmillan Company, 1964, pp. 437–468.

VAN ENGEN, HENRY, MAURICE L. HARTUNG, and JAMES E. STOCHL, *Foundations of Elementary School Arithmetic*, Chicago: Scott, Foresman and Co., 1965, pp. 331–359.

WARD, MORGAN, and CLARENCE HARDGROVE, *Modern Elementary Mathematics*, Reading, Mass.: Addison-Wesley, 1964, pp. 348–365.

Active exploration motivates a child to learn mathematics.

17

Classroom Management Techniques

17.1. *Introduction to Testing*

AT THE beginning of each school year, each child enters the classroom differing in every respect from each other child. No two children have had exactly the same set of experiences. Ideally, the teacher should meet the needs of each child during each moment of each school day. Even though the impossibility of such a task is self-evident, the goal of constantly trying to meet each child's needs is a desirable one.

We shall use as a basic theme in this chapter the idea of meeting the different needs of children within group-learning situations involving elementary school mathematics. In order to learn to meet individual needs, we shall need to discuss methods of identifying differences in terms of skill levels, abilities to abstract, abilities to pursue independent activities, abilities to organize and synthesize, abilities in related skills such as reading, science, language arts, and so forth.

After each child's abilities and deficiencies are identified, we shall examine techniques of meeting the needs of children who differ radically from the norms, such as the nonreader, the child transferring into the school system with gross deficiencies, the gifted child, the handicapped child, and the "slow" learner.

17.2. *Inventorying Skills and Concepts*

The teacher virtually lives with his students several hours a day, five days a week. If he is sensitive to his students, he will be able to develop a better insight into each child's over-all mathematical ability than any test ever devised.

But although the teacher can develop the ability to classify his students in terms of their general over-all competence, there are times when specially devised tests can identify "specifics" better than any amount of direct observation. One of these times is at the beginning of the school year when each child is usually "new" to the teacher. Another time is when the teacher is going to teach a particular unit and wants to identify each child's skill level relating to the unit. The teacher will also be interested in testing the attainment of particular skills and concepts at the completion of a unit.

Let us first examine the inventory test that is given at the beginning of the year. The first task in the construction of an inventory is a listing of those skills and concepts we want to inventory. A very good source for items for this list will come from your school system's curriculum guide. You will want to inventory not only those skills listed as major concepts and skills for the previous grade, but also those you plan to teach that year (in order to identify those children who may need special activities and assignments while certain concepts are being developed).

A second source of items for your inventory is an index of a textbook. Also, the teacher of the preceding grade is often helpful in suggesting items for inclusion.

In order to gain insight into how to go about developing such a test, let us pretend that you are a second-grade teacher. Let us assume that you have decided on inventorying the following major areas:

1. Sets
2. Place value
3. Order and relations
4. Addition of whole numbers
5. Subtraction of whole numbers
6. Numbers and numerals
7. Fractional numbers and fractions
8. Geometry
9. Measurement
10. Multiplication

Under each of these areas, there will be some items that are best inventoried with paper and pencil and others that will require oral responses. For example, let us examine some of the skills in the area of "number and numerals" and decide which of the two techniques—written or oral—might be the most appropriate for inventorying each skill. Consider the following:

Number and numerals:
1. Number concept of zero: oral
2. Cardinal number of a set: written
3. Number-numeral distinction: oral
4. Recognition of numerals: written and oral
5. Writing numerals: written
6. Reading numerals: oral
7. Counting: oral

After compiling a list of items you want inventoried, and after deciding on the mode of inventory, you will want to construct test items. Some skill levels can be ascertained by sampling techniques. For example, having a child count by fives, starting at 65 and counting to 95, is a good test of

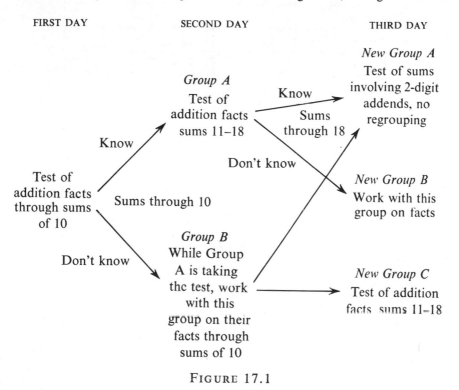

FIRST DAY   SECOND DAY   THIRD DAY

Figure 17.1

Checklist

	September	November	January
Money			
Cent	✓	✓	✓*
Nickel	✓	✓	✓
Dime			✓
Time			
Hour	✓	✓	✓
Half-hour	✓	✓	✓
Quarter-hour		✓	✓
Minute			✓
Day			✓
Month			
Season	✓	✓	✓
Linear measure			
Inch	✓	✓	✓
Foot	✓	✓	✓
Yard			
Liquid measure			
Pint		✓	✓
Quart	✓	✓	✓
Gallon			✓

* The child knew about a cent measure at each checking period.

FIGURE 17.2

whether he can start at five and count to 95. (If the child fails this test item, you can have him start at five and see how far he can count by fives.)

Other skills must be examined comprehensively. For example, you will want to inventory all of the basic addition facts involving six as an addend. It would not be possible to test two of the six facts and then render valid judgments about knowledge of the other six facts.

A useful technique in administering an inventory test is to stagger its administration. Figure 17.1 shows how a staggered administration might be used in order to inventory various addition skills.

Notice that when some of the students are occupied by the test, the teacher can be working with students found deficient in certain skills as measured by an earlier inventory test. As information is obtained from the test, the teacher may want to construct a checklist for each child. Figure 17.2 depicts a section of such a checklist for the area of measurement.

Notice that this checklist is being used to maintain a continuous inventory

	Group A	Group B	Group C
Longitudinal approach	Students are involved in determining areas of various regions by covering with units.	Students are involved in constructing rectangular arrays working with unit square regions where they record the rows and columns and area after constructing the rectangular array.	Students are involved in converting parallelogram regions to rectangular regions and deriving a formula for determining the area of a parallelogram.
Horizontal approach	Students are involved in determining the area of various rectangular regions by covering with various types of units.	Same as above.	Students are investigating ways that areas of rectangular regions were determined in the past.

FIGURE 17.3

of the child's skills. This type of record is a very valuable addition to the permanent records that accompany the pupil from one grade to the next.

We do not inventory the skills of a class in order to try to get everyone to the same skill level. On the contrary, to attempt to get everyone to the same skill level is most undesirable. However, inventory tests will prove useful in grouping your class for effective instruction in a particular unit.

These groups of students determined on the basis of inventory tests can be classified conveniently as one group of individuals whose skill level is below that necessary to profit by grade-level instruction; one group whose skill level matches the skills required for mastery of grade-level instruction; and one group that already possesses these grade-level skills.

In order to meet the needs of these three groups, it is necessary to develop very flexible teaching units. For example, assume that you are interested in developing the generalization that the area of a rectangular region is equal in measure to the product of the measure of the length and the measure of the width. Some of your students will need to work with the basic concept of area as being measured by the number of units of surface required to cover a given surface; others are ready for the generalization; whereas some students already possess this generalization and are ready for other concepts.

The teacher has several approaches he might use in meeting the needs of these three groups. Figure 17.3 shows two approaches he might use in meeting the needs of his students.

17.3. *Assessing Mental Potential*

Not only will you want to ascertain what skill levels various children have reached, but you will also want to determine each child's mental potential. While day-to-day observations of the children may lead you to make speculations about this or that child's potential, there will be times when obscure factors will lead you to faulty speculations. Such factors as vision defects, malnutrition, hearing defects, anemia, or lack of adequate sleep may lead you to identify a child as having little potential, when he really may have much potential once these defects or conditions are corrected. On the other hand, high motivation leading to intense concentration on a given area, possibly coupled with parental tutelage, may lead you to identify an individual as a gifted child when he is of only "average" potential but working inordinately more than the other children. (The author is defining gifted in mathematics as being capable of a high level of abstraction, coupled with creative and imaginative problem-solving ability.)

Because of the possibility of misclassifying a child on the basis of his potential, there exists the need to administer or to have administered to the children individual intelligence tests. These tests should be of such a nature as to yield profiles for each child. These profiles should include special aptitudes such as numerical comprehension, spatial apperception, numerical reasoning, and so on.

When the results of these tests deviate from your expectations, you should proceed to investigate what factors might account for such deviations. You will want to utilize the results of these tests in developing a flexible program to meet the different needs. Some characteristics of such a program for meeting the needs of children differing widely in mental potential are as follows:

Instructional materials:
1. Less abstract materials for the less mentally able
2. Differentiation in use of concrete materials, with the less able utilizing for a longer time the concrete materials

Instructional techniques:
1. Differentiation in the amount of independent study and self-direction
2. Differentiation in review and reteaching, with the less able receiving more frequent and intensive reviews and reteaching
3. Programmed materials and supplemented units for the more able student
4. Encouragement given to the more able student to deviate from prescribed routines in searching for new algorithms, properties, and patterns

EXERCISES (1)

1. Make up an inventory test for each of the following: division facts; addition of fractional numbers with common divisor; measure of volume (liquid); two-step story problems.
2. Look up the difference between a group intelligence test and an individual intelligence test.
3. Look up the difference between diagnostic tests and group achievement tests.
4. Look up what uses can be made of group achievement test scores.

17.4. *Testing Achievement*

As a unit is being administered, you will want to assess its value in raising skill levels and teaching concepts. This assessment may take many forms. For example, you might give a test, have the children summarize what they have learned, put on a play depicting the concepts learned, have the children write a report giving a self-evaluation of what they have learned, or measure the children's attainments on the basis of how they attack related problems. The most common type of assessment is probably a test. The types of concepts that might be tested, and suggested test items, are shown in Figure 17.4.

Every test need not be comprehensive, but may represent only a sampling of the concepts taught. You will use the results of the test to help identify

Sample Items

Vocabulary	1. In $3 + 4 = 7$, which numeral names the sum? 2. A figure formed by the join of two rays having a common endpoint is called either a line or an ____.
Meanings	1. In 342 the 4 names a number that is how many times as large as the number named by the 2? 2. In the division problem below, what does the 4 name? $$\begin{array}{r} 359 \\ \hline 7)\overline{2513} \\ 21 \\ \hline 41 \\ 35 \\ \hline 63 \\ 63 \\ \hline \end{array}$$
Computational skills	1. Find the product of 35 and 78. 2. Find the measure of the angle pictured below: 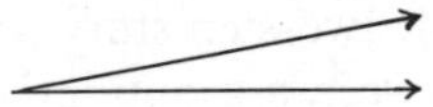 How many degrees less than 45° does this angle measure?
Problem-solving skills	1. What operations are needed to solve each of the following problems: (a) John buys 3 gallons of gasoline at 32 cents per gallon. How much did the 3 gallons of gas cost? (b) Mary bought 35 yards of ribbon. She cut the ribbon into 5-yard strips. How many strips could she get?
Generalizations	1. $3 + \square = \square + 3$ 2. $9 + \square = 9$

FIGURE 17.4

those individuals who would profit by more work in the area being tested. At the same time, the tests will point out weaknesses or misconceptions being developed that may require your immediate attention to correct.

17.5. *Assessing Nonmathematical Skills and Ability*

You will want to know which of your children have reading or language problems so that you can make provisions for these deficiencies. Standardized reading and language tests provide some useful information. However, you will want to supplement the information from these tests with mathematics-vocabulary tests and with oral reading tests of material of a mathematical nature. When children with special reading handicaps are identified, special provisions must be made for them. One or more of the following can be used to help the child who is handicapped in reading to develop problem-solving skills:

1. A variety of "story" problems placed on tape or inexpensive records the student can listen to with earphones
2. Filmstrips pictorially depicting stories the student can view
3. Another student acting as reader for the story problems. (Because the basic goal is to develop a child's ability to solve problems of a numerical nature and not to solve "word problems" per se, the teacher must be concerned with maintaining and developing the child's problem-solving skills until such time as he improves his reading skill level to the point of independence. If this is not done, the child will one day develop his reading skills only to find that the gap between his problem-solving ability and that of the others is so great as to be insurmountable. There is no reason to create a double handicap simply because the child is deficient in reading skills, providing his skills are not otherwise deficient.)

Sometimes a child's low skill level in mathematics is due to a physical disability. The diagnosis and treatment of these disabilities should be left to professionals. If no special provisions, such as special instruction, can be made for those who have visual or hearing defects, you should make every provision possible in your classroom to meet their needs.

17.6. *Introduction to Planning the Lesson*

How a learning experience in mathematics is organized depends to a large extent on the type of experience and the objectives of the experience. For example, disseminating information requires quite a different organization for learning than does the technique of having children discover structural

Learning-Sequence Chart

TYPE OF INSTRUCTION

Introduction of algorithm	Review skills and properties that will be needed for algorithm. Motivation: recognition of need for an efficient algorithm.	→	Basic presentation including: (1) format of algorithm; (2) meaning behind algorithm; (3) discussion of alternate algorithms.	→	(1) Practice. (2) Application.
Basic facts	Introduce basic meaning of the operation.	→	Exploration and discovery of facts.	→	(1) Practice. (2) Motivate a need for memorization; memorize. (3) Study properties that relate to this operation.
Geometric construction	Demonstration of construction technique.	→	Practice.	→	Application or utilization of construction in more complex construction.
Information	Presentation: a. Report b. Demonstration c. Display d. Exhibit e. Film or filmstrip f. Audio tape g. Television h. Books or magazines	→	Application.		
Vocabulary	Pronunciation. Meaning. Spelling.	→	Application.		

"Story" problems	See units at end of Chapters 4, 5, 6, and 7.
Properties	See specific units in chapters on operations.
Geometry	Exploration and → Application. classification. Constructions. Model building.
Generalizations	Discovery. ⟶ Application. Summarization. Presentation. Development via direct teaching.

FIGURE 17.5

properties. On the other hand, reteaching a concept requires that the teacher deviate from his original teaching plan to promote interest and meet the needs of those children who failed to attain the concept the first time. Reviewing a skill requires a different approach than does teaching for enrichment. Creative explorations require a freer learning environment than does the introduction of an algorithm.

Figure 17.5 suggests a framework for planning various types of learning experiences. It would not be possible to construct a chart to show every possible modification and deviation. This chart is designed solely for the purpose of exposing you to *a* framework—not *the* framework—for planning an activity. As your competence in teaching grows, you will develop many different learning sequences.

17.7. Organizing the Classroom

Ideally, when each new learning experience is begun, the classroom should be organized into as many groups as there are skill levels. Practically, however, a teacher can never attain this ideal. How many groups a teacher manages effectively will depend on his managerial ability. Some teachers can maintain an extremely effective learning environment with several groups simultaneously engaged in different learning experiences. Other teachers, lacking managerial skill, would have a better learning experience if they did not group, because confusion reigns within groups that are not receiving the teacher's attention.

Let us examine some of the basic principles for grouping in mathematics. The first principle is that the more groups you maintain, the greater variety of instructional materials you must have available to meet the needs of different groups. The more groups you have, the greater the amount of time you must spend in planning how these children will spend their time in the groups. The greater the number of groups, the more flexible these groups will be in terms of children moving from one group to another as new needs occur. The more groups you have, the better "chance" you will have of meeting the needs of your children.

Because our primary goal is to meet the educational needs of our students, this factor must take precedence when we decide to group. Groups organized for effective mathematics instruction are quite different from groups organized for other learning experiences in the elementary school. For example, groups organized for reading are semistable groups that do not have many children moving from one group to another throughout the year. In contrast, mathematics grouping is highly flexible, varying not only in who is in any given group on any given day, but also in the number of groups on any given day.

Let us examine two different types of grouping situations that can arise in teaching. The first of these involves introducing a multiplication algorithm. After an inventory test, we find that three children who transferred in from another system indicate that they have mastered this algorithm, seven children indicate that they are extremely weak in regard to the basic multiplication facts, and 19 give evidence of being ready to learn this algorithm. Thus, we have three groups. (Notice that these three groups are quite disproportionate in number.) Figure 17.6 depicts the types of activities we might plan for each of these groups.

Notice that it is possible to have a group where you do not do any formal introduction but where the nature of the learning experience is self-instructional.

Let us examine a second type of grouping situation where fewer groups are involved. Let us assume that you are going to develop the skill of partitioning a segment into five congruent pieces. Yesterday, we shall assume, you demonstrated how to copy an angle. Being able to copy an angle is prerequisite to learning today's skill. However, three children were absent yesterday and thus missed the instruction. In this case, you could present the technique to the whole group and, when you had finished, while the majority of students practiced partitioning a segment, you could work with the group of three children, demonstrating this skill to them. Or you might allow a child proficient in this skill to come over to the group of three and help them. After the three begin their practice, you could return to the larger group and aid those having trouble with partitioning a segment.

In planning your grouping, do not feel that you need to meet with each

Group A	Group B	Group C
Need to learn the basic facts.	Need to learn algorithm.	Need for extension.
1. Work with arrays, sets, recording of facts.	1. Presentation of the algorithm.	1. Allow these children to investigate how ancient peoples multiplied numbers
2. Work with flash cards or similar devices to aid in memorizing the facts.	2. Practice with the algorithm.	or
3. Practice tests.		2. Introduce them to a different algorithm.
4. Study on facts missed.		

Type of Teacher Involvement for Each Group:

Have planning session with group. Check with group to see that they are proceeding in an orderly way.	Check each child as he is practicing the algorithm in order to aid those having trouble.	Let the children report to you on their progress or let them construct an exhibit with your help in their search for materials to place in the exhibit.

FIGURE 17.6

group each day, although you may need to meet with some groups several times in one day. Utilize your better students to aid those who have been absent or recently transferred in. Let children participate in presenting instructional units.

Your skill in grouping will grow with your skill as a teacher. In your early experiences with grouping, limit the number of groups you attempt to co-ordinate. Remember that it is not the number of groups that you can maintain, but the effectiveness of the learning taking place within the groups that is most important.

17.8. *Introduction to Special Management Problems*

In this section, we shall suggest some general guidelines to serve as a nucleus of ideas around which you can add other techniques as you mature as a teacher.

Question: What do you do when a child transfers in?

When a child transfers in, you will want to determine his various skill levels as soon as possible. You should study his permanent records in order to determine if previous teachers have cited any unusual traits, skills, or deficiencies in the area of mathematics. You should talk with the child and inquire what concepts he has been learning and what self-image he has in regard to mathematics. If you are in the middle of a mathematics unit, administer the inventory test you used at the beginning of this unit. If several gaps are noted that are probably due to his transfer from a class studying topics at a different pace or in a different sequence from your class, you may want to utilize one or more of the following:

1. Assign the child a helper who can update his skills.
2. Request that the parents secure a tutor or provide the child with some assistance.
3. Assign the child programmed units on the topics that have been identified as deficiencies.
4. Give the child assistance after school or during your free periods.*

Question: What do you do with the child who always finishes early?

When a child finishes before the rest of his group, do not punish him by assigning him more of the same type of problem. Post in a conspicuous place activities of a mathematical nature that the children are free to engage in when they have completed their assignment. These activities may entail working with mathematical puzzles, reading biographies of mathematicians, writing a play on mathematics, constructing geometric models, constructing exhibits, reading the history of mathematics, working on a deficiency such as mastery of the basic facts.

You will probably want to question some who finish early. Their speed in completion may be contributing to excessive errors or sloppiness. When such is the case, you may want to encourage these children to take a little more time in order to reduce their error rates or improve the neatness of their papers. (Remember, however, that neatness per se is not a mathematical skill but a general study skill that relates to every area of learning. Excessive insistence on neatness when the child does not have adequate muscular control to write neatly can aid in developing negative attitudes toward mathematics.)

Question: What do you do with the child who is continually revealing to the class the discovery of a generalization before the class has had a chance to make the discovery?

You will want to prevent children from revealing a discovery before the others have had a chance to make the discovery. Possibly the best positive technique to use is to ask each child to test his discovery with other examples. Request that the children try to find a way to prove their discoveries. When you feel that further work will not significantly increase the number of

---

* Give preference to this technique.

children making discoveries, you can call on those children to announce their discoveries. (Notice that we have specified discoveries, rather than discovery. It is a good technique to structure more than one potential discovery in each learning situation. When the children come to expect more than one discovery, they will be less likely to reveal what they have discovered before they think that they have exhausted the number of possible discoveries.)

17.9. *Assessing a Year's Work*

Although you probably will want to maintain a constant evaluation of how your class is progressing from day to day, you will also want to know if your class is deficient in any major concepts normally taught at your grade level. For assessing your class's attainments and deficiencies, you have at your disposal any number of good standardized group achievement tests.

If you administer an achievement test at the beginning of the year, it will not only provide you with a "starting" point from which to measure the class achievement under your tutelage, but it will also show you in which areas the class has over-all weaknesses. You may want to postpone this first administration until you have had an opportunity for an over-all review.

You will want to administer an achievement test during the latter months of the school year. If you administer it when you think that the basic "core" of material has been presented, you will be able to reteach those areas showing weakness. You will want to record the scores from the mathematics achievement test in the child's permanent record, as this information will help his next teacher.

17.10. *Anecdotal Records*

In addition to the inventory checklist, achievement-test scores, and mental-ability scores, you will want to include anecdotal records within the child's permanent records. These anecdotal records consist of comments about any unusual behavior from a child with respect to mathematics. The following represent typical comments that might be included:

Johnny is quite motivated by measurement concepts. Following a unit on measurement, he constructed an exhibit on his own initiative that showed how the Egyptians found the area of land following a flood. He repeatedly brings in objects relating to measure and explains their uses to the class. He is an excellent resource person when the class is studying measurement.

Mary uses her fingers to determine sums and differences. I have found that since introducing her to a simple slide rule she has made less use of her fingers. (Later.) She now appears to be developing some independence of both her fingers and the slide rule.

Philip has very poor coordination. This must be considered in terms of the neatness one expects from him. He is extremely bright and is quick to anticipate generalizations. He has developed several unusual algorithms for multiplying and dividing. He is quite proficient with these algorithms, even though they require a high level of skill in mental calculation.

At the end of the year, you will want to screen your anecdotal records and remove any comments that did not prove to represent a consistent description of the child. For example, you may have recorded earlier that a child was weak in a particular area in which he has since become proficient.

EXERCISES (2)

1. Find out what each of the following words means when applied to an achievement test: reliability, validity, norms.
2. Go to an elementary school and study some children's permanent records. Record the types of information you find that might at some time be a factor in your teaching the child mathematics.
3. Observe a class being taught mathematics. Concentrate your observation on one or two children. Record specific comments on these children with respect to their performance, temperament, attitudes, skills, deficiencies, study habits, and apparent motivation.
4. Prepare a lesson plan for teaching a unit in geometry. Outline the objectives of your lesson and tell how you will evaluate whether the lesson has met each objective.

REFERENCES

BRUNER, J. S., *The Process of Education*, Cambridge, Mass.: Harvard University Press, 1960.

COLLIER, C. C., "Blocks to Arithmetical Understanding," *The Arithmetic Teacher*, vol. 6, pp. 262–269, November, 1959.

FEHR, HOWARD F., GEORGE MCMEEN, and MAX SOBEL, "Using Hand-Operated Computing Machines in Learning Arithmetic," *The Arithmetic Teacher*, vol. 3, pp. 145–150, October, 1956.

FLOURNOY, FRANCES, "The Effectiveness of Instruction in Mental Arithmetic," *Elementary School Journal*, vol. 55, pp. 148–153, November, 1954.

FLOURNOY, FRANCES, "Meeting Individual Differences in Arithmetic," *The Arithmetic Teacher*, vol. 7, pp. 80–86, February, 1960.

GLENNON, VINCENT J., "Arithmetic for the Gifted Child," *Elementary School Journal*, vol. 58, pp. 91–96, November, 1957.

GLENNON, VINCENT J., and STUDENTS, *Developing Meaningful Practices in Arithmetic*, Syracuse, N.Y.: Central New York School Study Council, Syracuse University, 1951, p. 123.

GRIME, HERSCHEL E., "Adapting the Curriculum in Primary Arithmetic to the Abilities of Children," *The Mathematics Teacher*, vol. 43, pp. 242–244, October, 1950.

HALL, DONALD E., "Bulletin Boards for Elementary School Arithmetic," *The Arithmetic Teacher*, vol. 2, pp. 114–115, February, 1964.

JACKSON, HUMPHREY C., "Motivation," *The Arithmetic Teacher*, vol. 2, pp. 402–406, October, 1964.

JUNGE, CHARLOTTE, "Depth Learning in Arithmetic—What Is It?" *The Arithmetic Teacher*, vol. 7, pp. 341–346, November, 1960.

JUNGE, CHARLOTTE, "The Gifted Ones—How Shall We Know Them?" *The Arithmetic Teacher*, vol. 4, pp. 141–146, October, 1957.

KIRK, SAMUEL A., and G. ORVILLE JOHNSON, *Educating the Retarded Child*, Boston: Houghton Mifflin Co., 1951, p. 434.

KOENKER, R. H., "Measuring the Meanings of Arithmetic," *The Arithmetic Teacher*, vol. 7, pp. 93–96, February, 1960.

MALONEY, JOHN P., "Arithmetic at the Primary Level," *The Arithmetic Teacher*, vol. 4, pp. 112–118, April, 1957.

MOYER, HAVERLY O., "Testing the Attainment of the Broader Objectives of Arithmetic," *The Arithmetic Teacher*, vol. 3, pp. 66–70, March, 1956.

NATIONAL COUNCIL OF TEACHERS OF MATHEMATICS, *Enrichment Mathematics for the Grades, Twenty-seventh Yearbook*, Washington, D.C.: The National Council of Teachers of Mathematics, 1963.

NATIONAL COUNCIL OF TEACHERS OF MATHEMATICS, *Evaluation in Mathematics, Twenty-sixth Yearbook*, Washington, D.C.: The National Council of Teachers of Mathematics, 1961.

NORTON, M. S., "Helping Pupils Help Themselves through Self-Evaluation," *The Arithmetic Teacher*, vol. 7, pp. 203–204, April, 1960.

RAPPAPORT, D., "Testing for Meanings in Arithmetic," *The Arithmetic Teacher*, vol. 6, pp. 140–143, April, 1959.

ROSS, R., "Diagnosis and Correction of Arithmetic Underachievement," *The Arithmetic Teacher*, vol. 10, pp. 22–27, January, 1963.

SCHMINKE, C. W., "The Arithmetic Folder," *The Arithmetic Teacher*, vol. 9, pp. 152–154, March, 1962.

SEARIGHT, FRANKLYN, "You Can Individualize Arithmetic Instruction," *The Arithmetic Teacher*, vol. 2, pp. 199–200, March, 1964.

SHAW, R. J., "Criteria for Evaluation of Teaching Procedures," *The Arithmetic Teacher*, vol. 4, pp. 248–249, December, 1957.

SOLE, DAVID, *The Use of Materials in the Teaching of Arithmetic*, Doctoral dissertation, New York: Teachers College, Columbia University, 1957.

VAN ENGEN, HENRY, "Which Way Arithmetic?" *The Arithmetic Teacher*, vol. 2, pp. 131–140, December, 1955.

VOLPEL, M. C., "The Hundred-Board," *The Arithmetic Teacher*, vol. 6, pp. 295–301, December, 1959.

WEAVER, J. FRED, "Big Dividends from Little Interviews," *The Arithmetic Teacher*, vol. 2, pp. 40–47, April, 1955.

Appendixes

APPENDIX A
Alternate Algorithms

THIS text has developed usually only one algorithm for each operation on each set of numbers studied. Although the algorithms selected for the body of the text represent algorithms for which certain points can be most easily emphasized, there exist many other good algorithms. Believing that a person who is teaching elementary mathematics should be familiar with many algorithms, the author has prepared this set of alternate algorithms.

1. *Alternate Addition Algorithms*

A. Addition algorithm for the slow learner

$$
\begin{array}{ll}
29 & \text{thought} \\
58 & 7 + 8 = 10 + 5 \\
+17 &
\end{array}
\longrightarrow
\begin{array}{ll}
& 1 \\
29 & \text{thought} \\
58 & 5 + 9 = 10 + 4 \\
+17 &
\end{array}
\longrightarrow
\begin{array}{l}
1 \\
1 \\
29 \\
58 \\
+17 \\
\hline
4
\end{array}
\longrightarrow
$$

$$
\begin{array}{l}
1 \\
1 \\
29 \\
58 \\
+17 \\
\hline
4
\end{array}
\quad
\begin{array}{l}
\text{thought} \\
1 + 5 = 6,\ 6 + 2 = 8,\ 8 + 1 = 9,\ 9 + 1 = 10
\end{array}
\longrightarrow
\begin{array}{l}
1 \\
1 \\
29 \\
58 \\
+17 \\
\hline
104
\end{array}
$$

B. Left-to-right addition algorithm

$$
\begin{array}{r}
94 \\
86 \\
+71 \\
\hline
\end{array}
\longrightarrow
\begin{array}{r}
94 \\
86 \\
+71 \\
\hline
24
\end{array}
\longrightarrow
\begin{array}{r}
94 \\
86 \\
+71 \\
\hline
241
\end{array}
\longrightarrow
\begin{array}{r}
94 \\
86 \\
+71 \\
\hline
241 \\
1 \\
\hline
251
\end{array}
$$

2. *Alternate Subtraction Algorithms*

A. Subtraction algorithm using compensation

	thought $\longrightarrow$		thought $\longrightarrow$	
374	$374 + 1 = 375$	375	$5 - 0 = 5$	375
-249	$249 + 1 = 250$	-250	$7 - 5 = 2$	-250
			$3 - 2 = 1$	125

B. Algorithm using compensation definition of subtraction

	reasoning $\longrightarrow$		thought $\longrightarrow$	
374	$374 + 10 = 37$ tens and 14 ones	37$\overset{\prime}{4}$	$9 + \boxed{5} = 14$	37$\overset{\prime}{4}$
-249	$249 + 10 = 25$ tens and 9 ones	$-2\overset{5}{\cancel{4}}9$	$5 + \boxed{2} = 7$	$-2\overset{5}{\cancel{4}}9$
			$2 + \boxed{1} = 3$	125

3. *Multiplication of Whole Numbers*

A. Left-to-right algorithm

Step 1	*Step 2*	*Step 3*	*Step 4*
372	372	372	372
× 28	× 28	× 28	× 28
	40	440	7440

Step 5	*Step 6*	*Step 7*
372	372	372
× 28	× 28	× 28
7440	7440	7440
6	76	2976
		10,416

B. Multiplication algorithm using the associative property $372 \times 28 = 372 \times (4 \times 7)$

$$
\begin{array}{r}
372 \\
\times \quad 4 \\
\hline
1488 \\
\times \quad 7 \\
\hline
10,416
\end{array}
$$

4. *Alternate Division Algorithms*

A. Division algorithm involving rounding the divisor

$37\overline{)1472}$ Thought process: If the digit in the ones place names 0, 1, 2, 3, 4, or 5, divide by the 3 tens, and if the digit in the ones place names 6, 7, 8, or 9, divide by 4 tens.

Therefore, $14 \div 4$ gives a trial quotient of 3. Because $40 \times 30 = 1200$, we place the 3 tens over the 7 tens.

$$
\begin{array}{r}
3 \\
37\overline{)1472} \\
111 \\
\hline
362
\end{array}
$$

Because the 7 in 37 names a number greater than 5, we again round 3 to 4 and find that $36 \div 4$ gives us a trial quotient of 9. Because $40 \times 9 = 360$, we place the 9 over the 2 ones.

$$
\begin{array}{r}
39 \\
37\overline{)1472} \\
111 \\
\hline
362 \\
333 \\
\hline
29
\end{array}
$$

We find that $1472 = 37 \times 39 + 29$.

B. Algorithm using the right distributive property for division

$$37\overline{)1472}$$

$$
\begin{array}{r}
10 + \ 10 + \ 10 + \ \ 7 \\
37\overline{)400 + 400 + 400 + 272} \\
370 \quad\ 370 \quad\ 370 \quad\ 259 \\
\hline
30 \quad\ \ 30 \quad\ \ 30 \quad\ \ 13
\end{array}
$$

and $30 + 30 + 30 + 13 = 103$

$$
\begin{array}{r}
2 \\
\text{and } 37\overline{)103} \\
74 \\
\hline
29
\end{array}
$$

therefore, quotient $= 10 + 10 + 10 + 7 + 2$
Remainder $= 29$

5. *Addition of Fractional Numbers Algorithms*

A. Finding the sum using a distributive property

$$n = \frac{3}{4} + \frac{2}{3}$$

$$n = \frac{1}{4} \times 3 + \frac{1}{3} \times 2$$

$$12n = 12 \times \frac{1}{4} \times 3 + 12 \times \frac{1}{3} \times 2$$

$$12n = 3 \times 3 + 4 \times 2$$

$$12n = 9 + 8$$

$$12n = 17$$

$$\frac{12n}{12} = \frac{17}{12}$$

$$n = \frac{17}{12}$$

B. Addition of fractional numbers using the principle $\frac{1}{a} + \frac{1}{b} = \frac{a+b}{ab}$, where:

$$n = \frac{2}{3} + \frac{3}{4}$$

$$\frac{1}{6}n = \frac{2}{3} \times \frac{1}{6} + \frac{3}{4} \times \frac{1}{6}$$

$$\frac{1}{6}n = \frac{1}{9} + \frac{1}{8}$$

$$\frac{1}{6}n = \frac{17}{72}$$

$$\frac{6}{6}n = \frac{17}{72} \times 6$$

$$n = \frac{17}{12}$$

6. *Subtraction of Fractional Numbers Algorithms*

A. Compensation algorithm

$$\frac{3}{4} - \frac{2}{5}$$

$$\left(\frac{3}{4} + \frac{1}{4}\right) - \left(\frac{2}{5} + \frac{1}{4}\right)$$

$$1 - \left(\frac{2}{5} + \frac{1}{4}\right)$$

$$1 - \frac{13}{20}$$

$$\frac{7}{20}$$

B. Subtraction of fractional numbers using the principle $\frac{1}{a} - \frac{1}{b} = \frac{a-b}{ab}$, where:

$$n = \frac{7}{5} - \frac{2}{3}$$

$$\frac{1}{14}n = \frac{7}{5} \times \frac{1}{14} - \frac{2}{3} \times \frac{1}{14}$$

$$\frac{1}{14}n = \frac{1}{10} - \frac{1}{21}$$

$$\frac{1}{14}n = \frac{21-10}{210}$$

$$\frac{1}{14}n = \frac{11}{210}$$

$$14 \times \frac{1}{14}n = 14 \times \frac{11}{210}$$

$$n = \frac{2 \times 7 \times 11}{3 \times 7 \times 2 \times 5}$$

$$n = \frac{11}{15}$$

7. Multiplication of Fractional Numbers Algorithm, Using the Commutative and Associative Properties and $\frac{1}{a} \times \frac{1}{b} = \frac{1}{a \times b}$

$$\frac{3}{4} \times \frac{5}{7} = \left(3 \times \frac{1}{4}\right) \times \left(5 \times \frac{1}{7}\right)$$

$$= (3 \times 5) \times \left(\frac{1}{4} \times \frac{1}{7}\right)$$

$$= 15 \times \frac{1}{28}$$

$$= \frac{15}{28}$$

8. Division of Fractional Number Algorithm, Using the Principle $\frac{a}{b} \times 1 = \frac{a}{b}$ and $\frac{a}{b} \div 1 = \frac{a}{b}$

$$\frac{3}{4} \div \frac{4}{7} = \frac{\frac{3}{4}}{\frac{4}{7}}$$

$$= \frac{\frac{3}{4} \times \frac{7}{4}}{\frac{4}{7} \times \frac{7}{4}}$$

$$= \frac{\frac{3}{4} \times \frac{7}{4}}{\frac{4}{7} \times \frac{7}{4}}$$

$$= \frac{\frac{21}{16}}{1}$$

$$= \frac{21}{16}$$

APPENDIX B
Geometric Constructions

As an elementary teacher, you will find occasions when you will need to know how to make and demonstrate various geometric constructions. This appendix has been included to meet this need.

The order of making arcs in the construction of the geometric figures has been indicated in order to simplify directions. However, this order can be varied and is only suggested as a guide to construction. This order should not be considered the only way in which the constructions can be performed.

1. *Making an Arc from a Fixed Point*

Hold compass like this and

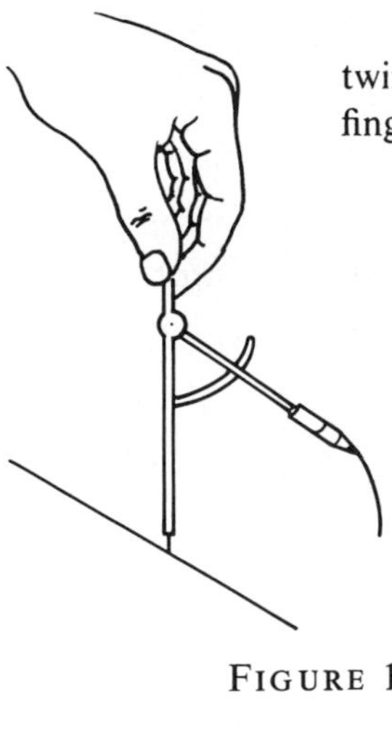

twirl or spin with fingers and thumb.

FIGURE 1

2. *Drawing a Circle*

1. Place the needle of the compass at the point you intend to be the center of the circle.

2. Spread the compass so that the distance between the point and the pencil point corresponds to the radius of your circle.

3. Tilt the compass slightly, as shown in Figure 2.

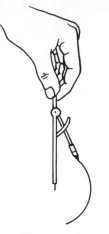

FIGURE 2

4. Pull the lead of your compass as shown in Figure 2.

3. *Constructing a Perpendicular at a Point*

1. Place your compass point at point *A* as shown in Figure 3.

2. Spread your compass and make arcs 1 and 2 as shown in Figure 3.

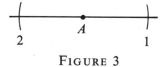

FIGURE 3

3. Spread the compass some more.

4. Place your compass point in the point where arc 1 crosses the line segment and make arc 3 as shown in Figure 4.

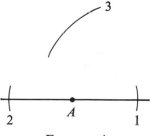

FIGURE 4

5. Place your compass point in the point where arc 2 crosses the line segment and make arc 4 as shown in Figure 5.

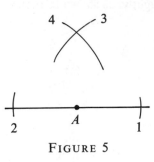

FIGURE 5

6. Connect the point where the arcs cross and point *A* with a line segment as in Figure 6.

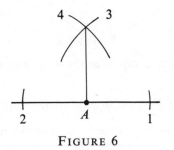

FIGURE 6

4. *Copying an Angle*

1. Draw a picture of a ray, as in Figure 7.

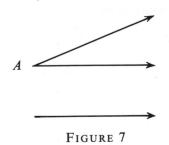

FIGURE 7

2. Place compass needle in point *A*.
3. Spread compass.

4. Swing two arcs crossing the two rays of the angle as in Figure 8.

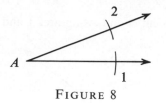

FIGURE 8

5. Make a large arc on your ray by placing the needle in the end point and swinging an arc as in Figure 9.

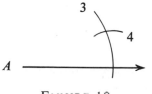

FIGURE 9

6. Place the needle of your compass in the point where arc 1 crosses the ray shown in Figure 8.

7. Decrease or increase the spread of your compass so that the pencil lead is on top of the point where arc 2 cuts the other ray in Figure 8.

8. Make an arc of this radius, placing your compass needle in the point where the large arc crossed your ray, as shown in Figure 10.

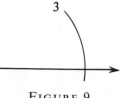

FIGURE 10

9. Connect with a line segment point A and the point where arcs 3 and 4 cross. Make this picture of a line segment a picture of a ray, as in Figure 11.

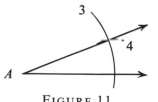

FIGURE 11

5. *Bisecting an Angle*

1. Place compass in point *A* and swing arcs 1 and 2 as in Figure 12.

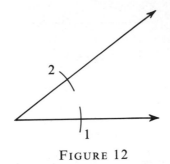

FIGURE 12

2. Place the needle of the compass in the point where arc 1 crosses the ray and make arc 3. (You may need to spread the compass.) See Figure 13.

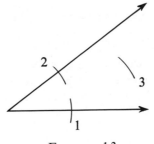

FIGURE 13

3. Place the needle of the compass in the point where arc 2 crosses the ray and make arc 4, as in Figure 14.

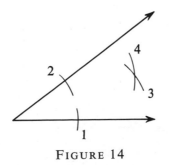

FIGURE 14

4. Connect with a line segment point *A* and the point where arcs 3 and 4 intersect. Extend this line segment to form a ray, as in Figure 15.

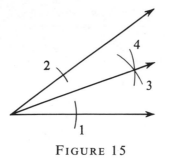

FIGURE 15

6. *Drawing a Line Through a Point Parallel to a Given Line*

1. Draw a ray from the line through point *P* as shown in Figure 16.

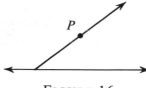

FIGURE 16

2. Copy angle *PRG* so that the new angle has *P* as a vertex and *PM* as a ray as shown in Figures 17 and 18.

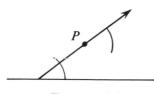

FIGURE 17

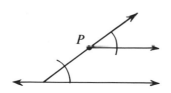

FIGURE 18

3. Extend $\overrightarrow{PK}$ to form line PK as shown in Figure 19.

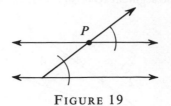

FIGURE 19

7. *Bisecting a Line Segment, or Constructing a Perpendicular Bisector*

1. Place the needle of the compass in point A and swing arcs 1 and 2, as in Figure 20.

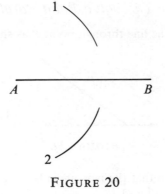

FIGURE 20

2. Place the needle of the compass in point B and swing arcs 3 and 4, as in Figure 21.

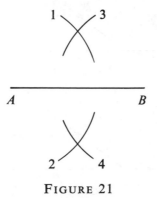

FIGURE 21

3. Connect with a line segment the point where arcs 1 and 3 cross and the point where arcs 2 and 4 cross. Where this line segment crosses the original line segment is the point that partitions the original line segment into two pieces of equal length. (See Figure 22.)

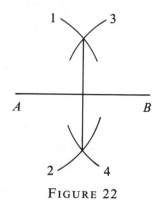

FIGURE 22

8. *Circumscribing a Circle About a Given Triangle*

1. Construct the perpendicular bisector of two sides of the triangle. (See Figure 23.)

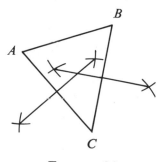

FIGURE 23

2. Place the needle of your compass in the point where the two constructed line segments cross. Set the spread of your compass to correspond to the distance from the needle point to one of the vertices. Circumscribe a circle, as in Figure 24.

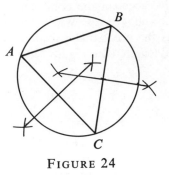

FIGURE 24

9. Constructing a Line Segment from a Given Point so that It Is Perpendicular to Another Line Segment

1. Place the needle of your compass in point *A*. Swing arcs 1 and 2, as in Figure 25.

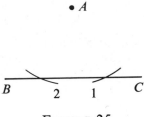

FIGURE 25

2. Place the needle of your compass in the point where arc 1 crosses $\overline{BC}$. Swing arc 3, as in Figure 26.

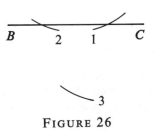

FIGURE 26

3. Place the needle of your compass in the point where arc 2 crosses $\overline{BC}$. Swing arc 4, as in Figure 27.

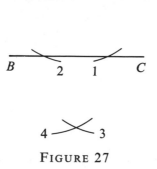

FIGURE 27

4. Connect with a line segment point A and the point where arcs 3 and 4 cross, as in Figure 28.

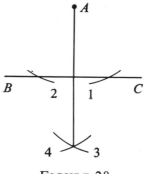

FIGURE 28

10. *Inscribing a Circle in a Fixed Triangle*

1. Bisect two of the angles determined by the triangle, as in Figure 29.

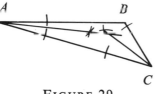

FIGURE 29

2. Construct a line segment perpendicular to $\overline{AC}$ through point Z where the two angle bisectors cross. (See Figure 30.)

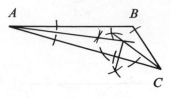

FIGURE 30

3. Let the distance from point A to $\overline{AC}$ serve as a radius and inscribe the circle, as in Figure 31.

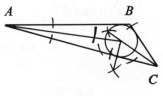

FIGURE 31

Answers to Exercises

CHAPTER 1

1. Structural approach; student involvement; greater flexibility; provisions for individual differences; unified approach; balance among computational, social, and creative aspects of mathematics; greater precision of language; greater emphasis on meanings; incorporation of recent research on learning; consistent approach.
2. A matter of degree.
3. SAMPLE ANSWERS: Aid in unifying the curriculum. Aid in the comparison of number systems. Economy of effort in discovering basic facts. Promotion of discovery. Aid in meeting individual needs.
4. SAMPLE ANSWER: Structured approach: the teacher presents a pattern leading to a simple discovery. Unstructured approach: the teacher provides a problem situation where several alternative paths to the solution are available for discovery.
5. SAMPLE ANSWER: By providing alternate algorithms for different ability groups; by using multiple methods of instruction; by using structural properties.
6. SAMPLE ANSWER: By recognizing the whole numbers as a subset of the sets of fractional numbers.
7. SAMPLE ANSWER: By giving more emphasis to the creative aspects of mathematics.
8. SAMPLE ANSWERS: By distinguishing between number–numeral; point–dot; angle–measure of an angle; equal–equal in measure.
9. SAMPLE ANSWERS: In providing concrete experiences; in understanding the structure of a number system.
10. Answers will vary.

CHAPTER 2

1. SAMPLE ANSWERS: Finding your way through a strange town. Finding the value of $f(x)$ for $0 < x < 1$, if $f(x) = \int(x^3 - e^x)dx$.
2. SAMPLE ANSWERS: Finding the way from your class to your dorm. Finding the value of x, if $x = 7 + 1$.
3. Answers will vary.
4. SAMPLE ANSWER: Find the driving distance from Columbus, Ohio, to San Diego, California. (Some possible paths to the solution are: automobile clubs, take the trip and check your odometer, an atlas, a bus company, a car rental company.)
5. SAMPLE ANSWERS: **a.** Being able to add   **b.** Being able to find the area of a rectangular surface   **c.** Being able to divide   **d.** Being able to make projections from data   **e.** Knowing an approximation for pi.

CHAPTER 3 (1)

1. SAMPLE ANSWER: An apple, a cherry, a grape, and a bald-headed man.
2. SAMPLE ANSWER:

Leafiness, greenness, shininess

3. SAMPLE ANSWER: $\{\triangle, \square\}$; triangle, square; $(\triangle, \square)$; $\triangle \square$
4. SAMPLE ANSWER: All sets will be said to have the number property of four if they can be matched one-to-one with $\{1, 2, 3, 4\}$.
5. All sets will be said to have the property of zero if they can be matched one-to-one with $\{\ \ \}$.
6. It should read: The teacher wrote the numeral 3 on the board.

CHAPTER 3 (2)

1. SAMPLE ANSWERS: I have two apples. I teach in a three-grade school.
2. SAMPLE ANSWERS: I took the second apple. I teach the third grade.
3. SAMPLE ANSWERS: "John Brown Had a Little Indian." "Blackbirds."
4. SAMPLE ANSWER: "A Fish Story."
5. SAMPLE ANSWERS: **a.** A block, a piece of chalk, a pencil, a glove
   b. A pin, a box, a tie, a chair   **c.** Eyes, ears.
6. SAMPLE ANSWERS:

7. SAMPLE ANSWER: Give a child 6 blocks and have him count them. Give a child 12 blocks and have him count out 6 blocks.
8. SAMPLE ANSWERS: I am thinking of the number of three-headed people in the world. I am thinking of the number of legs a fish has.
9. SAMPLE ANSWER:

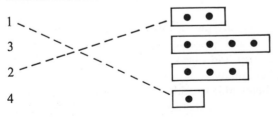

CHAPTER 3 (3)

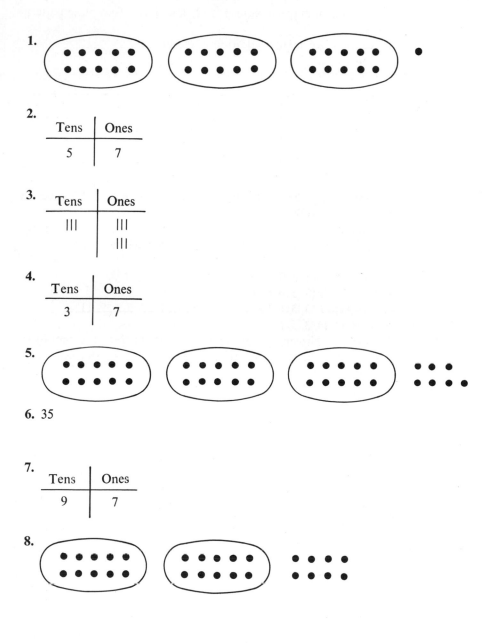

1.

2.

Tens	Ones
5	7

3.

Tens	Ones

4.

Tens	Ones
3	7

5.

6. 35

7.

Tens	Ones
9	7

8.

CHAPTER 4 (1)

1. Counting by 11s. Ones place pattern: 1, 2, 3, 4, 5, . . . Tens place pattern: 0, 1, 2, 3, 4, . . .
2. Provide readiness for mental addition of elevens.
3. Three, seven.
4. SAMPLE ANSWER:

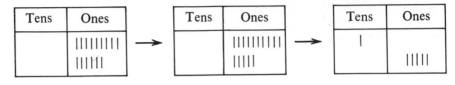

5. SAMPLE ANSWERS: $35 = 30 + \square$ $28 = \square + 8$ $\square = 60 + 6$
   $\square = 60 + 4$ $95 = 90 + \square$
6. Step 1: renaming or expanded notation. Step 2: associative property. Step 3: addition facts. Step 4: renaming or expanded notation.
7. SAMPLE ANSWER:

$$n\{A, B, C, D\} = 4$$
$$n\{3, 5, 6, 9, 11\} = 5$$
$$\{A, B, C, D\} \cup \{3, 5, 6, 9, 11\} = \{A, B, C, D, 3, 5, 6, 9, 11\}$$
$$n\{A, B, C, D, 3, 5, 6, 9, 11\} = 9$$

8. Six plus seven is thirteen; six plus seven equals thirteen; the sum of six and seven is thirteen; the sum of six and seven equals thirteen; seven added to six is thirteen.
9. Addends: 3, 9, 7, 4. Sums: 12, 11.
10. $6 + 0 = 6$; zero is called the identity element.
11. SAMPLE ANSWERS:
    Paired problems: $3 + 5 = \square$ $5 + 3 = \square$
    Single solution: $8 + 6 = 6 + \square$
    Multiple solution: $\square + 9 = 9 + \square$
12. SAMPLE ANSWERS:
    Paired problems: $6 + (7 + 8) = \square$ $(6 + 7) + 8 = \square$
    Single solution: $(9 + 3) + 2 = 9 + (\square + 2)$
    Multiple solution: $(8 + 4) + \square = 8 + (4 + \square)$

CHAPTER 4 (2)

1. SAMPLE ANSWERS:

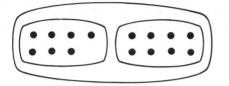

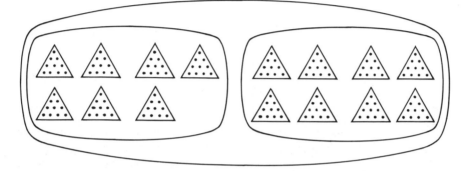

2.

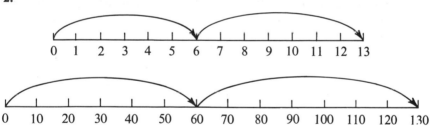

3. Answers will vary.

4. Step 1: renaming or expanded notation. Step 2: associative property. Step 3: addition facts. Step 4: renaming or expanded notation. Step 5: associative property. Step 6: addition of tens. Step 7: renaming or expanded notation.

5. Answers will vary.

6.   38 + 47

     (30 + 8) + (40 + 7)   expanded notation or regrouping

     30 + (8 + 40) + 7   associative property

     30 + (40 + 8) + 7   commutative property

$(30 + 40) + (8 + 7)$	associative property
$70 + 15$	addition of tens and basic facts
$70 + (10 + 5)$	renaming or expanded notation
$(70 + 10) + 5$	associative property
$80 + 5$	addition of tens
85	renaming or expanded notation

7. Answers will vary.

8. First $(2 + 2 + 5)$: only basic facts
Second $(3 + 5 + 6)$: can be worked using basic facts
Third $(1 + 9 + 4)$: need to know expanded notation

9. First $(21 + 32 + 45)$: no regrouping
Second $(48 + 16 + 29)$: regrouping from ones to tens
Third $(31 + 52 + 63)$: regrouping from tens to hundreds

CHAPTER 4 (3)

1–4. Answers will vary.

5. SAMPLE ANSWERS: **a.** John got 3 points in the first half of the game and 0 points in the second half. How many points did he get in all? **b.** Bill learned 15 new spelling words each week. How many words did he learn in three weeks? **c.** Bob spent thirty cents for balloons, forty cents for cookies, and ten cents for candles. How much money did he spend in all? **d.** A town has 4567 parking meters. It orders 3487 more meters. How many will it have in all?

CHAPTER 5 (1)

1. SAMPLE ANSWER:

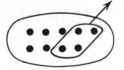

2. SAMPLE ANSWER:

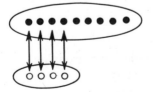

3. Six minus five equals one; six minus five is one; the difference of six and five is one; the difference of six and five equals one; five from six is one.

4. Minuends: 7, 8. Subtrahends: 3, 2. Differences: 4, 6. Sum: 7, 8. Known addends: 3, 2, 4. Unknown addends: 4, 6.

5. 53, 44, 35, 26, 17, 8; ones pattern: 3, 4, 5, 6, 7, 8; tens pattern: 5, 4, 3, 2, 1, 0.

6. Sample answer: Pair each block with one cylinder. How many are not paired?

7.

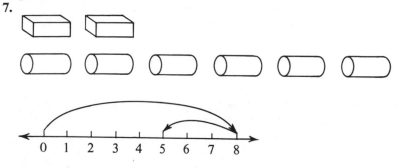

8. SAMPLE ANSWER:

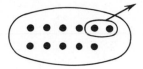

9. $7 + 6 = 13$; $6 + 7 = 13$; $13 - 6 = 7$.

10. Answers will vary.

11.

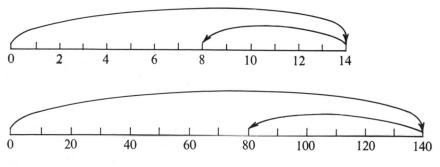

12–14. Answers will vary.

15. **a.** Yes   **b.** Yes   **c.** Compliment him   **d.** It would depend on the class' mastery of addition and subtraction of integers. This skill is not normally mastered at a third-grade level.

16. Sample answer: $(5 - 4) - 2 \neq 5 - (4 - 2)$.

17. Sample answers:

Paired problems: $6 - 4 = \square$ $(6 + 3) - (4 + 3) = \square$

Single solution: $8 - 5 = 9 - \square$

Multiple solution: $13 - \square = 20 - \triangle$

18. Sample answers:

Paired problems: $8 - (4 + 2) = \square$ $(8 - 4) - 2 = \square$

Single solution: $13 - (6 + 4) = (13 - 6) - \square$

Multiple solution: $18 - (5 + \square) = (18 - 5) - \square$

19. Sample answers:

Paired problems: $(9 + 8) - (5 + 2) = \square$ $(9 - 5) + (8 - 2) = \square$

Single solution: $(8 + 4) - (3 + 2) = (8 - \square) + (4 - 2)$

Multiple solution: $(13 + 5) - (4 + \square) = (13 - 4) + (5 - \square)$

20. Sample answers:

Paired problems: $(8 + 4) - 2 = \square$ $8 + (4 - 2) = \square$

Single solution: $(9 + 3) - 1 = 9 + (3 - \square)$

Multiple solution: $(9 + 5) - \square = 9 + (5 - \square)$

21. $\begin{array}{r} 35 \\ -7 \\ \hline \end{array}$ $\begin{array}{l}(20 + 15) - 7 = 20 + (15 - 7) \\ (\square + \triangle) - \bigcirc = \square + (\triangle - \bigcirc)\end{array}$

$\begin{array}{r} 30 \\ -2 \\ \hline \end{array}$ $\begin{array}{l}(20 + 10) - 2 = 20 + (10 - 2) \\ (\square + \triangle) - \bigcirc = \square + (\triangle - \bigcirc)\end{array}$

$\begin{array}{r} 30 + 4 \\ - \quad 2 \\ \hline \end{array}$ $\begin{array}{l}(30 + 4) - 2 = 30 + (4 - 2) \\ (\square + \triangle) - \bigcirc = \square + (\triangle - \bigcirc)\end{array}$

$\begin{array}{r} 20 + 8 \\ -(10 + 6) \\ \hline \end{array}$ $\begin{array}{l}(20 + 8) - (10 + 6) = (20 - 10) + (8 - 6) \\ (\square + \triangle) - (\bigcirc + \bigcirc) = (\square - \bigcirc) + (\triangle - \bigcirc)\end{array}$

CHAPTER 5 (2)

1–4. Answers will vary.

5. Sample answers: **a.** Beth has 29 ribbons. Nine of the ribbons are red. How many are not red?   **b.** Sam has 35 baseball cards. Henry has 25 baseball cards. How many more cards has Sam than Henry?   **c.** Ken has 35 cents. He spends some money at the store. He then has 28 cents. How much money did he spend at the store?   **d.** Sue has 88 pictures. She has 34 more than Ann. How many pictures does Ann have?   **e.** Jim has some pepper plants. Jill gave him 45 more plants. He now has 68 plants. How many plants did he have before Jill gave him some? **f.** John traveled 91 miles the first two hours of his trip. At the end of 4 hours he had gone a total of 155 miles. How far did he travel the second two hours?

CHAPTER 6 (1)

1. Counting by nines.

2. SAMPLE ANSWER:

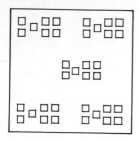

How many sets of seven are on the board? How many pieces are on the board? What is the product of 7 and 5 equal to?

3.

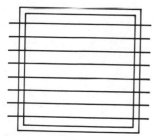

How many rows of pegs do we have? How many pegs in each row? How many pegs in all? Eight times 6 equals what?

4. SAMPLE ANSWER:

Put eight sticks on your frame in the same way I have done.

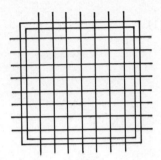

Now put seven sticks on your frame so that each new stick crosses the eight sticks. How many places do the sticks cross? What is eight times seven equal to?

5.

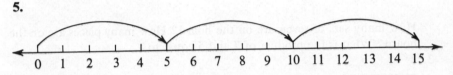

How long is each jump? How many jumps did we take? Three times five equals what?

6.

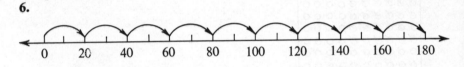

How long is each jump? How many jumps did we take? The product of 9 and 20 is equal to what?

7. $8 \times 90 = 8 \times (9 \times 10)$
$ = (8 \times 9) \times 10$
$ = 72 \times 10$
$ = 720$

8. $8 \times 28 = 8 \times (20 + 8)$
$ = (8 \times 20) + (8 \times 8)$
$ = 160 + 64$
$ = 224$

Dialogues will vary.

9. Answers will vary.

10.

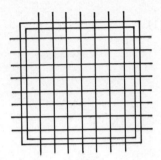

11.

12. SAMPLE ANSWER:

13. The product of 5 and 9 is 45; the product of 5 and 9 equals 45; 5 times 9 is 45; 5 times 9 equals 45; 9 multiplied by 5 is 45.

14. Factors: 8, 9, 6, 3. Products: 72, 18.

15. $88 \times 1 = 88$. Identity property for multiplication.

16. SAMPLE ANSWERS:
Paired problems: $7 \times 4 = \square$ $4 \times 7 = \square$
Single solution: $8 \times 5 = \square \times 8$
Multiple solution: $\square \times 3 = 3 \times \square$

17. SAMPLE ANSWERS:
Paired problems: $(3 \times 2) \times 5 = \square$ $3 \times (2 \times 5) = \square$
Single solution: $(4 \times 9) \times \square = 4 \times (9 \times 6)$
Multiple solution: $8 \times (5 \times \square) = (8 \times 5) \times \square$

18. SAMPLE ANSWERS:
Paired problems: $4 \times (5 + 6) = \square$ $(4 \times 5) + (4 \times 6) = \square$
Single solution: $8 \times (3 + 5) = (\square \times 3) + (\square \times 5)$
Multiple solution: $3 \times (7 + \square) = (3 \times 7) + (3 \times \square)$

19. SAMPLE ANSWERS:
Paired problems: $8 \times (9 - 3) = \square$ $(8 \times 9) - (8 \times 3) = \square$
Single solution: $4 \times (3 - 2) = (4 \times 3) - (4 \times \square)$
Multiple solution: $\square \times (8 - 1) = (\square \times 8) - (\square \times 1)$

CHAPTER 6 (2)

1–2. Answers will vary.

3.
$$
\begin{aligned}
300 \times 4000 &= (3 \times 100) \times (4 \times 1000) \\
&= 3 \times (100 \times 4) \times 1000 \\
&= 3 \times (4 \times 100) \times 1000 \\
&= (3 \times 4) \times (100 \times 1000) \\
&= 12 \times 100{,}000 \\
&= 1{,}200{,}000
\end{aligned}
$$

4. $35 \times 182 = 35 \times (100 + 80 + 2)$
$$= (35 \times 100) + (35 \times 80) + (35 \times 2)$$
$$= [(30 + 5) \times 100] + [(30 + 5) \times 80] + [(30 + 5) \times 2]$$
$$= (30 \times 100) + (5 \times 100) + (30 \times 80) + (5 \times 80)$$
$$+ (30 \times 2) + (5 \times 2)$$
$$= 3000 + 500 + 2400 + 400 + 60 + 10$$
$$= 6370$$

5.

$$
\begin{array}{r}
237 \\
\times\ \ 46 \\
\hline
42 \\
180 \\
1200 \\
280 \\
1200 \\
8000 \\
\hline
10{,}902
\end{array}
$$

6. Answers will vary.

CHAPTER 6 (3)

1–4. Answers will vary.

5. SAMPLE ANSWERS: **a.** A triangular piece of metal is .17 of an inch on a side. What is its perimeter? **b.** Betty bought three cans of beets for 17 cents a can. What was the total cost of the beets? **c.** Bill had 2 pages of stamps with 5 stamps on each page and 3 pages of stamps with 6 stamps on each page. How many stamps were on the five pages in all? **d.** The farmer planted 34 rows of pine trees. There were 67 trees in each row. What was the total number of pine trees planted?

CHAPTER 7 (1)

1.

$$
\begin{array}{r}
24 \\
\times\ \ 6 \\
\hline
144
\end{array}
$$

2. Because there is a whole number 8 that when multiplied by 9 gives the product of 72.

3.

$$
\begin{array}{r}
3 \\
\times\ 5 \\
\hline
15 \\
1 \\
\hline
16
\end{array}
$$

4. 3)$\overline{15}$ $\quad$ $15 \div 3 = 5$ $\quad$ $\frac{15}{3} = 5$ $\quad$ $15/3 = 5$

the small 5 above the division bracket.

5. The quotient of 6 and 2 is 3; the quotient of 6 and 2 equals 3; 6 divided by 2 is 3; 6 divided by 2 equals 3.

6. Products: 20, 16, 15. Divisors: 2, 3. Dividends: 15, 16, 20. Quotients: 8, 2.

7. SAMPLE ANSWERS:
Paired problems: $(18 - 6) \div 3 = \square$ $\quad$ $(18 \div 3) - (6 \div 3) = \square$
Single solution: $(24 - 12) \div 6 = (24 \div \square) - (12 \div 6)$
Multiple solution: $(36 - 12) \div \square = (36 \div \square) - (12 \div \square)$

8. SAMPLE ANSWERS:
Paired problems: $32 \div 8 = \square$ $\quad$ $16 \div 4 = \square$
Single solution: $10 \div 5 = (10 \times 2) \div (5 \times \square)$
Multiple solution: $72 \div 12 = (72 \div \square) \div (12 \div \square)$

CHAPTER 7 (2)

1. $12 \div 2 = 6$; $\quad$ $12 \div 6 = 2$; $\quad$ $12 \div 3 = 4$; $\quad$ $12 \div 4 = 3$; $\quad$ $(12 \div 1 = 12$ and $12 \div 12 = 1$ are not basic facts, but could be discovered).

2. SAMPLE ANSWER:

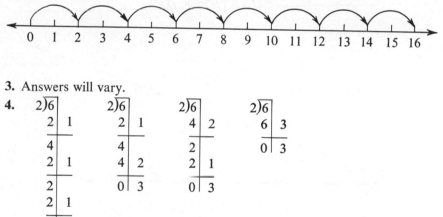

3. Answers will vary.

4.

2)$\overline{6}$		2)$\overline{6}$		2)$\overline{6}$		2)$\overline{6}$	
2	1	2	1	4	2	6	3
4		4		2		0	3
2	1	4	2	2	1		
2		0	3	0	3		
2	1						
0	3						

5. $36 \div 4 = \square$ $\quad$ You would introduce the algorithm working with a division problem for which he already knew the answer. In this way he could focus on the mechanics of the algorithm.

6. SAMPLE ANSWERS: $600 - (2 \times 100) = \square$ $\quad$ $1524 - (2 \times 500) = \square$

7. SAMPLE ANSWERS: $356 - (4 \times 70) = \square$ $\quad$ $890 - (7 \times 30) = \square$

8. Answers will vary.

9. 39 tens; 39 hundreds; 39 tens.

CHAPTER 7 (3)

1–4. Answers will vary.

5. SAMPLE ANSWERS: **a.** A farmer had 394 peaches. He placed 6 peaches in each package. How many packages did he pack? **b.** Six boys earned a total of four dollars and ninety-four cents. If they each earned the same amount of money, how much did each boy earn? **c.** Tom took a bag of 36 quarters and a bag of 40 quarters to the bank. How many dollar bills could he get in exchange for these quarters? **d.** Judy had 16 shells and found 4 more at the beach. If she packed these shells 5 to a box, how many boxes would she use? **e.** Robert put up a fence for 3 days. He put up the same amount of fence each day. If he put up 900 feet of fence in all, how many feet did he put up each day? **f.** Mary made 80 pieces of chocolate candy and 60 lemon drops. She bagged the chocolate 5 pieces to the bag and she boxed the lemon drops 11 pieces to the box. If she sold a bag for a nickel and a box for a nickel how many nickels could she get by selling all the bags and boxes?

CHAPTER 8 (1)

1. SAMPLE ANSWER:

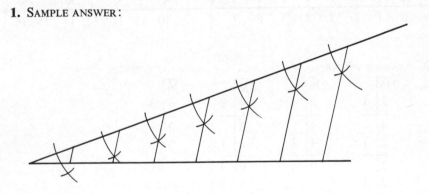

2. SAMPLE ANSWER: Pentagon: fifths, tenths. Octagon: halves, fourths, eighths, sixteenths.

3. Check to see that each disjoint subset has the same number of elements and that there are six of these subsets equal in number.

4. SAMPLE ANSWER:

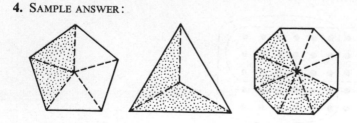

5. SAMPLE ANSWER:

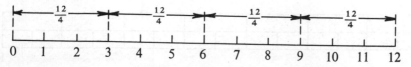

6. SAMPLE ANSWER:

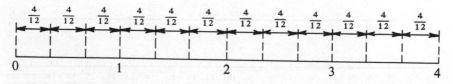

7. SAMPLE ANSWER:

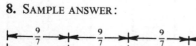

8. SAMPLE ANSWER:

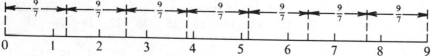

CHAPTER 8 (2)

1. SAMPLE ANSWER:

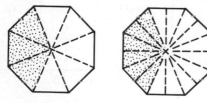

2. Sample answer:

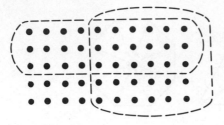

3.

0 1

4.

$$\frac{0}{4} \quad \frac{1}{4} \quad \frac{2}{4} \quad \frac{3}{4} \quad \frac{4}{4} \quad \frac{5}{4} \quad \frac{6}{4} \quad \frac{7}{4}$$

$$\frac{0}{12} \; \frac{1}{12} \; \frac{2}{12} \; \frac{3}{12} \; \frac{4}{12} \; \frac{5}{12} \; \frac{6}{12} \; \frac{7}{12} \; \frac{8}{12} \; \frac{9}{12} \; \frac{10}{12} \; \frac{11}{12} \; \frac{12}{12} \; \frac{13}{12} \; \frac{14}{12} \; \frac{15}{12} \; \frac{16}{12} \; \frac{17}{12} \; \frac{18}{12} \; \frac{19}{12} \; \frac{20}{12} \; \frac{21}{12}$$

5.

$$\frac{30}{10} \quad \frac{30}{10} \quad \frac{30}{10} \quad \frac{30}{10} \quad \frac{30}{10} \quad \frac{30}{10} \quad \frac{30}{10} \quad \frac{30}{10} \quad \frac{30}{10} \quad \frac{30}{10}$$

$$\frac{15}{5} \quad \frac{15}{5} \quad \frac{15}{5} \quad \frac{15}{5} \quad \frac{15}{5}$$

0　2　4　6　8　10　12　14　16　18　20　22　24　26　28　30

$$\frac{12}{16} \; \frac{12}{16} \; \frac{12}{16} \; \frac{12}{16} \; \frac{12}{16} \; \frac{12}{16} \; \frac{12}{16} \; \frac{12}{16} \; \frac{12}{16} \; \frac{12}{16} \; \frac{12}{16} \; \frac{12}{16} \; \frac{12}{16} \; \frac{12}{16} \; \frac{12}{16} \; \frac{12}{16}$$

$$\frac{6}{8} \; \frac{6}{8} \; \frac{6}{8} \; \frac{6}{8} \; \frac{6}{8} \; \frac{6}{8} \; \frac{6}{8} \; \frac{6}{8} \; \frac{6}{8}$$

$$\frac{3}{4} \quad \frac{3}{4} \quad \frac{3}{4} \quad \frac{3}{4}$$

0　1　2　3　4　5　6　7　8　9　10　11　12

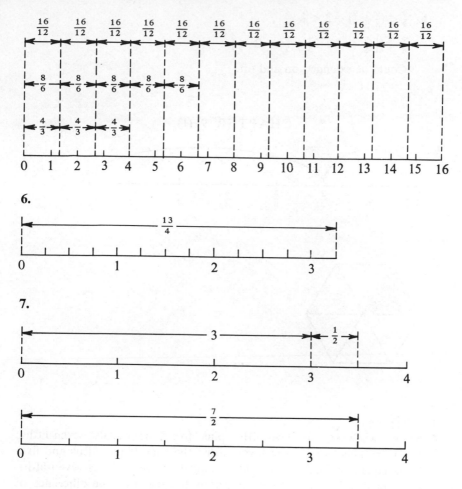

6.

7.

8. a. Yes.   **b.** There are many names for zero.

9. SAMPLE ANSWERS:

a. $\frac{9}{7} \times \frac{8}{8} = \frac{72}{56}$

$\frac{9}{8} \times \frac{7}{7} = \frac{63}{56}$

$\frac{9}{8} = \frac{63}{56} = \frac{63 \times 1,000,000}{56 \times 1,000,000} = \frac{63,000,000}{56,000,000}$

$\frac{9}{7} = \frac{72}{56} = \frac{72 \times 1,000,000}{56 \times 1,000,000} = \frac{72,000,000}{56,000,000}$

9 million fractional numbers with denominators of 56,000,000 from $\frac{9}{8}$ to $\frac{9}{7}$. By a similar argument you could extend the number to 9 billion, 9 trillion, etc.

b. $\frac{9}{8} < (\frac{9}{8} + \frac{9}{7}) \div 2 < \frac{9}{7}$

$\frac{9}{8} < \{[(\frac{9}{8} + \frac{9}{7}) \div 2] + \frac{9}{7}\} \div 2 < \frac{9}{7}$

Could be extended on and on.

CHAPTER 9 (1)

1.

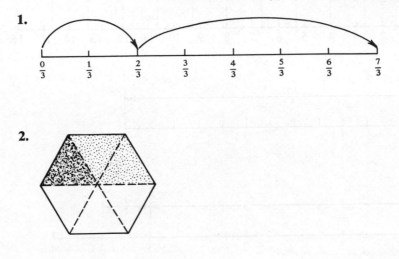

2.

3. $\frac{4}{3} + \frac{\triangle}{\square} = \frac{7}{3}$

4. SAMPLE ANSWERS: **a.** Two-fifths plus five-fifths equals seven-fifths; two-fifths plus five-fifths is seven-fifths; the sum of two-fifths and five-fifths equals seven-fifths; five-fifths added to two-fifths is seven-fifths. **b.** Seven-eighths minus three-eighths is four-eighths; the difference of seven-eighths and three-eighths equals four-eighths; three-eighths subtracted from seven-eighths is four-eighths; seven-eighths less three-eighths is four-eighths.

5. Sum: $\frac{8}{4}$. Addends: $\frac{3}{4}$, $\frac{5}{4}$.

6. Differences: $\frac{1}{4}$ in **a**, $\frac{3}{4}$ in **b**. Minuend: $\frac{4}{4}$. Subtrahend: $\frac{1}{4}$. Known addend: $\frac{3}{4}$. Unknown addend: $\frac{1}{4}$. Sum: $\frac{4}{4}$.

7. SAMPLE ANSWERS:

Paired problems: $\frac{3}{4} + \frac{5}{7} = \frac{\triangle}{\square}$ $\frac{5}{7} + \frac{3}{4} = \frac{\triangle}{\square}$

Single solution: $\frac{6}{7} + \frac{3}{5} = \frac{\triangle}{\square} + \frac{6}{7}$

Multiple solution: $\frac{\triangle}{\square} + \frac{2}{3} = \frac{2}{3} + \frac{\triangle}{\square}$

8. SAMPLE ANSWERS:

Paired problems: $(\frac{1}{5} + \frac{4}{6}) + \frac{2}{3} = \frac{\triangle}{\square}$ $\frac{1}{5} + (\frac{4}{6} + \frac{2}{3}) = \frac{\triangle}{\square}$

Single solution: $(\frac{4}{9} + \frac{1}{7}) + \frac{2}{5} = \frac{4}{9} + (\frac{\triangle}{\square} + \frac{2}{5})$

Multiple solution: $(\frac{\triangle}{\square} + \frac{3}{4}) + \frac{7}{8} = \frac{\triangle}{\square} + (\frac{3}{4} + \frac{7}{8})$

CHAPTER 9 (2)

1. SAMPLE ANSWERS:

Paired problems: $\frac{6}{7} - \frac{1}{5} = \frac{\triangle}{\square}$ $(\frac{6}{7} + \frac{2}{9}) - (\frac{1}{5} + \frac{2}{9}) = \frac{\triangle}{\square}$

Single solution: $\frac{13}{11} - \frac{4}{11} = (\frac{13}{11} + \frac{2}{5}) - (\frac{4}{11} + \frac{\triangle}{\square})$

Multiple solution: $\frac{11}{5} - \frac{7}{5} = (\frac{11}{5} - \frac{\triangle}{\square}) - (\frac{7}{5} - \frac{\triangle}{\square})$

2. a.

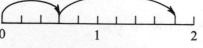

b.

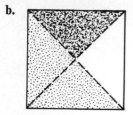

c.

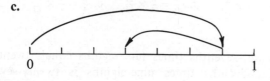

3. a. $\frac{6}{2} + \frac{8}{2} = \frac{6+8}{2}$ **b.** $\frac{12}{5} + \frac{4}{5} = \frac{12+4}{5}$

c. $\frac{4}{7} - \frac{2}{7} = \frac{4-2}{7}$ **d.** $\frac{30}{6} - \frac{12}{6} = \frac{30-12}{6}$

4–5. Answers will vary.

6. $3 + \frac{4}{7} \rightarrow 3 + \frac{44}{77}$

$\underline{2 + \frac{9}{11} \rightarrow 2 + \frac{63}{77}}$

$\qquad 5 + \frac{107}{77} = 5 + \frac{77}{77} + \frac{30}{77} = 6\frac{30}{77}$

7. Answers will vary.

8. $\qquad 3 + \frac{4}{7} \quad \rightarrow \quad 3 + \frac{44}{77} \rightarrow 2 + \frac{77}{77} + \frac{44}{77} \rightarrow \quad 2 + \frac{121}{77}$

$\underline{-(2 + \frac{9}{11}) \rightarrow -(2 + \frac{63}{77}) \rightarrow -(2 + \frac{63}{77}) \quad \rightarrow -(2 + \frac{63}{77})}$

$\qquad\qquad\qquad\qquad\qquad\qquad\qquad\qquad\qquad\qquad \frac{58}{77}$

9. SAMPLE ANSWERS: **a.** If you are interested in comparing the $\frac{6}{10}$ to a decimal expression. **b.** If you are interested in comparing $\frac{75}{100}$ with a percent expression. **c.** If you are being paid by the half hour. **d.** If you are making change in quarters of a dollar. **e.** If you are buying yards of cloth.

CHAPTER 10 (1)

1.

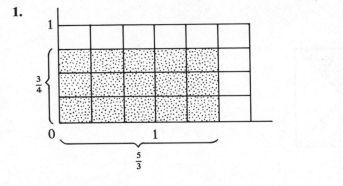

2. SAMPLE ANSWERS: **a.** $\frac{3}{8} = \frac{7}{8} \times \frac{\triangle}{\square}$ **b.** $\frac{2}{9} = \frac{8}{3} \times \frac{\triangle}{\square}$ **c.** $\frac{2}{4} = \frac{3}{4} \times \frac{\triangle}{\square}$

   d. $\frac{3}{4} = \frac{4}{3} \times \frac{\triangle}{\square}$

3. SAMPLE ANSWERS: **a.** Three-sevenths times nine-eighths equals twenty-seven fifty-sixths; three-sevenths times nine-eighths is twenty-seven fifty-sixths; the product of three-sevenths and nine-eighths is twenty-seven fifty-sixths; the product of three-sevenths and nine-eighths equals twenty-seven fifty-sixths. **b.** Three-sevenths divided by nine-eighths is twenty-four sixty-thirds; the quotient of three-sevenths and nine-eighths is twenty-four sixty-thirds; the quotient of three-sevenths and nine-eighths equals twenty-four sixty-thirds.

4. Factors: $\frac{3}{8}$, $\frac{8}{7}$, $3\frac{1}{2}$. Products: $\frac{24}{35}$, $12\frac{1}{4}$. Partial products: $\frac{1}{4}$, $\frac{3}{2}$, $9\frac{3}{2}$.

5. Products: $\frac{6}{35}$, $\frac{16}{3}$. Dividend: $\frac{16}{3}$. Divisor: $\frac{5}{2}$.

6. SAMPLE ANSWERS:

Paired problems: $\frac{4}{7} \times \frac{9}{3} = \frac{\triangle}{\square}$ $\frac{9}{3} \times \frac{4}{7} = \frac{\triangle}{\square}$

Single solution: $\frac{6}{5} \times \frac{3}{4} = \frac{\triangle}{\square} \times \frac{6}{5}$

Multiple solution: $\frac{1}{2} \times \frac{\triangle}{\square} = \frac{\triangle}{\square} \times \frac{1}{2}$

7. SAMPLE ANSWERS:

Paired problems: $(\frac{3}{4} \times \frac{6}{7}) \times \frac{1}{5} = \frac{\square}{\triangle}$ $\frac{3}{4} \times (\frac{6}{7} \times \frac{1}{5}) = \frac{\square}{\triangle}$

Single solution: $(\frac{7}{9} \times \frac{6}{5}) \times \frac{2}{3} = \frac{\triangle}{\square} \times (\frac{6}{5} \times \frac{2}{3})$

Multiple solution: $(\frac{11}{3} \times \frac{4}{2}) \times \frac{\triangle}{\square} = \frac{11}{3} \times (\frac{4}{2} \times \frac{\triangle}{\square})$

8. SAMPLE ANSWERS:

Paired problems: $\frac{3}{4} \times (\frac{11}{2} - \frac{1}{2}) = \frac{\square}{\triangle}$ $(\frac{3}{4} \times \frac{11}{2}) - (\frac{3}{4} \times \frac{1}{2}) = \frac{\square}{\triangle}$

Single solution: $\frac{8}{3} \times (\frac{6}{7} - \frac{4}{5}) = (\frac{\square}{\triangle} \times \frac{6}{7}) - (\frac{\square}{\triangle} \times \frac{4}{5})$

Multiple solution: $\frac{\triangle}{\square} \times (\frac{35}{3} - \frac{17}{2}) = (\frac{\triangle}{\square} \times \frac{35}{3}) - (\frac{\triangle}{\square} \times \frac{17}{2})$

9. SAMPLE ANSWERS:

Paired problems: $\frac{7}{9} \times (\frac{16}{3} + \frac{4}{5}) = \frac{\triangle}{\square}$ $(\frac{7}{9} \times \frac{16}{3}) + (\frac{7}{9} \times \frac{4}{5}) = \frac{\triangle}{\square}$

Single solution: $\frac{2}{13} \times (\frac{4}{7} + \frac{2}{5}) = (\frac{2}{13} \times \frac{\triangle}{\square}) + (\frac{2}{13} \times \frac{2}{5})$

Multiple solution: $\frac{5}{4} \times (\frac{3}{2} + \frac{\triangle}{\square}) = (\frac{5}{4} \times \frac{3}{2}) + (\frac{5}{4} \times \frac{\triangle}{\square})$

10. SAMPLE ANSWERS:

$\frac{6}{4} \times \frac{4}{6} = \frac{\triangle}{\square}$ $\frac{3}{5} \times \frac{\triangle}{\square} = \frac{15}{15} = 1$ $\frac{\triangle}{\square} \times \frac{9}{8} = \frac{72}{72} = 1$

$\frac{8}{3} \times \frac{3}{8} = \frac{\triangle}{\square}$ $\frac{4}{7} \times \frac{\triangle}{\square} = 1$

CHAPTER 10 (2)

1. SAMPLE ANSWERS:

Single solution: $\frac{3}{4} \div \frac{5}{8} = (\frac{3}{4} \times \frac{5}{6}) \div (\frac{5}{8} \times \frac{\triangle}{\square})$

Multiple solution: $\frac{4}{9} \div \frac{2}{7} = (\frac{4}{9} \times \frac{\square}{\triangle}) \div (\frac{2}{7} \times \frac{\square}{\wedge})$

2. SAMPLE ANSWERS:

Paired problems: $(\frac{6}{5} + \frac{3}{5}) \div \frac{7}{3} = \frac{\triangle}{\square}$ $\qquad$ $(\frac{6}{5} \div \frac{7}{3}) + (\frac{3}{5} \div \frac{7}{3}) = \frac{\triangle}{\square}$

Single solution: $(\frac{21}{13} + \frac{4}{11}) \div \frac{7}{10} = (\frac{21}{13} \div \frac{7}{10}) + (\frac{4}{11} \div \frac{\triangle}{\square})$

Multiple solution: $(\frac{8}{5} + \frac{3}{7}) \div \frac{\triangle}{\square} = (\frac{8}{5} \div \frac{\triangle}{\square}) + (\frac{3}{7} \div \frac{\triangle}{\square})$

3. SAMPLE ANSWERS:

Paired problems: $(\frac{7}{2} - \frac{4}{2}) \div \frac{6}{17} = \frac{\triangle}{\square}$ $\qquad$ $(\frac{7}{2} \div \frac{6}{17}) - (\frac{4}{2} \div \frac{6}{17}) = \frac{\triangle}{\square}$

Single solution: $(\frac{4}{6} - \frac{1}{6}) \div \frac{3}{7} = (\frac{4}{6} \div \frac{3}{7}) - (\frac{1}{6} \div \frac{\triangle}{\square})$

Multiple solution: $(\frac{14}{2} - \frac{\triangle}{\square}) \div \frac{3}{4} = (\frac{14}{2} \div \frac{3}{4}) - (\frac{\triangle}{\square} \div \frac{3}{4})$

4. Answers will vary.
5. **a.** Compensation property **b.** Multiplication algorithm **c.** Reciprocal property **d.** Multiplication facts **e.** Division by one
6. **a.** Compensation property **b.** Multiplication algorithm **c.** Multiplication facts **d.** Concept of $\frac{3}{6}$ and $\frac{4}{6}$ **e.** Compensation property **f.** Fraction notation
7–8.

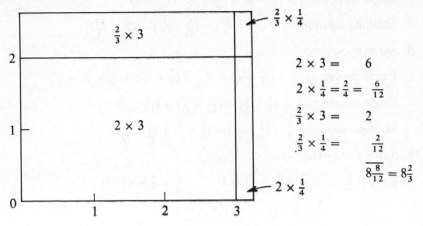

CHAPTER 11 (1)

1. Repetitive, no place value, no zero, additive, base 4.
2. Not repetitive, place value, no zero, additive, base 3 (note *aa* means 1 three 1 one).
3. Not repetitive, place value, zero, additive, base 4.
4. Repetitive (in *kak* both *k*s mean five), no place value, no zero, additive and subtractive, base 5.

5. Repetitive, no place value, no zero, multiplicative, additive, no base.
6. Repetitive, no place value, no zero, additive, base 5.

CHAPTER 11 (2)

1. a. Pile *a:* 75 cups; pile *b:* 10 cups; pile *c:* 2 cups. Total cups: 87.
   b. Pile *a:* 4 cups; pile *b:* 2 cups; pile *c:* 0 cups. Total cups: 6.
   c. Pile *a:* 18 cups; pile *b:* 0 cups; pile *c:* 2 cups. Total cups: 20.
2. SAMPLE ANSWERS:
   $4567_{eight} \rightarrow (\_ \times 8^3) + (\_ \times 8^2) + (\_ \times 8^1) + (\_ \times 8^0)$
   $3 \times 8^3 + 7 \times 8^0 \rightarrow$ _____eight
3. SAMPLE ANSWER:

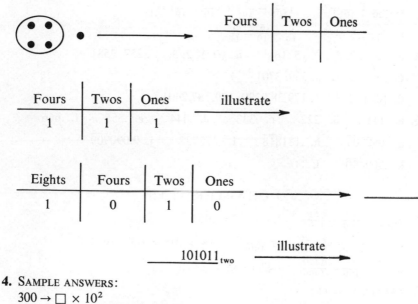

Fours	Twos	Ones
1	1	1

illustrate

Eights	Fours	Twos	Ones
1	0	1	0

101011_{two} illustrate

4. SAMPLE ANSWERS:
   $300 \rightarrow \square \times 10^2$
   $7000 \rightarrow 7 \times 10^{\square}$
   $460 \rightarrow 4.6 \times 10^{\square}$
   $3854 \rightarrow$ _____ $\times 10^3$
   Express in scientific notation: **a.** 40,000   **b.** 3,700,000   Express in standard notation: **a.** 3.6×10^6 **b.** 4.798×10^8

CHAPTER 12 (1)

1. a. $\frac{375}{2} \times \frac{5}{5} = \frac{1875}{10} = 187.5$ **b.** $\frac{41}{5 \times 5} = \frac{41}{5 \times 5} \times \frac{2 \times 2}{2 \times 2} = \frac{164}{100} = 1.64$
   c. $\frac{3714}{2 \times 5 \times 3} = \frac{3714}{2 \times 5 \times 5} \times \frac{2}{2} = \frac{7428}{100} - 74.28$

2. a. $\frac{3}{10} + \frac{6}{10} = \frac{9}{10}$ $.3 + .6 = .9$

   b. $\frac{4}{10} + \frac{7}{100} = \frac{40}{100} + \frac{7}{100} = \frac{47}{100}$ $.40 + .07 = .47$

   c. $\frac{3}{10} - \frac{1}{10} = \frac{2}{10}$ $.3 - .1 = .2$

   d. $\frac{8}{10} - \frac{9}{100} = \frac{80}{100} - \frac{9}{100} = \frac{71}{100}$ $.80 - .09 = .71$

3. SAMPLE ANSWERS: **a.** $\frac{3}{10} + \frac{5}{100} = \frac{\triangle}{\square}$ $\frac{5}{100} + \frac{3}{10} = \frac{\triangle}{\square}$

   b. $(\frac{4}{1000} + \frac{3}{10}) + \frac{25}{100} = \frac{\triangle}{\square}$ $\frac{4}{1000} + (\frac{3}{10} + \frac{25}{100}) = \frac{\triangle}{\square}$

   c. $\frac{8}{10} - \frac{3}{10} = \frac{\triangle}{\square}$ $(\frac{8}{10} - \frac{4}{100}) - (\frac{3}{10} - \frac{4}{100}) = \frac{\triangle}{\square}$

   d. $\frac{17}{100} - \frac{3}{100} = \frac{\triangle}{\square}$ $(\frac{17}{100} + \frac{4}{10}) - (\frac{3}{100} + \frac{4}{10}) = \frac{\triangle}{\square}$

   e. $\frac{35}{100} + \frac{1}{10} = \frac{\triangle}{\square}$ $(\frac{35}{100} - \frac{2}{10}) + (\frac{1}{10} + \frac{2}{10}) = \frac{\triangle}{\square}$

   f. $\frac{6}{10} + \frac{0}{10} = \frac{\triangle}{\square}$ $\frac{0}{10} + \frac{6}{10} = \frac{\triangle}{\square}$

4. a. {0, 1, 2, 3, . . . 15, 16}   **b.** {0, 1, 2, 3, . . . 257, 258}

   c. {0, 1, 2, 3, . . . 369, 370}

   d. {0, 1, 2, 3, . . . 179,387,239, 179,387,240}

5. a. $.11\bar{1}$ **b.** $.22\bar{2}$ **c.** $.33\bar{3}$ **d.** $.44\bar{4}$ **e.** $.55\bar{5}$ **f.** $.66\bar{6}$

   g. $.0909\overline{09}$ **h.** $.1818\overline{18}$ **i.** $.2727\overline{27}$ **j.** $9.0909\overline{09}$

   k. $.9090\overline{90}$ **l.** 11

CHAPTER 12 (2)

1. a. $\frac{3}{10} \times \frac{17}{100} = \frac{51}{1000}$ $.3 \times .17 = .051$

   b. $\frac{4}{100} \times \frac{5}{100} = \frac{20}{10,000}$ or $\frac{2}{1000}$ $.04 \times .05 = .0020$ or $.002$

   c. $\frac{42}{10} \times \frac{35}{100} = \frac{1470}{1000}$ $.42 \times .35 = .1470$

2. SAMPLE ANSWER:

a.

```
      64)471.00
         384.00 | 6
         ───────
          87.00
          64.00 | 1
         ───────
          23.00
          19.20 | .3
         ───────
           3.80
           3.20 | .05
         ───────
            .60 | 7.35 or 7.4 to the nearest tenth
```

b.

$$64\overline{)47.10}$$
$$\begin{array}{r|l} 44.80 & .7 \\ \hline 2.30 & \\ 1.92 & .03 \\ \hline .38 & \text{.73 or .7 to the nearest tenth} \end{array}$$

c. $47.1 \div 6.4 = (47.1 \times 10) \div (6.4 \times 10)$ or $471 \div 64$ by the same methods as **a** and **b**; answer: 7.36 **d.** $471 \div .064 = (471 \times 1000) \div (.064 \times 1000)$; use the same method as **a** and **b**; answer: 7359.4
e. $47.1 \div .64 = (47.1 \times 100) \times (.64 \times 100) = 4710 \div 64$; use the same method as **a** and **b**; answer: 73.6

3. a. 120 miles **b.** 12 feet **c.** 27

4. SAMPLE ANSWERS: $\frac{6}{14}, \frac{9}{21}, \frac{12}{28}, \frac{15}{35}, \frac{18}{42}$.

5. SAMPLE ANSWER: $\frac{4 \times 16}{7 \times 16} = \frac{64}{112}$ and $\frac{9}{16} \times \frac{7}{7} = \frac{63}{112}$.

6. $\frac{3}{100}$ and $1\frac{30}{100}$ or $1\frac{3}{10}$ or $\frac{130}{100}$

7. .22, .04, .001.

8. SAMPLE ANSWERS: **a.** John could make a ringer about 3 out of every 5 times he threw a horseshoe. About how many ringers would he make after throwing 100 times? **b.** Bill could walk 4 feet for every 1 foot his baby brother could crawl. How far could Bill walk while his baby brother was crawling 100 feet? **c.** Betty used 14 yards of ribbon for each 10 yards of material. How many yards of ribbon would she need for 100 yards of material? **d.** Sam had wrenches in eighths of an inch sizes. What size wrench did he need to turn a bolt with a head width of $\frac{25}{100}$ of an inch? **e.** Felix saves 25 percent of his tulip bulbs each year. If he grew 456 bulbs, how many would he save?

CHAPTER 13 (1)

1. ● ● ● ● ● ● ● ● ● ● ●
● ● ● ● ● ● ● ● ● ● ●
● ● ● ● ● ● ● ● ● ● ●

2.

1	7	13	19	25	31	37	43	49	55	61	67	73	79	85	91	97
2	8	14	20	26	32	38	44	50	56	62	68	74	80	86	92	98
3	9	15	21	27	33	39	45	51	57	63	69	75	81	87	93	99
4	10	16	22	28	34	40	46	52	58	64	70	76	82	88	94	100
5	11	17	23	29	35	41	47	53	59	65	71	77	83	89	95	
6	12	18	24	30	36	42	48	54	60	66	72	78	84	90	96	

3. If the tens and ones digit name a number divisible by 4, then the number itself is divisible by 4.

4. If the sum of the digits equals a number divisible by 3 and the ones digit names a 0 or 5, then the number is divisible by 15.

5. SAMPLE ANSWER: If the sum of the thousands and tens when divided by eleven either is equal to the remainder of hundreds and ones when divided by eleven, or if the difference of the remainders is a multiple of eleven, then the number is divisible by eleven.

6. If a number is divisible by 2 and by 3, then it is divisible by 6.

7. a. An infinite set   **b.** Two consecutive odd numbers which are also primes   **c.** 2, 3, 5   **d–e.** Reading assignment

CHAPTER 13 (2)

1. d.

2. a.

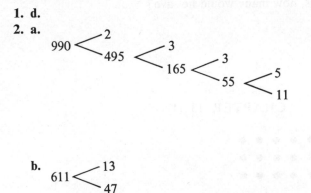

b.
611 < 13
      47

c.

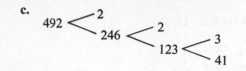

d.

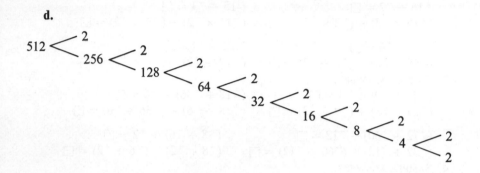

3. a. 1638   **b.** 13,500   **c.** 442   **d.** 4232

4. 1

1 + 4

1 + 4 + 7

1 + 4 + 7 + 10

1 + 4 + 7 + 10 + 13

1 + 4 + 7 + 10 + 13, ... + [1 + 3(n − 1)]

5. Reading assignment.

CHAPTER 14 (1)

1. A number "followed by" its opposite equals zero.
2. A number "followed by" zero equals that number, and zero "followed by" a number equals that number.
3. "Followed by" is a commutative operation.
4. "Followed by" is an associative operation.

CHAPTER 14 (2)

1. Commutative property for subtraction of integers. The operation of subtraction on the set of integers is not commutative.
2. Associative property for subtraction of integers. (It does not hold.)
3. n plus m is equal to n minus the opposite of m.
4. Compensation property.

CHAPTER 14 (3)

1. a. Because $^-3 \times {}^-2 = {}^+6$ then $^+6 \div {}^-3 = {}^-2$
  b. Because $^-3 \times {}^+2 = {}^-6$ then $^-6 \div {}^-3 = {}^+2$
  c. Because $^+3 \times {}^+2 = {}^+6$ then $^+6 \div {}^+3 = {}^+2$

2. SAMPLE ANSWERS:

$^+16 \div {}^-2 = \square$ $^-15 \div {}^-3 = \square$
$(^+16 \times {}^-3) \div ({}^-2 \times {}^-3) = \square$ $(^-15 \times {}^-2) \div ({}^-3 \times {}^-2) = \square$

$^-48 \div {}^+6 = \square$ $^-12 \div {}^-4 = \square$
$(^-48 \div {}^+3) \div ({}^+6 \div {}^+3) = \square$ $(^-12 \div {}^-2) \div ({}^-4 \div {}^-2) = \square$

3. SAMPLE ANSWERS:

$(^-27 + {}^+9) \div {}^+3 = \square$ $(^+18 + {}^-36) \div {}^-6 = \square$
$(^-27 \div {}^+3) + ({}^+9 \div {}^+3) = \square$ $(^+18 \div {}^-6) + ({}^-36 \div {}^-6) = \square$

$(^-72 + {}^-60) \div {}^-12 = \square$ $(^-8 + {}^-6) \div {}^+2 = \square$
$(^-72 \div {}^-12) + ({}^-60 \div {}^-12) = \square$ $(^-8 \div {}^+2) + ({}^-6 \div {}^+2) = \square$

4. SAMPLE ANSWERS:

$(^-14 - {}^+16) \div {}^+2 = \square$ $(^-21 - {}^-6) \div {}^-3 = \square$
$(^-14 \div {}^+2) - ({}^+16 \div {}^+2) = \square$ $(^-21 \div {}^-3) - ({}^-6 \div {}^-3) = \square$

CHAPTER 14 (4)

1. SAMPLE ANSWERS: Which sentences are false?

  a. $^-6 < {}^-7$ **g.** $^-6 < {}^-7$
  b. $^-6 \times {}^+4 < {}^-7 \times {}^+4$ **h.** $^-6 \times {}^-4 < {}^-7 \times {}^-4$
  c. $^-4 < {}^+8$ **i.** $^-4 < {}^+8$
  d. $^-4 \times {}^+5 < {}^+8 \times {}^+5$ **j.** $^-4 \times {}^-5 < {}^+8 \times {}^-5$
  e. $^+8 < {}^+11$ **k.** $^+8 < {}^+11$
  f. $^+8 \times {}^+2 < {}^+11 \times {}^+2$ **l.** $^+8 \times {}^-2 < {}^+11 \times {}^-2$

2. SAMPLE ANSWERS: Which sentences are false?

$^-2 < {}^+6$ $^+24 < {}^+32$
$^-2 \div {}^+2 < {}^+6 \div {}^+2$ $^+24 \div {}^+8 < {}^+32 \div {}^+8$
$^-2 \div {}^-2 < {}^+6 \div {}^-2$ $^+24 \div {}^-8 < {}^+32 \div {}^-8$

$^-12 < {}^-6$
$^-12 \div {}^+3 < {}^-6 \div {}^+3$
$^-12 \div {}^-3 < {}^-6 \div {}^-3$

3. a. 3×10^{-1} **b.** 3×10^{-3} **c.** 3.4×10^{-3} **d.** 4.71×10^{-3}

4. a. .04   **b.** .0000000034   **c.** .0000000000647

5. Answers will vary.

CHAPTER 15 (1)

1. A small dot.
2. SAMPLE ANSWER: R
3. SAMPLE ANSWERS: Surface of a table top extended; surface of a wall extended; surface of a ceiling extended; surface of a floor extended; surface of a smooth lake extended.
4. A and E have to be drawn with two-point origins; B, C, D were most probably drawn with a one-point origin.
5. A: crosspoints B: endpoints C: crosspoints and endpoints D: endpoints E: crosspoints
6. Convex: A, D, E; concave: B and C.

CHAPTER 15 (2)

1. SAMPLE ANSWER: R S

2. A: not the join of just line segments B: crosspoints C: endpoints D: endpoints E: crosspoints
3. A, B, C: not the join of three line segments D: endpoints E: endpoint
4. A: not the join of 4 line segments B: not the join of only line segments C and D: crosspoints E: an endpoint
5. A and C: not the join of only 4 line segments B: diagonals are not congrunet D and E: not the join of only line segments
6. B: scalene A and C: isosceles C: equilateral

CHAPTER 15 (3)

1. Diameter.
2. Z M

3.

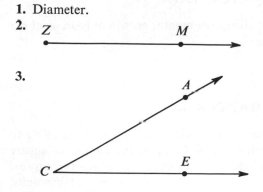

4. 180°.
5. Yes.
6. No.
7. Each angle determined by each pair of sides is 60°.
8. $\overleftrightarrow{RK}$.
9. A rhombus is a quadrilateral with four congruent sides which has parallel opposite sides.
10. A rectangle.

CHAPTER 15 (4)

1. No.
2.

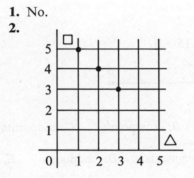

3. Yes.
4. SAMPLE ANSWERS: (2, 3), (4, 1), (0, 5), ($\frac{1}{2}$, $4\frac{1}{2}$).
5. **a.** yes　　**b.** no　　**c.** yes

CHAPTER 15 (5)

1. SAMPLE ANSWERS: sales of ice cream per month; growth of bean plant per day; automobile accidents per year.
2–5. Answers will vary.

CHAPTER 16

1. Answers will vary. *Hint:* Select a grid with markings corresponding to a whole number of units for the radius. Compare the number of square units completely within the circle to the number within plus the number of square units containing the border. Select smaller and smaller units. Show that the true area is approximated by $\frac{22}{7} \times r \times r$ or $\frac{22}{7} \times r^2$.

2. SAMPLE ANSWER: Compare weights on a balance board. Equality of measure determined by the balance board. A small cube or similar object is selected to serve as a unit of weight. Select cubes of multiple weights of the small cube to serve as the scale (for example: 1-unit weights, 2-unit weights, 4-unit weights). Establish the concept that the smaller the unit of weight the more precise the measure of weight. Investigate some of the standard units of weight measure (pound, gram). Investigate direct and indirect measurements of weight. Involve the students in conversion from one scale to another (pounds, tons, grams, kilograms). Explore some of the generalizations which relate to weight (specific gravity, comparative weights on various planets, etc.).

3–4. Answers will vary.

5. SAMPLE ANSWER: **d.** Tie several different strings on a pole. Tie a rock to one of the strings. Tie rocks of increasing weights until the string breaks. Repeat this process with the other strings. Note which strings had the greatest resistance to breaking and which had the least resistance. Select a unit of weight and repeat the process, determining the breaking point in units of weight. Repeat this process, using standard units of weight. Discuss, using direct and indirect techniques to determine the breaking point. Discuss applications (fishing lines, threads, etc.).

CHAPTER 17 (1)

1. Answers will vary.
2–4. Reading assignment.

CHAPTER 17 (2)

1. Reading assignment.
2–3. Observation experience.
4. Preparation of a lesson plan (see Section 17.6).

INDEX